# THE KENSINGTON DIET™ COOKBOOK

*Also by Stephen Twigg*
*and published by Bantam Books*

THE KENSINGTON DIET™

# THE
# KENSINGTON
# DIET™
# COOKBOOK

## STEPHEN TWIGG

**BANTAM BOOKS**

LONDON · NEW YORK · TORONTO · SYDNEY · AUCKLAND

**THE KENSINGTON DIET™ COOKBOOK**
**A BANTAM BOOK: 0 553 506102**

First publication in Great Britain

PRINTING HISTORY
Bantam edition published 1998

Copyright © 1998 by Stephen M. Twigg
*The Kensington Diet* and associated device is a trade mark of
Stephen M. Twigg and may not be used
or reproduced without explicit permission. International
management by The Alta Vista
Corporation Ltd.

Photographs copyright © Tim Hill
Food stylist: Zoë Hill
Home economist: Una Vandenburg

The right of Stephen M. Twigg to be identified as the author of this
work has been asserted in accordance with sections 77 and 78 of
the Copyright Designs and Patents Act 1988.

Set in Monotype Times by Deltatype Ltd, Birkenhead, Merseyside

Bantam Books are published by Transworld Publishers Ltd,
61–63 Uxbridge Road, London W5 5SA,
in Australia by Transworld Publishers (Australia) Pty Ltd,
15–25 Helles Avenue, Moorebank, NSW 2170
and in New Zealand by Transworld Publishers (NZ) Ltd,
3 William Pickering Drive, Albany, Auckland.

Reproduced, printed and bound in Great Britain by
Mackays of Chatham Plc, Chatham, Kent.

# THE KENSINGTON DIET™ COOKBOOK

## PUBLISHER'S NOTE

# CONTENTS

PUBLISHER'S NOTE                                               7
*INTRODUCTION*                                                17
  KD TAKES FOOD COMBINING A QUANTUM LEAP FORWARD    18
  '1 IN 5' ROTATION                                 22
  IN BRIEF – AN OVERVIEW OF KD RULES AND ADVICE     23
  THE 10% RULE FOR EMERGENCY WEIGHT CONTROL         24
  KD COOKING                                        25
  KD FOR VEGGIES, TOO!                               26
  THE SUBTLE ART OF SERVING                         27
  KD COOKING GEAR                                   28
  KD INGREDIENTS                                    29
  HOW TO USE THIS BOOK                              30

*BREAKFASTS AND BRUNCHES*                                     32
  Everything you need to know about breakfasts      32
    Mixed fruit salad (v)                 33
    Citrus fruit salad (v)                34
    Exotic fruit salad (v)                34
    Stewed fruit compôte (v)              35
    Summer berries and yogurt with blackcurrant coulis (v)   36
    Grilled spiced fruits (v)             36
    Grilled grapefruit (v)                38
    Fruit smoothies                       38
    Banana and strawberry smoothie (v)    39
    Stewed apricot smoothie with whole blueberries (v)   39
    Scrambled eggs with smoked salmon     40
    Scrambled eggs with mushrooms, tomatoes and bacon   41

Grilled gammon rashers with eggs, mushrooms and tomatoes   42
Bubble and squeak (v)   43

*EATING LIGHT*   45
Everything you need to know about soups   45
  Cream in soups   45
    Basic vegetable stock (v)   48
    Quick vegetable stock (v)   49
    Chicken stock   50
    Watercress soup (v)   51
    Creamy celery soup (v)   52
    Gazpacho (v)   53
    Avocado soup (v)   54
    French-style onion soup (v)   56
    Thick vegetable soup (v)   57
    Root soup (v)   58
    Bean soup (v)   60
    Black olive purée (v)   61
    Lentil soup (v)   61
    Pumpkin soup (v)   62
    Fish soup   63
  Chinese-style 'Five morsels' soups   64
    Chinese mushroom and bean curd soup   65
    Chinese chicken and bamboo shoot soup   66
    Chinese salmon and vegetables soup   67

  Soup accompaniments   68
    Wheat croutons (v)   68
    Polenta croutons (v)   69

*SERVING SALADS*   71
Everything you need to know about salads   71
  Basic salad ingredients   72
    Basic vinaigrette (v)   73
    Twice-cooked duck salad   75
    Chicken liver salad   78
    Spicy quick roast chicken salad with salsa dressing   79
    Turkey, bacon and walnut salad   80
    Smoked salmon, dill and caper salad   81
    Prawn and avocado salsa salad   82

KD Niçoise salads 84
  Niçoise-style tuna salad 85
  Niçoise-style potato salad Ⓥ 86
  Caesar-style salad 87
  KD Waldorf salad Ⓥ 88
  Cashew nut salad Ⓥ 90
Pasta salads 91
  Pasta salad with herb dressing Ⓥ 92
  Pasta salad with sun dried tomato dressing Ⓥ 93
  Tabbouleh Ⓥ 95
  Curry and rice salad Ⓥ 96
  Lentil salad Ⓥ 99
  Bean salad Ⓥ 100
  Warm vegetable salads Ⓥ 102
  Warm salad of mixed mushrooms Ⓥ 104
Crudités 105
  Warm walnut and anchovy dip 107
  Shredded vegetable crudités with classic sauces 108
    Yogurt and mint sauce Ⓥ 108
    Herb and onion vinaigrette Ⓥ 109
    Blue cheese sauce Ⓥ 109
    Shredded vegetable crudités Ⓥ 110
  Oriental-style shredded vegetable crudités 110
    Tomato and ginger sauce Ⓥ 110
    Horseradish mayonnaise Ⓥ 111
    Black bean sauce Ⓥ 111
    Oriental-style crudités Ⓥ 111

MORE STARTERS, LOVELY LUNCHES AND SUPPERS 113
Pâté 113
  Chicken liver pâté 113
  Bean pâté Ⓥ 114
  Cheese and herb soufflé omelette Ⓥ 115
  Scrambled eggs with ratatouille Ⓥ 117
  Spanish-style omelette Ⓥ 118
Rarebits 119
  Ploughman's rarebit Ⓥ 121
  Four seasons rarebit 121
  Stuffed leek rarebit 123

Quiches                                                                  124
  Basic quiche filling (v)                                      124
  Bacon, onion and tomato quiche                                125
  Goat's cheese and Roquefort quiche in a pot (v)               126

Pastries, pizzas, pancakes, crostini and röstis                          127
  Shortcrust pastry (v)                                         128
  Mushroom tartlets (v)                                         128
  Tatin-style tart of peppers and onions with sour cream and
    chives (v)                                         130
  Quenelles of sour cream and chives (v)                        132
  Pizza KD style (v)                                            132
  Polenta crostini (v)                                          133
  Wheat bread crostini (v)                                      134
  Socca with mixed roast peppers (v)                            134
  Rösti and seasonal vegetables (v)                             136

Stuffed vegetables                                                       138
  Courgettes                                                    138
  Marrow                                                        138
  Onions                                                        139
  Mushrooms                                                     139
  Peppers                                                       139
  Kohlrabi and turnips                                          140
  Autumn medley of stuffed vegetables (v)                       140
  Courgettes                                                    140
  Onions                                                        141
  Turnips                                                       143
  Spring medley of stuffed vegetables (v)                       144
  Aubergine purée (v)                                           146

*PROTEIN MAIN COURSES*                                                   147
  Everything you need to know about Main Courses with Proteins  147
  Spaghetti Bolognese KD style                                  148
  Beef Stroganoff                                               150
  Roast French rack of lamb                                     152
  Lamb kebabs                                                   153
  Stuffed pork fillets                                          155
  Pork steaks with onion and garlic sauce                       157
  Salmon fillet with a charred oriental spice crust             158

Grilled haddock 159
Griddle fried tuna 161
Hot and sour fish 162
Chicken breast stuffed with goat's cheese and sage 164
Roast chicken with rich chicken and vegetable sauce 165
Turkey satay 167
Liver in tomato sauce 169
Liver with oregano 170
Frittata-style omelette (v) 172

CARBOHYDRATE MAIN COURSES 174
Everything you need to know about Main Courses
    with Carbohydrates 174
Wheat and Gluten Grains 176
Spaghetti with herbs and olives (v) 177
Pasta Stroganoff (v) 178
Summer vegetable cous cous (v) 179
Rice 181
Paella (v) 182
Vegetable rice curry (v) 183
Potatoes 184
Roast of crispy potatoes and onions (v) 185
Spicy potatoes in tomato sauce (v) 186
Potatoes and root vegetables boulangère style (v) 188
Corn 190
Polenta stacked with ratatouille vegetables (v) 190
Spicy vegetable peanut satay (v) 192
Pulses 194
Basic lentils (v) 195
Spaghetti with lentil sauce (v) 196
Lentil lasagne (v) 197
Lentil moussaka (v) 199
Lentil chilli (v) 200
Lentil curry (v) 202
Casserole of beans and vegetables with filled
    dumplings (v) 203
Stuffing 206
Herb stuffing (v) 206
Other Carbohydrates 206

# MIX WITH ANY FOODS – MAINLY VEGETABLES 208

Vegetable preparation and cooking KD style 209
Ribbon 'pasta' 211
Carrot, courgette and leek ribbon 'pasta' (v) 212
Leek and parsnip ribbon 'pasta' sauté (v) 212
Noodle 'pasta' 213
Carrot and courgette noodle 'pasta' (v) 214
Penne-style 'pasta' 214
Mixed root penne-style 'pasta' with herbs (v) 215
Aubergine 'noodles' (v) 216
Mix With Any vegetable 'rice' 217
Carrot and courgette boiled vegetable 'rice' (v) 217
Carrot and courgette fried 'rice' (v) 218
Julienne Mix With Any vegetables 219
Grated Mix With Any vegetables 219
Side salad of grated Mix With Any vegetables (v) 220
Mashed and puréed Mix With Any vegetables 221
Buttered parsnip mash (v) 222
Purée of swede (v) 222
Carrot purée (v) 223
Carrot and parsnip purée with garlic (v) 223
Purée of Brussels sprouts (v) 224
Presentation ideas 224
Layered spinach and carrots (v) 224
Steaming Mix With Any vegetables 226
Medley of seasonal steamed vegetables (v) 226
Stir frying 227
Stir fry of a variety of Mix With Any vegetables (v) 228
Stir fry of Mix With Any vegetables Thai-style (v) 230
Stir fried spinach and bean sprouts (v) 232
Roasted Mediterranean vegetables (v) 233
Roasted winter vegetables (v) 235
Pressed terrine of vegetables (v) 236
Oven cooked ratatouille (v) 238
Quick sauté ratatouille (v) 239
Mix With Any vegetable casserole (v) 241
Griddled chicory hearts (v) 243
Griddled courgettes (v) 244
Griddled asparagus and leeks (v) 245
Tomato and onion side salad (v) 246

Green side salad (v) 247
Herby green side salad (v) 247
Mixed vegetable curry (v) 248
Aubergine curry (v) 250

DESSERTS AND DRINKS 252
Everything you need to know about desserts 252
Sweet desserts 253
Little bites 253
Nut macaroons (v) 255
Cups of chocolate (v) 255
Lemon pot (v) 256
BL's potted cheesecake (v) 258
Bakewell pot (v) 259
Floating meringues on custard with hot chocolate (v) 259
Lemon rice pudding (v) 261
Tiramisu KD (v) 262
Treacle tartlets (v) 264
Papaya fool (v) 265
Yogurt with chopped nuts (v) 267
Dessert salads (v) 267
Goat's cheeses and crudités with walnuts (v) 269
Cow's milk cheeses with crudités and salsa (v) 270

EMBELLISHMENTS 271
Basic tomato sauce (v) 271
Rich tomato sauce (v) 272
Sage and onion sauce (v) 273
Creamy mushroom sauce (v) 274
Onion gravy (v) 275
Sweet pepper coulis (v) 276
Warm herb vinaigrette (v) 277
Fennel vinaigrette (v) 277
Mustard mayonnaise (v) 278
Simple mayonnaise (v) 279
Tartare sauce (v) 279
Green salsa (v) 280
Summer tomato salsa (v) 281

## GARNISHES AND TASTE SENSATIONS ......... 283
Basic pesto (v) ......... 283
Alternative pesto (v) ......... 284
Purée of roasted garlic (v) ......... 285
Mint purée (v) ......... 285
Garlic chips (v) ......... 286

## CONVERSION TABLES ......... 287
DRY MEASURES ......... 287
LIQUID MEASURES ......... 287
USEFUL MEASURES ......... 288
OVEN TEMPERATURES ......... 288

## THE KD FOOD DIRECTORY ......... 289
Key To The Directory ......... 289

# INTRODUCTION

As you'll know if you've read *The Kensington Diet*, the KD way of food combining is the most exciting and radical new arrival on the food scene for decades. Before *The Kensington Diet*, you basically had two choices: you could either choose to eat boring 'healthy' food – or you could indulge in wickedly enjoyable food . . . while watching your waistline expand, and your cholesterol count go through the roof!

*The Kensington Diet* revolution has swept all that away. Founded on the proven principles of classical food combining, KD's sophisticated yet practical approach to eating delivers *both* health *and* taste . . . to the max! With KD, you *can* have your cake (properly combined, of course) . . . *and* eat it! In short, KD is the healthiest way of eating I know. After years of study and experience, I don't have a shadow of a doubt that it's the most universally beneficial way of dramatically improving your health, and getting your weight under control, if you need to.

KD is an approach to diet for the new millennium. One that not only combines food in a way that will profoundly benefit you, but does so in ways which fit in with your modern – undoubtedly hectic – lifestyle. The recipes are more delicious than you ever imagined healthy food could be: they are easy to prepare and cook – and they use the foods you like to eat.

The main and overriding purpose behind *The Kensington Diet Cookbook* is to make it possible for you to eat a wide variety of meals in the KD way. For you to make KD eating a way of life, I need to be able to demonstrate to you that it can fit into *any* meal situation . . . from a snack to a fast family lunch . . . through to a complete dinner party, and any eating occasion in between. I need to show you it can be enjoyable for everyone and easy to do. I need to show you how all your favourite foods fit into the KD style of eating. I want to convince you that KD meals are, if anything, *better* than your present favourite meals. I want to make you *want* to eat The Kensington Diet way! That's what this book has been created for.

I've chosen the recipes in this book so you'll always be able to find something that fits into your KD eating strategy at any time, but I also hope they'll inspire you to be creative and imaginative in your own cooking.

## KD TAKES FOOD COMBINING A QUANTUM LEAP FORWARD

Food combining, or the art of compatible eating, is effective because foods eaten in good combinations do not oppose each other in your body like poorly combined foods do.

The fact is that different types of food are digested best in different chemical environments, sometimes in different parts of your digestive system. Put the wrong foods together in a meal, and neither is digested particularly well; and *that* increases the toxicity your body has to deal with. The results are increasing levels of discomfort and harm as your body is forced to do its best with what you're giving it every day. But when you eat food that is well combined, your body is not put under the stress of having to deal with foods it can't digest easily, nor their toxic end-products.

If you've ever tried following old-fashioned food combining, you'll know that it really can bring enormous benefits. Sadly, you'll also know that it can be impossible to stick to. But once you start eating the KD way – as explained in my first book, *The Kensington Diet* – you can have all the benefits of food combining, with none of the drawbacks.

## HOW THE KENSINGTON DIET IMPROVES ON TRADITIONAL FOOD COMBINING

| Old fashioned food combining insists that . . . | The Kensington Diet says . . . |
|---|---|
| You must carefully monitor the amount of acidifying and alkalising foods in your diet and change so you are eating mostly alkalising foods. | There's no need! Your intake of acidifying and alkalising foods will adjust naturally as your body and mind are transformed and improved. If you alter very rapidly to an alkalising diet your temperament and mood will be severely disturbed. Some people's diets have tended towards an acid-forming diet because they need it so for the time being, in order to feel comfortable in themselves and maintain their equilibrium. Don't worry about acidifying and alkalising foods – they'll be taken care of in due course. |
| You must eat an additive-free diet. | You needn't go out of your way to avoid all foods with additives. In the real world you can't avoid additives and toxins completely and you can cope with a certain amount of most of them. That's one of the things your body is supposed to do, deal with toxins and foreign material. On The Kensington Diet you'll find your tastes shifting quite naturally away from additive-rich foods, while at the same time your ability to cope with them will improve as your body systems become more efficient. Don't concern yourself too much about additives. |
| You must eat a predominantly unrefined whole food diet. | Absolutely not. You are going to eat what you like in the way that makes sure your body will get the best from the foods you choose. Everything you need in the way of a good balance of foods is available at the average supermarket. If you enjoy eating whole foods use them as much as you want, if not, don't give them a second thought. |
| You must make sweeping, wholesale changes to your diet and lifestyle to get any real benefit. | You choose the level at which you want to participate in your own health. Every meal combined The Kensington Diet way will help you. You'll soon find yourself enjoying KD meals more than your old ones. |

KD food combining improves on traditional food combining because it asks you to concentrate only on the most effective and necessary changes to your eating, so you are not distracted by non-essential and ineffective changes. This makes it easier and at the same time more successful. *You get the best from doing less.*

In *The Kensington Diet*, I explained that KD food combining coupled with food rotation (summarised below) provide you with two of the most powerful methods of healthy eating yet devised. Each one is a wide-ranging and far-reaching technique for improving your health and managing your weight and size with food – together, they are the most effective and formidable system of eating for health you will find.

Correct food combining and '1 day in 5' food rotation work together to resolve many of the most common health problems. By doing so, they enable your body to both recover (cure) from situations from which you are already suffering and improve (prevent) your underlying health process from which many problems can arise. This comprehensive approach to using food for health is far more effective than tinkering with your intake of one or two supposed problem foods – such as salt, or fat – or any single aspect of diet, such as calories or fibre. KD eating is based on the latest understanding of the way your body works and applies that understanding to your eating to directly help you.

The golden rule of KD food combining is:

> Eat your proteins and carbohydrates so they will not be in your stomach at the same time

How do you recognise which foods are proteins and which carbohydrates? That's easy – just check the following chart! You'll also find a very comprehensive alphabetical list of foods with more information in the KD Food Directory at the back.

# YOUR KD QUICK REFERENCE GUIDE TO EASY FOOD COMBINING

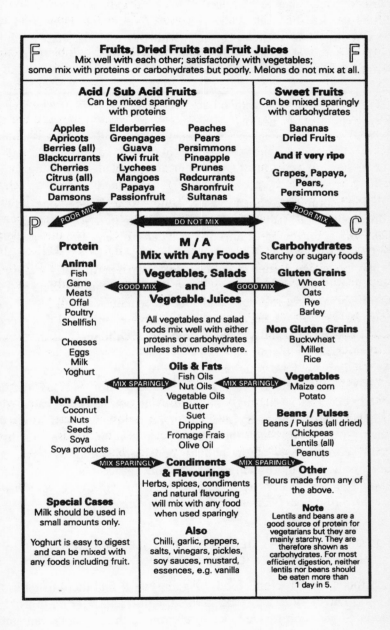

**F** **Fruits, Dried Fruits and Fruit Juices** **F**
Mix well with each other; satisfactorily with vegetables;
some mix with proteins or carbohydrates but poorly. Melons do not mix at all.

**Acid / Sub Acid Fruits**
Can be mixed sparingly
with proteins

| | | |
|---|---|---|
| Apples | Elderberries | Peaches |
| Apricots | Greengages | Pears |
| Berries (all) | Guava | Persimmons |
| Blackcurrants | Kiwi fruit | Pineapple |
| Cherries | Lychees | Prunes |
| Citrus (all) | Mangoes | Redcurrants |
| Currants | Papaya | Sharonfruit |
| Damsons | Passionfruit | Sultanas |

**Sweet Fruits**
Can be mixed sparingly
with carbohydrates

Bananas
Dried Fruits

**And if very ripe**

Grapes, Papaya,
Pears,
Persimmons

**P** *POOR MIX* ←→ DO NOT MIX ←→ *POOR MIX* **C**

**Protein**

**Animal**
Fish
Game
Meats
Offal
Poultry
Shellfish

Cheeses
Eggs
Milk
Yoghurt

**Non Animal**
Coconut
Nuts
Seeds
Soya
Soya products

**Special Cases**
Milk should be used in
small amounts only.

Yoghurt is easy to digest
and can be mixed with
any foods including fruit.

**M / A**
**Mix with Any Foods**

**Vegetables, Salads**
*GOOD MIX* ← **and** → *GOOD MIX*
**Vegetable Juices**

All vegetables and salad
foods mix well with either
proteins or carbohydrates
unless shown elsewhere.

**Oils & Fats**
Fish Oils
*MIX SPARINGLY* ← Nut Oils → *MIX SPARINGLY*
Vegetable Oils
Butter
Suet
Dripping
Fromage Frais
Olive Oil

*MIX SPARINGLY* → **Condiments** ← *MIX SPARINGLY*
**& Flavourings**
Herbs, spices, condiments
and natural flavouring
will mix with any food
when used sparingly

**Also**
Chilli, garlic, peppers,
salts, vinegars, pickles,
soy sauces, mustard,
essences, e.g. vanilla

**Carbohydrates**
Starchy or sugary foods

**Gluten Grains**
Wheat
Oats
Rye
Barley

**Non Gluten Grains**
Buckwheat
Millet
Rice

**Vegetables**
Maize corn
Potato

**Beans / Pulses**
Beans / Pulses (all dried)
Chickpeas
Lentils (all)
Peanuts

**Other**
Flours made from any of
the above.

**Note**
Lentils and beans are a
good source of protein for
vegetarians but they are
mainly starchy. They are
therefore shown as
carbohydrates. For most
efficient digestion, neither
lentils nor beans should
be eaten more than
1 day in 5.

Throughout the book, protein foods and recipes are labelled 'P', carbohydrates are 'C' and foods and recipes which can be safely combined with either are labelled 'M/A' for 'mix with any'.

Fruits need to be dealt with carefully in your diet. They need very little digestion and combining them with other foods simply inhibits proper use of what you mix them with. As a result, I strongly recommend that you:

> Eat fruits mixed only with other fruits, and don't mix melon with anything but other melon

## '1 IN 5' ROTATION

While food combining comes close to being an ideal diet, it doesn't have all the answers. But there is a powerful technique you can add to it which will give your diet an edge over any other eating system. It's called *food rotation*.

Some foods, when eaten too often, can provoke particularly unpleasant chemical responses in the body. These responses can manifest as food sensitivities, allergic reactions and food dependencies that, in the most serious instances, have been connected to severe emotional disorders in adults, hyperactivity and violent behaviour in children, and to a whole raft of physical problems.

At its simplest, food rotation is a way of making sure you don't eat some foods too often. Most people's eating, for various reasons, gradually becomes surprisingly habitual. A monotonous diet can deplete the vital digestive chemistry needed for proper digestion of foods that are being over-used. Much the same as bad combining, this results in toxicity, compromise of individual body and mind systems, and disorganisation of the underlying body/mind processes.

*Food rotation, therefore, is as important to improving your health and controlling your weight as food combining.*

### FOODS WHICH MAY BECOME A PROBLEM FROM OVERUSE SHOULD BE EATEN ONE DAY ONLY IN ANY FIVE DAYS

Which foods are 'problem' foods? Again, you'll find them listed in the KD Food Directory at the back, marked with * and referred to as '1 in 5' foods. So you don't have to keep referring to the directory, remember as a general rule: *'1 in 5' foods are the proteins, the carbohydrates and any other food you are eating very often, which means daily or almost daily.*

When you analyse it carefully, there are actually only a few foods which most people need to consider as potential problems. The most common are the cereals and particularly wheat products (especially bread), soya products, eggs, cow's milk dairy products (especially cheese), yeast extracts, potatoes, chocolate and caffeine products (tea, coffee, cola etc.). These foods can have very potent effects. They can alter what's happening in your body or mind in dramatic ways.

Not many people eat the same protein daily, and meat protein sensitivity is very rare. (Do you eat chicken or pork every day? Almost certainly not). Also, the rule applies to individual foods, not entire groups, so although you may be over-using a single kind of nut for example, you can easily *change* to eating a different type of nut *every* day and *still* comply with the '1 in 5' rule. The same applies to different types of fish, so you can have fish every day – so long as it is of different kinds. You can have different kinds of meat or poultry, and if you choose to have cow's milk cheese one day, sheep's the next and goat's cheese the next, you'll still be within the '1 in 5' rule. How's *that* for a rule that invites you to eat anything you want?

While plenty of people do eat several carbohydrates every day, you can probably imagine the benefits you'll get for your health and weight by controlling your intake of potatoes, bread and pasta, and rice. Food rotation is the way to do it – *without* giving up any of them. Just make them '1 in 5' foods.

The '1 in 5' rule makes sure you vary your diet and don't eat anything too often. That will automatically mean you are breaking the cycle of any food to which you may be becoming allergic, and enables your body to restore itself to full health without dietary crutches.

> If you find it difficult to rotate one or other of the main habit foods to the '1 in 5' rule because they cause you withdrawal symptoms, reduce them to '1 in 2' or '1 in 3' and slowly withdraw from them until you are eating them only '1 in 5'.

## IN BRIEF – AN OVERVIEW OF KD RULES AND ADVICE

Here is a complete list of all you need to know about how to eat The Kensington Diet way:

*KD food combining requires you to follow this single golden rule—*
- **Eat your proteins and carbohydrates so they will not be in your stomach at the same time**

*KD food rotation requires you to follow this single golden rule—*
- **All proteins, carbohydrates and foods liable to be eaten very often, other than vegetables, salads and fresh fruits, should be eaten one day only in any five days: '1 in 5'**

*The Kensington Diet strongly recommends that you—*
- **Mix fruits only with other fruits, and don't mix melon with anything but other melon.**

*KD special tips—*
- *Do* eat simple meals – they are easier to digest.
- *Do* make fresh salads, vegetables and fruits the major part of your diet.
- *Do* have only moderate portions of protein, carbohydrate and fat.
- *Do* choose only one protein or carbohydrate for each meal whenever possible.
- Do *not* add large amounts of fats to carbohydrate meals.
- Do *not* eat foods marked '1 in 5' in the food directory more than one day in every five.
- Do *not* drink with meals except wine, champagne, vegetable juice and black tea or coffee.

## THE 10% RULE FOR EMERGENCY WEIGHT CONTROL

If, at any time, you need to improve your control of your health or dimensions, the basic Kensington Diet and your chosen KD Strategy (these are fully explained, with sample menus and easy-to-follow charts, in *The Kensington Diet*) offer a wealth of resources on which to fall back. In case of emergency, however, use the '10% Rule'.

The KD 10% Rule is simplicity itself. All you have to do is *reduce* your intake of Proteins, Carbohydrates and fats by 10% and *increase* your physical activity by – you've got it – 10%. Of course, you must carry on your good food combining and '1 in 5' food rotations at the same time.

This straightforward adjustment to your established eating/activity ratio can bring about a major shift in your metabolism. You'll be responding to the demands of more activity with less food by using the fuel available from what you eat more efficiently and not wasting (or waisting!) it as excess fat on your body.

Here are a few tips:

- Use 10% more stairs, even if it means retracing your steps a little.
- Walk 10% more than you do now, even if it means taking the long-cut rather than the short-cut.
- Make love 10% more, dig a tenth of the garden over twice, take the dog for that extra walk, and so on.

And when you are ready to eat, simply use a plate that's 10% smaller or prepare 10% less in the first place. If you are still hungry, steam some vegetables or make a salad and dress them with a squeeze of lemon juice and some freshly ground black pepper. As a last resort, donate 10% to the dog or the dustbin and think of it not as waste but as an investment in your waist.

The KD 10% Rule really is your Emergency Button, for it accomplishes quickly and with little effort a true paring down in your food and your figure, and prepares you for a lengthier, more detailed approach when the time is right.

## KD COOKING

You most emphatically *don't* need to be a wizard in the kitchen to use *The Kensington Diet Cookbook*. Every recipe has been carefully devised and painstakingly tested for people with average cooking ability, and the average amount of time available for meal preparation to modern people in a fast-moving world.

Just as you'd expect, every KD recipe will automatically give you instructions for correctly combining your ingredients to keep you on track with your healthy eating. For example, sauces which contain starch thickeners will *never* be used with proteins in a meal, so you'll find coulis, purées and butter sauces instead.

You'll realise this has many advantages – for a start you'll quickly see the cooking methods are just as easy as you're used to, and often more simple. You'll find the results are as tasty and often better to look at on the plate. The biggest upside is – of course – that they will be doing you good instead of harm. You'll discover recipes and ideas which take old favourites and give them a new twist to make them suitable for your diet

– for example, quiches without pastry – and dishes which you can make into new favourites. Rather than use eccentric or bizarre recipe titles, I've decided to keep them very simple and straightforward – I feel this helps you to know in advance what you're going to get! Don't be misled into thinking, however, that the dishes are at all commonplace or ordinary – every single one is an exquisite and delectable gem, and most prove conversation-stoppers at any dinner party.

Remember that cooking is always easier and more enjoyable if you have everything to hand and prepared in advance before you begin. This is particularly true when starting out with food combining. If you don't have what you need for a correctly combined meal you will become frustrated and liable to revert to your old way of cooking and eating.

## KD FOR VEGGIES, TOO!

The Kensington Diet is entirely compatible with vegetarian eating; indeed it improves the average vegetarian diet and makes it even more healthy and weight-friendly.

A common problem for veggies is over-use of some foods. They often replace animal protein foods with a limited selection of carbohydrates, which results in over-use of certain foods – particularly wheat, potatoes, rice and the pulses. The consequences are far from the good diet most vegetarians aim for. Weight and health can both suffer.

Poor combining is not such a great problem for vegetarians, although it can occur when nuts, seeds or soya are mixed with carbohydrates in a meal. Another problem is mixing too many main carbohydrates or proteins together in the same meal, even if proteins and carbohydrates are being properly separated. A complicated meal which contains rice, potatoes and pulses would be quite common, and can easily be simplified to great benefit.

Apply The Kensington Diet food combining and food rotation rules to vegetarian foods and you have the best of both worlds. If you separate non-animal proteins (like nuts and soya) from your carbohydrates and vary them to '1 in 5' you'll get wonderful benefits. The best thing to do is to feature just one of these foods in each meal and really enjoy as many vegetable or salad foods as you can put with it.

Vegetables can be stir-fried, curried, roasted, grilled, crudité and made into salads and all can be delicious when accompanied by a non-animal protein or one of the carbohydrates. Every vegetarian recipe in this book is clearly identified with a Ⓥ.

# THE SUBTLE ART OF SERVING

I always stress that attractive presentation is crucial to the full enjoyment of KD eating. You're more likely to feel good about eating food that looks good on the plate, and you can make your meals a special experience every time with just a little attention to a few details.

Don't leave presentation to the last minute, or view it as an afterthought. Remember, the best restaurants employ battalions of chefs dedicated to making their cuisine look as attractive as possible. The keyword here is: *plan!* Think about the way you're going to serve your meal at the same time as you're buying the raw ingredients, and you won't go wrong.

- **Colour** has an almost instantaneous effect and if it's not right, the whole meal is in question. Aim for soft backgrounds, deep, rich tones in places and one or two sharp colour contrasts to tie the whole thing together. Use the plate or a serving of grains, purée or sauce as the soft background, the oranges and deep-yellows of carrots and pumpkins and the luscious dark greens of broccoli and spinach, for instance, as the rich tones. Your garnish or a dollop of sauce can be the sharp contrast.

- **Texture** must be obvious in the meal you serve. In fact, three different textures in the food items are about the minimum you should aim for before you can expect the response. That's why, in any recipe you read, some ingredients will be described by their texture: finely chopped, crushed, sliced julienne, roughly torn, and so on. On your plate, count the textures and try to arrange them in a dramatic and pleasing order.

- **Garnish** is that little bit of something or other that may be thrown away at the end of the meal, but at the moment of presentation it does its bit. Garnish is the final touch for colour, texture and placement or proportion of the meal on the plate. It may also be a taste sensation and it can, if you let yourself, have a bit of quirky or poetical expression.

Please take the opportunity at each meal time to explore the total environment of your meal so that you can elevate it to a peaceful, pleasurable occasion.

Finally, remember that the temperature at which you serve food involves both presentation and health considerations. Don't make the mistake of serving meals which are always 'piping hot' – at this temperature, it's not only difficult to savour the taste of your lovingly-prepared meal, but you'll also find that your digestive system won't be able to efficiently absorb essential nutrients later in the digestive process.

## KD COOKING GEAR

If you need a special pan or piece of equipment, which will be rarely, I'll mention it at the beginning of the recipe 'Method', but here's a list of what I find indispensable in my kitchen:

- Heavy based, non-stick **pans** offer the twin benefits of good heat distribution for even and predictable cooking while being easy to clean. It's also helpful if your saucepans can be used on the hob and in the oven. I use Le Creuset pans.
- A **steamer** is excellent for cooking vegetables with little loss of nutrients and flavour. There are various types of steamers available and all are suitable. Choose from expensive sets of purpose made pans which stack on top of each other, bamboo baskets from Chinese supermarkets which fit over boiling water in woks or saucepans, or expanding fan type steamers which fit inside standard saucepans over simmering water.
- **Knives** should be the best you can afford and kept sharp. Make sure you have a variety of sizes and types suited to the various foods you want to prepare. I also find a Chinese cleaver very useful for many different jobs, from delicate chopping and slicing to beating out cuts of meat and poultry.
- A **wok** isn't just useful for Chinese stir fries, it can be used for quick sautéing and poaching of foods of all types. Use a wok as heavy as you can handle – thin metal doesn't conduct the heat efficiently and will not cook your food evenly and quickly. I have two woks, a small one with a long single handle and a bigger one with twin side handles. Both have flattened bases for stability on the hob.
- A ridged **griddle pan** made of heavy cast iron is one of my favourite pans. Cuts of meat, fish and poultry or slices of vegetables cook very rapidly with less oil than is required by a conventional flat frying pan and the charred ridges on the food add an attractive feature and extra flavour.

- **Tongs**, preferably metal, are useful for moving food around frying pans without burning yourself.
- **Food processors**, mixers and blenders come in handy for making sauces or soups. I have a processor for meals which require it but I find an electric hand blender quite sufficient for most basic processing of liquid-based foods.
- A hand **whisk** is all you really need for whisking or mixing small amounts of liquids or dressings.
- A mandolin type **food slicer** and shredder, when used with care, is very useful for preparing small amounts of vegetables for fast cooking and attractive presentations (see Mix With Any recipes).
- Fine and coarse **graters** and a swivel type potato peeler will also help you produce attractive vegetables.
- A **trivet** or wire roasting mesh enables you to roast or grill foods, particularly meats, poultry and fish, with less fat than they would acquire in a flat tin.
- A **microwave** will cook vegetables quickly, efficiently and with very little loss of nutrients but it's also very good for reheating. When cooking large meals for a number of people it can be a boon if you can cook some items early then warm them through without losing any of their taste, texture and colour, and a microwave makes time management much easier when cooking.
- **Moulds** and special dishes are a good investment for providing simple and effective presentation options. You only need a couple each of simple ring and cup shaped moulds to be able to produce wonderfully attractive displays on the plate. A few attractive large plates and bowls will add new dimensions to the appearance of the simplest foods when they reach the table.

## KD INGREDIENTS

I want you to realise how accessible good eating for your health and figure really is. That shouldn't mean you have to have special cooking skills, or that you should need to look for unusual ingredients that aren't easily available in the average supermarket. With KD you won't have to do either.

What about processed food? While we know that fresh is best, and home-cooked is healthier than mass-produced, there are many excellent processed food products around which *will* fit into a healthy diet. If you are short of time or expertise, or if there are commercially-prepared products you enjoy and which will fit into your healthy eating the KD way, then it's fine to use them. I'll tell you about a few I use as we go. The main thing is 'read the labels'. Check for bad combinations or starches used as thickeners in sauces and soups you want to put with protein meals – they won't go! Wheat flour and soya are heavily used in prepared and processed foods, which doesn't help if you are trying to keep them to '1 in 5' or less – avoid them. Check for additives like monosodium glutamate which, in my experience, can be unhelpful to your body and weight control or high salt, fat or sugar content if you are trying to deal with your weight. One of the best pieces of advice I can give you is 'never open a packet or tin of food without adding something of your own to make it special'.

Some people are surprised to find that I use cream in recipes. Cream is a 'Mix With Any' food which, when used in moderation, has no health or weight penalty for the majority of people. However, if you have reason to believe that you have a definite problem with cream, fats or other 'unhealthy foods' such as salt, sugar etc., then you can easily avoid them or modify these recipes.

Many of the recipes in this book use olive oil, and I'd advise you to buy the very best you can find, preferably extra-fine virgin, which comes from the first pressing of the olives and has a straw-yellow colour. You will find that ethnic grocery shops, particularly those specialising in Mediterranean foods, may offer the best quality and the best value.

In the final analysis, any meal, no matter how well-designed, is only as good as its ingredients. I urge you to purchase the best ingredients you can and to gradually restock your larder with even the 'basics' boasting real quality. Treat yourself, as well, as you want to be treated.

## HOW TO USE THIS BOOK

This is how to use your *Kensington Diet Cookbook* to satisfy the basic rules of KD eating:

1.  **Decide** which main Protein or Carbohydrate will feature in your meal and fit into the '1 in 5' requirement of your KD eating (e.g. chicken or potatoes). Find a recipe you like which features that food and which is appropriate for the meal you want to serve (e.g. lunch, dinner or supper).

2. **Browse** through the recipes for starters, desserts and Mix With Any dishes which you can add to your main dish to create the meal you would most like to serve. To help you choose dishes and courses which will go together, the category (Protein, Carbohydrate or Mix With Any) is shown for every recipe and any '1 in 5' foods used are listed. Tips, advice, serving suggestions and variations to many recipes, are offered throughout, to give you a huge range of possibilities, so you'll always be able to create a meal which suits you. Bear in mind the presentation ideas I mentioned earlier.

3. **Check** your store cupboard and make a shopping list for the extra ingredients you'll need, then purchase them.

Now you're ready to cook delicious meals which will fit perfectly into your Kensington Diet combining and rotating rules.

Plan your meals ahead for several days to make sure you always have the foods you need available and to help you keep track of your '1 in 5' food rotation. This is explained in more detail in *The Kensington Diet*, which includes a Five Day Menu Arranger to make it easy for you.

In the years since first creating KD food combining, I've transformed my own health, and that of many of my clients. I promise you that if you read and follow the advice in *The Kensington Diet*, you can do the same, too. I offer you *The Kensington Diet Cookbook* with the wish that it will make your journey towards better health, improved vitality, effective weight control and maximum zest for living as delicious and luscious as it can possibly be!

*Stephen M. Twigg*

# BREAKFASTS AND BRUNCHES

## EVERYTHING YOU NEED TO KNOW ABOUT BREAKFASTS

Breakfasts don't have to be the same day in day out. Apart from being boring it isn't healthy and it certainly isn't The Kensington Diet way, where variety is the spice of health. Whatever the size of your appetite and whatever your taste there's something here for you which will keep you combining and rotating correctly.

Here are a few tips to think about first.

Fruits make excellent breakfast food. They are cleansing, nutritious and refreshing but fruits don't mix well with other types of foods and in general ought to be eaten only with other fruits. Melon definitely should not be mixed with anything at all but other melons, not even other fruits.

There are a few exceptions regarding what you can mix with fruit and yogurt, although it is a protein, is one of them. Yogurt is so easy to digest it can be mixed with fruit without harm – although still not with melon or carbohydrates. Ring the changes too by using cow's milk yogurt sometimes and sheep's or goat's milk at others.

And here's another bending of the 'Don't mix fruit' rule you can use occasionally. Some fruits, if they are very ripe, are so sweet they can be regarded as virtually all carbohydrate. They can therefore be mixed with cereals or spread on breads and crispbreads if you really want, without harm to your healthy diet. Examples are ripe bananas and dried fruits.

If you must have something sweet to spread on your toast or crispbreads it's OK too to use most jams or marmalades. Yes they may be fruit as well, but the fairly small amount of fruit compared with all the sugar that's present, means you can give them the benefit of any dubious doubt and treat them as carbohydrate as well.

Some breakfast carbohydrates are badly over used. Wheat as bread, toast, crispbreads or cereals is the most obvious example. If you enjoy carbohydrate breakfasts choose from Rye – bread or crispbreads, Oats – cakes or porridge, Corn – cereals, Rice – cereals, Potatoes and Baked Beans. Ring the changes and rotate them all at least '1 in 5'.

And one final thing, milk is a protein as is soya milk, so they don't go well on cereals. Instead use single cream diluted to your taste, at least half and half, with water, or the milk-like product made from rice, called Rice Dream, available from health food stores.

Here are some breakfast recipes to get you going:

# Mixed Fruit Salad Ⓥ

Just about any combination of fresh or tinned fruit can be used to make fruit salad. The healthiest way is to choose at least five ripe and reasonably firm fresh fruits from what is seasonal.

Food category – F
Serves – 4

INGREDIENTS

- ½ pint/300 ml apple juice
- 4 tablespoons clear honey
- 1 tablespoon grated fresh root ginger
- 2 nectarines, stoned and diced

- 1 apple, cored, skin on, diced
- 4 apricots, stoned and diced
- 2 pears, cored, skin on, diced
- 4 plums, stoned and diced

TASTE SENSATION
freshly ground nutmeg

METHOD
In a small saucepan over a moderate heat, warm the apple juice, honey and ginger for 3–4 minutes. Do not boil. Remove from heat, transfer to a non-metal jug or container and allow to cool. Arrange the fruit in a non-metal bowl and pour the cooled liquor over. Serve immediately with a little fresh nutmeg grated over.

# Citrus Fruit Salad ⓥ

This scrumptious salad can be made the night before.

Food category – F
Serves – 4

INGREDIENTS
- ½ pint/300 ml orange juice
- 4 tablespoons clear honey
- 5 cardamom pods, crushed
- 5 whole cloves
- 1 tablespoon grated orange zest

- 1 ruby grapefruit, segmented
- 1 yellow grapefruit, segmented
- 1 large orange, segmented
- 1 blood orange, segmented
- 1 ugli fruit, segmented

METHOD
In a small saucepan over a moderate heat, warm the orange juice, honey, cardamom, cloves and orange zest for 3–4 minutes. Do not boil. Remove from heat, transfer to a non-metal jug or container and allow to cool.

> Prepare the citrus fruits into segments. Grate and retain a tablespoon of zest from the orange before segmenting it in this way. Take a slice from top and bottom of the fruit. With one flat sliced end on a cutting board, and using a sharp knife, slice the rind and pith from the flesh in strips working from the top downwards to the board. You will now be able to cut the flesh out in segments from between the tough divisions that separate them.

Mix the segments of citrus fruit together in a non-metal bowl and pour the cooled liquor over.

Eat immediately or, for stronger flavours, leave to stand in a cool place for a few hours but no longer than overnight, until ready to serve. Serve into individual bowls with a little of the liquor.

# Exotic Fruit Salad ⓥ
Food category – F
Serves – 4

INGREDIENTS
- 4 tablespoons clear honey
- ½ pint/300 ml pineapple juice

- 3 kiwi fruit, peeled and sliced
- 1 large banana, peeled and sliced

- 1 papaya, seeded, peeled and diced
- ¼ pineapple, diced

- 1 mango, peeled and diced

TASTE SENSATION

maple syrup
ground cinnamon

METHOD

Dissolve the honey in the pineapple juice. Mix the fruit together in a non-metal bowl and pour the liquor over. Leave to stand for at least 30 minutes and serve into separate bowls with a trickle of maple syrup and a pinch of ground cinnamon.

# Stewed Fruit Compôte ⓥ

There are so many dried and semi-dried fruits available you'll be spoilt for choice, but the method remains the same whichever you use. This fruit compôte is prepared the day before it is needed.

Food category – F
Serves – 4

INGREDIENTS

- 1 pt/600 ml apple juice
- 4 tablespoons clear honey
- ½ teaspoon cinnamon
- 6 whole cloves
- juice and zest of an orange
- 4 oz/125 g prunes, pitted

- 4 oz/125 g dried apricots
- 4 oz/125 g dried apple
- 4 oz/125 g dried pears
- 4 oz/125 g sultanas
- crème fraîche to serve

METHOD

In a small saucepan over a moderate heat, warm the apple juice, honey, cinnamon, cloves, orange juice and zest for 3–4 minutes. Do not boil. Mix the fruits together in a non-metal bowl, pour the hot liquor over and set aside in a cool place overnight. In the morning, transfer to a saucepan and bring to boiling point over a moderate heat. Remove from heat immediately and set aside to cool a little before serving into individual bowls, with a topping of crème fraîche if desired.

# Summer Berries and Yogurt with Blackcurrant Coulis ⓥ

This is another dish easily prepared overnight. The flavours just tingle and glow with this combination and the colours are sensational.

Food category – F and P
Serves – 4

INGREDIENTS

- 6 oz/175 g raspberries
- 6 oz/175 g blueberries
- 6 oz/175 g blackberries
- 6 oz/175 g strawberries

- 5 fl oz/150 ml water
- 1 tablespoon lemon juice
- 1 tablespoon balsamic vinegar
- 2 tablespoons brown sugar

FOR THE COULIS

- 1–2 tablespoons clear honey
- 6 oz/175 g blackcurrants

- 8 oz/250 g plain Greek yogurt

METHOD

Prepare the fruit by removing stalks and leaves, then washing and draining. Halve or quarter large strawberries. Mix the raspberries, blueberries, blackberries and strawberries together, gently in a non-metal dish.

In a small saucepan warm the water, lemon juice and balsamic vinegar over a medium heat until close to simmering. Pour the hot liquor over the mixed fruit, sprinkle with the sugar, cover and set aside overnight in a cool place.

In a small saucepan warm the honey, then add the blackcurrants and keep warm for 5 minutes without boiling. Liquidise in a blender then sieve through a non-metal sieve or mash straight through the sieve. Allow to cool then taste the coulis for flavour and adjust, adding a little more honey if necessary. Serve the mixed fruits into individual bowls, top with yogurt and drizzle with blackcurrant coulis.

# Grilled Spiced Fruits ⓥ

A taste of heaven on a stick.

Food category – F
Serves – 4

You'll need some wooden or bamboo skewers about 6–8 inches long for this recipe. These are available from many supermarkets now because they're used for Thai-style kebabs.

INGREDIENTS

- 2 medium peaches, stoned and cut into approx. 1 inch/ 2.5 cm dice
- 8 oz/250 g whole tinned lychees, peeled and stoned, juice retained
- 2 bananas, firm but ripe, peeled and cut into 1 inch/ 2.5 cm slices
- 1 medium mango, flesh only, in approximately 1 inch/ 2.5 cm dice

- 8 oz/250 g tinned pineapple in large chunks, juice retained
- 6 whole cloves
- ground cinnamon
- freshly ground nutmeg

METHOD

Put 8 wooden skewers to soak in a bowl of warm water. Put the juice from the tinned lychees and pineapple into a small saucepan with the cloves, bring to a simmer and simmer, uncovered, over a medium to low heat to reduce, about 15–20 minutes. When reduced to a thickish syrup, remove from heat and keep warm until ready to use. Watch carefully and stir occasionally to avoid burning. While reducing the liquor line a grill pan with foil and heat the grill.

Remove the skewers from the water and thread with pieces of fruit, alternating the types and leaving at least an inch at both ends of each skewer to allow handling. Prepare two skewers per person. Sprinkle the skewered fruits with cinnamon and freshly ground nutmeg, place in the lined grill pan and grill for 5–6 minutes, turning occasionally until the fruits are well coloured around the edges but not burned. Serve onto individual plates with a little warm, but not hot, liquor over.

VARIATION

- Cut the bananas lengthways and the other fruits into long pieces or segments instead of chunks. Keep the lychees whole. Heat the grill. Arrange the fruits in the bottom of a large non-stick frying pan, scatter the whole lychees over and sprinkle with spices and a tablespoon brown sugar. Place under the hot grill until the fruits are softened and have some colour and the sugar has drawn the juices and melted to a syrup. Serve the hot spicy fruit with cool crème fraîche or Greek yogurt, if desired.

# Grilled Grapefruit ⓥ

It may not be hot but it's sharp and refreshing in the mouth.

Food category – F
Serves – 4

INGREDIENTS

- 2 large grapefruits, halved, segments loosened
- 8 whole cloves
- 2 teaspoons clear honey
- ground cinnamon

METHOD

Line a grill pan and heat the grill to a medium to high heat. To prepare the grapefruits halve them and trim the rounded ends, without cutting through to the flesh, so they will stand without falling over. Using a grapefruit knife or other small sharp knife cut all the way around the inside of the skin of each half to sever the tough divisions between the segments, then slice each side of the divisions to loosen the segments of fruit flesh.

Stick two whole cloves into the flesh of each grapefruit half, drizzle with honey and sprinkle with cinnamon.

Place the grapefruit halves on the grill pan and grill at a moderate heat about 2 inches from the grill for about 4–5 minutes until the fruits are softened and warmed right through. Carefully, using tongs or a pair of spoons to protect your fingers from the hot juice which will have been drawn from the fruit, place each half into individual dishes just large enough to hold them firmly. Serve immediately.

## FRUIT SMOOTHIES

Smoothies are an art form requiring imagination and patience, but only as much patience as it takes to stop yourself eating the ingredients before you've blended them into a healthy whole which somehow transcends the sum of its component parts! That takes about 3–4 minutes.

Virtually any soft fruit will do for a smoothie; it's especially good for using up over-ripe fruits. The key to an exceptional smoothie is in what flavours you can get into it from the limited range of bonafide ingredients, fruit, yogurt and natural flavours. Recipes are jealously guarded. Are flavoured yogurts or plain best? Is cow's milk yogurt better than sheep's; Greek or set? Is chocolate allowed in a real fruit smoothie? Is a smoothie only genuine if it requires a spoon, or is it still a smoothie if you can drink it? The debate goes on – see what you think. Here are a couple of my favourites to get your imagination and taste buds going. These recipes are for one. (Smoothies are fairly private things – let others make their own!) You'll need a liquidiser, food blender or at least an electric hand blender to become a true smoothie person.

# Banana and Strawberry Smoothie Ⓥ

Food category – F and P
Serves – 1

INGREDIENTS

- 1 whole ripe banana, roughly chopped
- 4 oz/125 g ripe strawberries
- 5 fl oz/150 ml vanilla yogurt
- cold water, a few tablespoons only

TASTE SENSATION
3 drops natural orange flavour or essential oil

METHOD
In a blender, or in a jug using a hand blender, purée the fruit and half the yogurt. When you have a smooth mixture add the orange oil and the remaining yogurt and blend again to a smooth liquid. Blend in enough water to make a smoothie thin enough to drink. Serve in a tall glass.

> Pre-chilled glasses are, some say, essential to perfect smoothies. Keep one or two in your freezer compartment if you become a smoothie aficionado. Or fill a glass with ice-cubes while you prepare the ingredients. Then turn the cubes out and pour in the smoothie.

# Stewed Apricot Smoothie with Whole Blueberries Ⓥ

This recipe uses stewed dried apricots which should be cooked according to the packet instructions. Just wait until you taste what happens when you bite into the blueberries while you're eating this creamy apricot and yogurt smoothie.

Food category – F and P
Serves – 1

INGREDIENTS

- 1 cup stewed dried apricots, stoned and drained
- 6 oz/175 ml sheep's yogurt
- 2–3 oz/60–90 g half cup whole ripe blueberries, washed and stalks removed

METHOD

How to Stew Apricots: Cover the stoned apricots in water in an enamel saucepan and bring to a soft boil over a medium heat. Simmer for 10–15 minutes, remove from heat and leave to cool before draining. Keeping at least a third of a cup of the apricots in reserve, blend the yogurt with enough apricots to make a thick, spoonable, smooth apricot cream. Spoon the mixture into a bowl. Add the blueberries and use a spoon to fold them in carefully without breaking any. Pour into the chilled glass. Rinse the blender jar in cold water and blend the retained apricots to a smooth purée. Top the smoothie with this purée and serve.

# Scrambled Eggs with Smoked Salmon

Food category – P
'1 in 5' – eggs, salmon
Serves – 4

INGREDIENTS

- 10 eggs, size 2
- 2 oz/60 g unsalted butter
- 4–6 oz/125–185 g smoked salmon cut into thin strips
- sea salt and freshly ground black pepper, to taste

METHOD

Beat the eggs together in a bowl. In a non-stick saucepan over a medium heat melt half the butter until it starts to foam. Add the egg mixture and stir continuously while it warms and begins to thicken. When over half the mixture has thickened into creamy scrambled egg, continue to stir well while adding a small pinch of salt and the remaining butter. Stir vigorously until only a little of the egg remains to be cooked. Be sure not to allow any of the mixture to remain unmixed with the butter or undisturbed in the pan where it can solidify. Remove from heat, then fold in the smoked salmon strips straight away. Serve immediately onto warm plates, sprinkle with a little coarsely ground black pepper.

TIPS

☞ Successful scrambled eggs are creamy and soft, not runny or set hard. This means they have to have enough butter and cook for just the right amount of time. The main thing to remember is they will continue to cook in the hot saucepan even after you have removed them from the heat, so take them off early enough and continue to mix in the pan while you add your finishing touches. Scrambled eggs must be served immediately or they will go rubbery, so whoever is going to eat them must be primed to tuck in at once.

VARIATIONS

• Try smoked haddock, skinned and flaked, in place of the salmon.
• To make this dish as a light lunch or supper just add two tablespoons of well drained chopped capers and two tablespoons of chopped fresh dill with the salmon before serving with a dressed green salad garnished with shavings of Parmesan.

# Scrambled Eggs with Mushrooms, Tomatoes and Bacon

A version of scrambled egg using the perennial Mix With Any accompaniments to any Protein breakfast, mushrooms and tomatoes.

Food category – P
'1 in 5' – eggs, bacon
Serves – 4

INGREDIENTS

• 8 rashers lean streaky bacon
• 6 oz/175 g white button mushrooms, wiped clean and chopped into $\frac{1}{4}$ inch/6 mm dice
• 2 oz/60 g unsalted butter
• 4 medium sized tomatoes, seeded and coarsely chopped

• sea salt and freshly ground black pepper, to taste
• Tabasco sauce, optional
• 8 eggs, size 2

METHOD

Grill the bacon both sides until crisp and remove to kitchen paper so it will drain off excess fat. When cool enough to handle, chop into $\frac{1}{4}$ inch/

6 mm pieces on fresh kitchen paper to further remove excess fat. Set aside. Sauté the mushrooms over a high heat in about 1 oz/30 g butter until they are just soft and a little browned. Remove from the heat, add the tomatoes, salt and pepper and a few drops of Tabasco if used, to taste. Mix and leave so the tomatoes warm in the pan without becoming over-soft.

Beat the eggs together while you heat about 1oz/30 g of butter in a non-stick saucepan until it is just foaming. Scramble the eggs as described above but without any ingredients other than salt and extra butter. Serve onto warm plates, make a depression in the middle of each egg portion and fill with spoons full of mushroom and tomato mixture. Top with chopped bacon and serve immediately.

## Grilled Gammon Rashers with Eggs, Mushrooms and Tomatoes

Food category – P
'1 in 5' – bacon, eggs
Serves – 4

INGREDIENTS

- 4 gammon rashers 3–4 oz/ 90–125 g each, excess fat removed
- 2 oz/60 g unsalted butter
- 8 medium flat field mushrooms, cleaned, stalks trimmed
- sea salt and freshly ground black pepper, to taste
- 4 eggs, size 2
- 4 ripe tomatoes, halved
- balsamic vinegar

METHOD

Heat the grill to a high heat, warm the oven to keep plates and cooked food warm without further cooking. With foil, line a large grill pan (or other suitable pan) large enough to take all the gammon rashers. Warm 1 oz/30 g butter until it just melts in a heavy based non-stick frying pan. Brush the mushrooms both sides with melted butter and season with salt and freshly ground black pepper. Arrange the mushrooms and tomatoes in the grill pan: the tomatoes cut side down and the mushrooms stalk side down. Grill both sides until cooked. When turning the tomatoes season the cut sides with salt and pepper and a few drops of balsamic vinegar. The tomatoes will probably cook more quickly than the mushrooms and should be soft but not falling apart and tinged with colour from grilling. The mushrooms should be softened and a little browned. When both are cooked, remove to a plate in the warm oven. Season the gammon rashers with pepper only, place under the grill and cook both sides for 3–4 minutes until browned at the edges and cooked through to your taste. Remove to keep warm while you fry the eggs.

Fry the eggs two at a time in butter in your favourite way. This will give you time to arrange two servings at a time. To serve, arrange on each warm plate a gammon rasher topped with a fried egg and accompanied by two halves of grilled tomato and two grilled mushrooms. Serve immediately.

VARIATIONS
• Try poached eggs instead of fried or even poached kipper fillets and poached eggs with the tomatoes and mushrooms.

# Bubble and Squeak ⓥ

No need to wait for leftover potatoes and greens to make this delicious and filling old favourite. Cook the ingredients and prepare your bubble and squeak the night before, leave them in the fridge and your breakfast will take almost no time at all in the morning.

Food category – C
'1 in 5' – potato
Serves – 4

INGREDIENTS
• 10 oz/315 g Savoy cabbage leaves, washed and trimmed of thick stalks and veins (or use other cabbage greens such as spring greens, spinach or Brussels sprouts)
• 2 small onions, finely chopped
• 2 oz/60 g unsalted butter
• 1½ lbs/750 g potatoes, boiled and mashed with 1 tablespoon cream
• 1 teaspoon of English prepared mustard
• 1 teaspoon whole grain or other French mustard
• sea salt and freshly ground black pepper, to taste
• 2 tablespoons olive oil

METHOD
Fill a large bowl with cold water for refreshing the cabbage leaves.

Bring a large pan of unsalted water to the boil and blanch the cabbage leaves for about 2 minutes then transfer to the cold water. Drain, pat dry and shred coarsely.

In a small frying pan sauté the onions in 1 oz butter until lightly coloured. In a large mixing bowl mix the mashed potatoes with the contents of the onion pan, butter included. Add the mustards and season with salt and pepper. Add the cabbage greens and fold together well. Shape into 4 cakes about ¾ inch/2 cm thick, placing them on oiled greaseproof paper. If they are to be kept for frying later, keep covered in the refrigerator.

To cook, heat the olive oil and remaining butter in a large heavy based non-stick frying pan until the butter is melted and hot. Pan-fry the bubble and squeak over a medium heat for 6–8 minutes on each side, turning halfway through cooking. The patties should be crusted and well browned both sides. Serve onto warm plates with your choice of cooked mushrooms, tomatoes, onions and baked beans.

VARIATION

- For a light lunch or supper, replace a quarter of the potato with parsnips, add a tablespoon each of chopped fresh parsley and sage with the cabbage greens and serve with freshly made tomato sauce (see page 271).

# EATING LIGHT

## EVERYTHING YOU NEED TO KNOW ABOUT SOUPS

Winter or summer, lunch or supper there's a soup for the occasion. And soups, whether home made or shop bought, have a very useful role to play in Kensington Diet eating for health and weight control. The fascinating thing is how easy they are to make.

Soups are amongst the healthiest dishes you can eat. High fluid content, loads of nutrients, easy to digest and low in most problem foods all adds up to a very good deal indeed for your body. Soups can be substantial enough to make a light meal in themselves or light enough to form a filling starter which will take the thick edge off your appetite and help you to avoid eating too much of other courses which are less good for you and your figure. Soups are serious good news.

The most versatile soups for Kensington Diet purposes are made from Mix With Any ingredients. Which means M/A vegetables, vegetable stock, no added starchy thickeners, cream where it is called for to smooth out textures and flavours and M/A garnishes. This means you can enjoy KD Mix With Any soups in any meal with either carbohydrate or protein accompaniments or main courses with no concerns about combinations or even '1 in 5' rotation.

### CREAM IN SOUPS

I've already mentioned the use of cream in KD eating (see page 30). It's used in soups to give smoothness and body as well as flavour, and because it is a Mix With Any food you don't have to worry what it's combined with. The small amount used does not cause a health or weight problem for the vast majority of people. However, it's still a good idea to make sure you don't have too much cream too often, so be aware, there are many other soups without cream you could choose instead.

Where cream is used in a KD Mix With Any soup it can be replaced with yogurt or with skimmed or semi-skimmed milk to make a lighter soup with even fewer calories and less fat. To do so, though, will change it to a protein soup and it will become incompatible with carbohydrate dishes. Milk shouldn't be used to replace cream where it's used in soups containing carbohydrates, because milk and carbohydrates don't combine well.

When making or buying soups that are not made entirely from Mix With Any ingredients they should never contain both proteins and carbohydrates together. So take a soup which contains meat, chicken or fish as stock or main ingredient, it's fine if milk or yogurt is used to make it smoother but it shouldn't have any starch as a thickener. Similarly, in a carbohydrate soup while you might find potato, wheat or corn starch used to thicken it and pasta, rice, pearl barley or potatoes as main ingredients, you wouldn't want meat, fish or chicken as either stock or a main ingredient.

The garnishes suggested for Kensington Diet soups are, wherever possible, Mix With Any foods for the reasons I've already explained. Protein or carbohydrate garnishes are suggested only for soups with which they will combine correctly. Be quite careful that what you put with your soup as garnish or accompaniments, actually combines well with other ingredients in the soup and in other dishes in the meal it's to be served with. Croutons and the universal companion to soup, bread, may be fine with carbohydrate soups but they won't go with protein soups or even Mix With Any soups which are a part of a meal containing proteins. We've already considered the fact that wheat is much overused in most people's diet and is the cause of many problems (see page 23). Croutons and bread with soup are part of the all too familiar epidemic of wheat overuse and in KD eating they're something to be avoided most of the time if you're to be successful making wheat '1 in 5' or less.

The stock you use when you make your soup is obviously very important, not only in how to treat the soup for combining and rotation but for the nutrition and flavour it brings as well. Vegetable stock is used most extensively in Kensington Diet soups because it adds flavour and nutrition, as well as for the fact that it will combine well with either proteins or carbohydrates.

For ease and speed commercial vegetable stock cubes and extracts can be useful but they vary considerably. Many contain additives such as monosodium glutamate or colourings and flavourings which won't do you a lot of good. Others have a very high salt content and few other flavourings, so they don't do much to enhance your food and frequently spoil it with excess salt.

My favourite vegetable stock cube is one you can get from most health food shops and, now, many supermarkets as well. It's called Kallo and it's a good product to have available as a back up in case you need stock very quickly or to strengthen the flavour of your own home made stock if you need to. Vegetable stock from the cold cabinet of most big supermarkets is also a good option if you don't have your own available.

In general, though, if you have time and like good food, you'll make your own vegetable stock. I find it's best to regularly make up fresh amounts of the basic KD vegetable stock and keep some available all the time. It's not only useful for soups but can be used in many other recipes for all the same reasons it's used here. You can also recover nutrients lost from vegetables when they are cooked just by adding the cooking liquor from steamed or boiled vegetables to your stock.

Some recipes do benefit from a protein-based stock such as chicken or fish, and where it is within the food combining rules, it's OK to use them, and you might like to replace the vegetable stock used in an otherwise Mix With Any soup, with a chicken or fish stock. I've included an excellent Chicken Stock recipe for you below. Just remember it will change the food category of the soup. In general, though, I prefer to use my own, freshly made, vegetable stock for most purposes.

If I do need protein stocks, particularly if I need **fish stock** which can become bitter if not made well, I use tubs of ready made stock available from the cold cabinets of supermarkets. I choose brands which have the firm jelly consistency of a good stock and a strong flavour. I also use ready made sauces and consommés if their labels show them to be compatible with what I'm cooking and if they have no additives I feel unhappy about. I prefer not to use protein stock cubes or extracts.

Below is a recipe for a good Basic Vegetable Stock. It's really easy and well worthwhile taking a little time to make, but if you haven't the time even for that, then there's also a super fast version you can make in just 15 minutes.

You really do need some form of food processor or blender for easy soup making. Blending in the pot with an electric hand blend, followed by stirring the soup through a fine sieve with a wooden spoon, does the job very well though, and you can make do with simply forcing the soup through a sieve – at a push.

One last word about cooking with any stock: be careful with your seasoning. The flavours and seasoning already in stocks, especially ready made products, can affect how much added flavouring and seasoning you'll need to put into your final dish. The best time to add salt and pepper is at the end of cooking when you can taste and assess the finished product, and adjust it to your own pallet.

# Basic Vegetable Stock ⓥ
Food category – M/A
Makes approximately 1¾ pints/1 litre

INGREDIENTS
- 2 tablespoons olive oil
- 3–4 medium carrots, washed, trimmed and coarsely chopped
- 4 stalks celery, washed, trimmed and coarsely chopped
- 2 leeks washed, trimmed and coarsely chopped
- 2 medium onions, chopped
- 2 bay leaves
- small bunch fresh thyme
- 6 whole peppercorns
- 2½ pints/1.5 litres cold water

METHOD
Place a large saucepan or stock pot over a low heat, warm the oil, then add the vegetables, herbs and peppercorns. Cook stirring occasionally, until the onions are clear and the vegetables softening, about 5–10 minutes. Add the water and bring to a simmer. Simmer uncovered for 30–40 minutes until the stock is reduced by about one third. Strain through a fine sieve, discard the vegetables. Use immediately or store for later use.

VARIATIONS
- Changes to this Basic Stock can be made during preparation or at the time of use, by adding garlic, different herbs or spices suitable for the other foods with which it is to be used. Salt and pepper should only be added to the final recipe.
- A small beetroot, washed, topped and tailed, may be added to the stock during preparation to give it a beautiful ruby colour and earthy flavour.

☞ Basic Vegetable Stock can be kept in your refrigerator in an airtight container for up to three days after making and for up to three months in your freezer. For freezing, line a half pint bowl or straight sided jug with a large freezer bag. Pour half a pint of stock into the bag and place it, bowl and all, into the freezer to freeze. When frozen seal and remove the bag with its frozen stock inside and keep until ready to use. Another handy way to keep frozen stock in useful portions is to fill an ice-cube tray. Drop one or two cubes into chilled summer soups such as Gazpacho.

# Quick Vegetable Stock ⓥ

Not as strong in flavour as the Basic Vegetable Stock, above, but still an excellent stock for when you want it quickly.

Food category – M/A
Makes approximately 20 fl oz/600 ml

INGREDIENTS

- 3–4 medium carrots, washed, trimmed and diced
- 4 stalks celery, washed, trimmed and diced
- 2 leeks washed, trimmed and cut into half-inch lengths
- 2 medium onions, diced
- 3 bay leaves, torn in half
- 2 small bunches fresh thyme
- 6 whole peppercorns
- 1 pint/600 ml cold water

METHOD

In a large capacity saucepan – allow for a good rolling boil – place all the ingredients together with just enough of the water to cover them. Bring to a rapid boil over a medium/high heat, cover and boil strongly for ten minutes. Strain through a fine sieve and discard the vegetables. Add enough water to the stock to bring it up to the amount you need for your recipe and use immediately. This stock should not be stored.

VARIATIONS

- Add small amounts of concentrates such as yeast extract, tomato purée, soy sauce, Worcestershire sauce, Tabasco or mushroom sauce to the final stock where appropriate to taste. See also variations to Basic Vegetable Stock, above.

# Chicken Stock

Food category – P
Makes approximately – 2 pints/1200 ml

INGREDIENTS

- 1 oz/25 g unsalted butter
- 3–4 medium carrots, washed, trimmed and coarsely chopped
- 4 stalks celery, washed, trimmed and coarsely chopped
- 2 leeks washed, trimmed and coarsely chopped
- 2 medium onions, chopped
- 2 bay leaves
- small bunch fresh parsley
- small bunch fresh thyme
- 6 whole peppercorns
- 2 lbs/1 kg mixed chicken bones and trimmings, roughly chopped
- 3 pints/1.8 litres cold water

METHOD

Place a large saucepan or stock pot over a low heat, warm the butter, then add the vegetables, herbs and peppercorns. Cook stirring occasionally, until the onions are clear and the vegetables softening, about 5–10 minutes. Add the chicken trimmings and water and bring to a simmer. Simmer, partially covered, for 2–3 hours, regularly skimming off any foam that floats to the surface. The stock should reduce by about a third during simmering. Strain through a fine sieve, discard the vegetables and chicken trimmings. Leave to cool overnight in the refrigerator. Remove excess fat that will have risen to the surface. Use immediately or store for later use (see below).

TIPS

☞ Hard boiling breaks down any meat and soft tissue on the bones and produces large quantities of foam, so instead simmer just at boiling point with very little movement at the surface of the stock. After 10 minutes, skim off the foam at the top of the stock.

☞ You can extract a wonderful stock from just about any chicken bones and trimmings. Time allowing, if I need boneless breasts or thighs of chicken I'll buy them on the bone, remove the meat myself and use the bones and skin for my stock. The leftover carcass from a roast chicken, giblets too of course, will also produce plenty of flavour.

☞ Keep bones and trimmings in your freezer until you have accumulated enough ingredients and time to make a batch of stock, then freeze the end product for future use. If, when made, you want to store your stock in the refrigerator, keep it in an airtight container, use within three days and boil it again.

☞ If you want a clearer stock for any purpose you can get a good result just by straining through fine muslin. The classic way of course is to boil the strained stock with the whites of 2 or 3 eggs for a few minutes then to strain again through cloth. If time does not allow, the best ready made supermarket chill cabinet stocks are good and clear already, very quick and much less fuss.

VARIATIONS

• Changes to this Chicken Stock can be made during preparation or at the time of use, by adding garlic with the onion, different herbs or spices suitable for the other foods with which it is to be used. Salt and pepper should only be added to the final recipe.

# Watercress Soup ⓥ

A glorious soup with a peppery flavour that's as good cold as it is hot.

Food category – M/A
Serves – 4

INGREDIENTS

• 1 small onion, finely chopped
• 2 stalks celery, washed, trimmed and finely chopped
• 1 tablespoon olive oil
• 3 large bunches or packs of watercress, washed, thick stalks and damaged leaves removed (4 nice sprigs retained for garnish)

• ¼ teaspoon freshly ground nutmeg
• 1½ pint/900 ml Basic Vegetable Stock (see page 48)
• 1 tablespoon lemon juice
• small carton single cream
• sea salt and ground white pepper, to taste

METHOD

In a large saucepan over a low heat, sweat the onion and celery in the olive oil until the onion is soft and clear, but not browned, about 5–10 minutes. Add the watercress and nutmeg, cover and continue to cook for 2–3 minutes. Add two-thirds of the vegetable stock and the lemon juice, bring to the simmer and cook for 10 minutes. Transfer to processor or blender and purée to a smooth soup, adding additional stock and some single cream to produce the consistency you desire. Return to the saucepan (through a fine sieve if a smoother soup is required) and adjust for flavour, season with salt and white pepper. Serve in warm bowls garnished with sprigs of watercress and a swirl of single cream.

TIP

☞ To serve this soup or its variation as a cold soup, cool after blending and adjust for final consistency and flavour when cold, just before serving.

VARIATION

• For a thicker soup add 1 cup diced potato with the onion and celery and ensure that it is completely cooked before blending. This will make it a Carbohydrate soup.

## Creamy Celery Soup Ⓥ

Celeriac is added to this recipe to enhance the celery flavour and make this soup rich and smooth.

Food category – M/A
Serves – 4

INGREDIENTS

• 1 small onion or leek, trimmed and finely chopped
• 1 tablespoon olive oil
• 6 stalks celery, washed, trimmed and coarsely chopped
• 1 medium celeriac, peeled, diced

• 1½ pints/900 ml Basic Vegetable Stock (see page 48)
• small carton single cream
• sea salt and white pepper, to taste
• 2 tablespoons fresh parsley, finely chopped, for garnish

METHOD

In a large saucepan over a medium heat sweat the onion in the olive oil until soft, without browning, about 5–10 minutes. Add the celery, celeriac and quarter pint of stock, cover and continue to cook, stirring occasionally until the vegetables have softened, 5–10 minutes. Add all but a cup of the remaining stock, bring to the simmer and cook until all the vegetables are completely soft. Transfer to a processor or blender and purée until smooth, adding single cream and extra stock to produce the consistency required. Return to the pan (through a fine sieve if a smoother soup is desired) and keep warm while adjusting the flavour to taste with salt and white pepper. Serve into warm bowls, each garnished with half a tablespoon of chopped parsley swirled into the soup just before serving.

# Gazpacho Ⓥ

Probably the perfect cold soup for summer. A classic and always a favourite, and about as healthy as a soup can get. Here are some KD versions.

Food category – M/A
Serves – 4

INGREDIENTS

- 1 lb/500 g fresh, ripe plum tomatoes, skinned, seeded and roughly chopped (or 1 large tin of chopped tomatoes)
- 1 red pepper, seeded, cored and roughly chopped
- 1 yellow pepper, seeded, cored and roughly chopped
- 1 green pepper, seeded, cored and roughly chopped
- 1 medium cucumber, peeled, seeded and roughly chopped
- 1 red or Spanish onion, roughly chopped

- 1–2 cloves garlic, crushed
- 2 tablespoons wine vinegar, white or red
- 2 tablespoons olive oil
- 1 teaspoon lemon juice
- 4–6 fresh basil leaves, torn coarsely
- 1¾ pints/1 litre tomato juice
- sea salt and freshly ground black pepper, to taste
- pinch sugar

FOR GARNISH
- 2 tablespoons finely chopped fresh herbs (parsley, mint, oregano or coriander)

METHOD

Mix all ingredients (except half a pint of the tomato juice, and the salt, pepper and sugar), in a large mixing bowl. If you have time, cover and leave to stand in the refrigerator for a few hours, to cool and allow the flavours to blend. When ready, transfer to a food processor or blender and purée until smooth. Adjust texture with as much of the remaining tomato juice as necessary, mix well. Season to taste with salt, pepper and sugar. Serve in chilled bowls garnished with chopped herbs.

VARIATIONS

I love to serve food that people can 'customise' to their own taste and Gazpacho is perfect for it. It's fun to watch what different people choose when they have the chance. Just serve lots of small dishes of garnish from which people can help themselves to make their bowl of basic soup into their own special creation. You just have to be sure the garnishes are compatible with other dishes, if any, in the meal. Here are some ideas to get your imagination going. Use as many M/A garnishes as you like and, if your combining and rotating requirements allow, some carbohydrate or protein options too:

- Food category – M/A
  Red, green and yellow peppers, finely diced
  Cucumber, peeled and seeded, finely diced
  Onions, red, Spanish or spring, finely chopped
  Olives, black or green, stoned and finely chopped
  Capers
  Tabasco or Worcestershire sauce
- Food category – P
  Anchovy fillets (drained and finely chopped)
  Almond flakes (toasted)
  Eggs (hard boiled and chopped)
- Food category – C
  Croutons (plain, herb or garlic, see below)
  Corn kernels
  The soup can be thickened by adding 2 – 3 slices of white bread, crusts removed, and blended in with all the other ingredients.

# Avocado Soup Ⓥ

An unusual cold soup with more than a touch of Mexico to make it taste wonderful, and no cooking either. Perfect for a summer meal.

Food category – M/A
Serves – 4

INGREDIENTS

- 1 tablespoon olive oil
- 1 small onion, finely chopped
- 1 small green chilli seeded, and very finely chopped
- 1 tablespoon lemon juice
- 2 ripe avocados
- 1–2 tablespoons sour cream
- 1½ pints/900 ml chilled Basic

Vegetable Stock (see page 48)
- Tabasco sauce, to taste

- sea salt and freshly ground black
  pepper, to taste

FOR GARNISH
- 2 ripe tomatoes, skinned, seeded
  and finely chopped

- 1 tablespoon fresh coriander,
  finely chopped

---

**Preparing Chilli Peppers**

Care is needed when preparing chilli peppers because of the irritation their juices can cause to sensitive tissues like the eyes. With a sharp knife split and remove the stalk and seeds of the chilli onto kitchen paper and immediately discard the trimmings. Chop the chilli on fresh kitchen paper, tip immediately into a small bowl, discard the paper, wash the knife and wash your hands thoroughly to remove any remaining juices.

---

METHOD

In a small bowl mix the olive oil, onion, chilli and lemon juice and set aside to chill. Halve and destone the avocados and scoop the flesh into a mixing bowl with the sour cream and mix briefly. Put the onion and chilli mix with the avocado mixture into a processor or blender and add half the chilled stock. Blend until smooth. Add as much of the remaining stock as you require to make a smooth creamy soup. Adjust the flavouring with Tabasco sauce (about 10 drops), salt and freshly ground black pepper. Serve with 2–3 Basic Vegetable Stock ice-cubes for extra chill, if desired (see page 48).

FOR THE GARNISH

Mix the chopped tomatoes with the chopped coriander and a little salt and black pepper. Serve the soup in individual bowls topped with a tablespoon of chopped tomato and coriander garnish. If your combining and rotation requirements allow, try the garnish suggestion below.

GARNISH OPTION

Food category – C
- Serve avocado soup with plain natural (yellow) or blue corn chips or scatter a tablespoon of sweetcorn kernels over each serving.

# French-Style Onion Soup Ⓥ

A variation of another old favourite – this time to warm you up in winter.

Food category – M/A
Serves – 4

INGREDIENTS

- 1 lb/500 g onions, thinly sliced
- 1–2 cloves garlic, finely crushed
- 2 tablespoons olive oil
- 1 dessertspoon yeast extract
- 1½ pints/900 ml Basic Vegetable Stock (see page 48)
- ½ pint dry cider
- sea salt and freshly ground black pepper, to taste

METHOD

In a large heavy based saucepan, over a medium heat, fry the onions and garlic in the oil, stirring once in a while so the onions acquire plenty of colour but do not burn, about 10 minutes. Reduce the heat under the pan. While frying the onions dissolve the yeast extract in the stock and add to the onions with the cider and freshly ground black pepper to season. Bring to a simmer over a low heat. Simmer, partly covered, for 25–35 minutes until the onions are soft. Serve hot soup into warm bowls with garnish or accompaniment from below if your combining and rotating requirements allow.

GARNISH OPTION

Food category – C
- Serve the soup into individual warmed bowls and sprinkle with croutons (see page 68) or float a slice of toasted garlic or herb bread on each bowl.

VARIATION
- French-style onion soup intended for a Carbohydrate meal can be given a different flavour by replacing the cider with half a pint of real ale.

# Thick Vegetable Soup Ⓥ

Virtually anything can go into thick, filling soups like this. It's a soup for eating, not drinking, so the key is to cut the vegetables chunky and cook them long enough so the soup thickens into a broth.

Food category – M/A
Serves – 4

INGREDIENTS

- 1 small onion, finely diced
- 1 cup medium diced pumpkin flesh
- 3 tablespoons olive oil
- 1–2 cloves garlic, finely crushed
- 2 medium carrots, peeled, trimmed and diced
- 2 medium leeks, trimmed and cut into ½ inch/1 cm slice
- 2 sticks celery, washed, trimmed and cut into ½ inch/1 cm slice
- 2 pinches powdered saffron (or ½ tsp turmeric)
- 1 cup ripe, skinned, seeded and roughly chopped tomatoes
- 1¾ pints/1 litre Basic Vegetable Stock (see page 48)
- 1 cup tinned (or frozen) artichoke hearts, drained and quartered
- 1 cup frozen (or fresh) petit pois
- 2 tablespoons finely chopped fresh herb (parsley or thyme), for garnish
- sea salt and freshly ground black pepper, to taste

METHOD

In a large heavy based saucepan over a moderate heat, fry the onions and pumpkin in the oil until they take on a little colour and the onions soften. Reduce to a low heat. Add the garlic, carrots, leeks, celery and a little salt and pepper seasoning, turn gently until well mixed and cook over a low heat for 5 minutes. Add the saffron, mix and cook for 2 minutes. Add the chopped tomatoes and two-thirds of the stock, stir and bring to a simmer. Add more stock if the soup thickens while it simmers, covered, for 15–20 minutes. Add the artichokes (and the petit pois if they are fresh), cover and simmer for a further 8–10 minutes. Add the peas if they are frozen and simmer for 3–4 minutes. The soup should be a thick broth with all the vegetables well cooked. Serve hot soup into warm bowls, garnish with chopped fresh herbs.

VARIATIONS

Food Category – C
- Add pasta, rice, beans (butter or haricot) or medium diced potatoes

(about 1 cup) at the same time as the tomatoes and stock, if your combining and rotation requirements allow.

- Note: these additions will tend to thicken the soup, so you may need to add extra stock as the soup cooks.

GARNISH OPTIONS

Food Category – M/A
- Garnish with thinly sliced onions, fried until crisp in a little hot oil.

Food Category – C
- Serve with garlic or herb bread, or croutons (see page 68) if your combining and rotating requirements allow.

# Root Soup ⓥ

Similar to the Thick Vegetable Soup but benefiting from the earthy, rustic flavours and fibre of root vegetables.

Food category – M/A
Serves – 4

INGREDIENTS
- 2 tablespoons olive oil
- 1 small onion, finely chopped
- 1 cup carrots, peeled, trimmed and diced
- 1 cup celeriac, peeled, trimmed and diced
- 1 cup parsnip, peeled, trimmed and diced
- 1 cup swede, peeled, trimmed and diced
- 1 cup kohlrabi, peeled, trimmed and diced

- 1–2 cloves garlic, finely crushed
- 2 pints/1.2 litres Basic Vegetable Stock (see page 48)
- 2 bay leaves
- 1 small sprig thyme
- sea salt and freshly ground black pepper, to taste
- 1 tablespoon single cream (optional)

FOR GARNISH
- 1 small parsnip, peeled, trimmed
- 1 dessertspoon olive oil

- Worcestershire sauce

METHOD
Heat the oil in a large heavy based saucepan over a low heat and sauté the onions until softened and clear, without browning, about 5 minutes.

Add the root vegetables and garlic, mix, cover and cook for 4–5 minutes stirring occasionally. Add two-thirds of the stock, the bay leaves and the thyme, season lightly and bring to a simmer. Simmer for 15–20 minutes until the vegetables are cooked but not breaking down, adding a little more stock if required to keep the liquid over the vegetables. Remove about two-thirds of the vegetables to a bowl and set aside. Remove and discard the bay leaf and thyme.

Cook the remaining vegetables in the saucepan stock until soft, 5–8 minutes. Transfer the stock and its vegetables to a processor or blender and purée into a smooth soup base. If a very smooth soup base is required press through a sieve after blending. Return the soup base to the pan and warm, without boiling, while adjusting to taste with cream, salt and pepper. Replace the diced vegetables set aside earlier, warm through while adjusting the consistency with extra stock if required. Serve into warm bowls garnished with crisp ribbons of parsnip (see below) and a few drops of Worcestershire sauce.

---

### How To Make Parsnip Ribbons

Using a swivel type potato peeler, shave the parsnip into ribbons.

In a large, heavy based frying pan, heat the olive oil and pan-fry the ribbons until they take plenty of colour and start to crisp. They will soften first and need to be kept reasonably loose and separate in the pan. When cooked enough, set aside on kitchen paper to drain. Alternatively, use a frying pan with an ovenproof handle and cook the parsnip ribbons in the oven at 200C/400F/Gas Mark 6 for about 10 minutes, tossing occasionally until crisped and coloured.

---

VARIATION

Food category – C

• Replace a cup of mixed root vegetables with a cup of potato cut into medium dice. You may need a little extra stock with this option, otherwise the method is as before.

# Bean Soup ⓥ

A pretty soup with a rich, contrasting garnish ... filling and full of goodness.

Food category – C
'1 in 5' – beans/pulses
Serves – 4

INGREDIENTS

- 8 oz/250 g dried cannelloni beans, soaked overnight in twice their volume of water
- 2 tablespoons olive oil
- 1 large onion, finely chopped
- 1-2 cloves garlic, finely crushed
- 1 stalk celery, washed, trimmed and sliced
- 2 bay leaves

- large bunch fresh thyme
- large sprig fresh rosemary
- 3 pints/1.8 litres Basic Vegetable Stock (see page 48)
- sea salt and white pepper, to taste
- 2 tablespoons finely chopped fresh parsley

METHOD

Drain the soaked beans, rinse well and drain again. While the beans are draining, heat the oil in a large, heavy based saucepan over a low heat and sauté the onions and garlic until the onions are soft and clear without browning, about 5–10 minutes. Add the beans, celery, bay leaves, thyme, rosemary and a little pepper, stir together and cook through for another 2–3 minutes. Add the stock, bring to a simmer, cover and cook, just simmering and stirring occasionally, for 1¼–1½ hours, until the beans are soft.

Allow to cool a little then transfer to a processor or blender, removing the herbs at the same time, purée and then pass back into the saucepan through a fine sieve to produce a smooth soup. Keep warm while adjusting to taste with salt and pepper. Stir in the fresh chopped parsley and serve immediately into warm bowls. Garnish with a drizzle of Black Olive Purée (see below).

VARIATION

Food category – C
- As a Carbohydrate dish this soup can be served with croutons (see page 68) or bread of any description, if your food rotation requirements allow it.

# Black Olive Purée Ⓥ

Use this as an essential garnish for the Bean Soup.

Food category – M/A

INGREDIENTS
- 1 cup black olives, pitted
- 1 dessertspoon lemon juice
- freshly ground black pepper
- olive oil

METHOD

In a food processor or blender, purée the pitted black olives with the lemon juice, plenty of freshly ground black pepper and sufficient olive oil, added as you go, to produce a thick smooth black olive purée.

# Lentil Soup Ⓥ
Food category – C
'1 in 5' – beans/pulses
Serves – 4

INGREDIENTS
- 2 tablespoons olive oil
- 1 small onion, finely diced
- 1 clove garlic, finely crushed
- 2 finely grated carrots
- 1 medium finely grated celeriac
- 1 bay leaf
- ½ teaspoon cumin powder
- ½ teaspoon coriander powder
- 6 oz/175 g red lentils, twice rinsed and drained
- sea salt and black pepper, to taste
- 1¾ pints/1 litre Basic Vegetable Stock (see page 48)
- 1 medium tomato, skinned, seeded and chopped (or use tinned)
- 2 tablespoons fresh coriander, finely chopped, for garnish

METHOD

Heat the oil in a large heavy based saucepan over a low heat, sweat the onions and garlic without browning until the onion is soft and clear, about 5–10 minutes. Add the carrot, celeriac, bay leaf, cumin and coriander, stir, cover and cook for 2 minutes. Add the lentils and season with freshly ground black pepper, stir, cover and cook for 2–3 minutes more. Add three-quarters of the stock, stir, bring to a simmer, cover and simmer for 25 – 35 minutes, stirring occasionally, adding more stock or water if the soup becomes too thick.

Remove about a third of the soup to a processor or blender and purée until smooth. Return the puréed soup to the pan, add the chopped tomatoes, mix well and while warming on a low heat, check and adjust the seasoning with salt and black pepper. Serve into warm bowls and sprinkle with chopped coriander.

GARNISH OPTIONS

Food category – M/A

- GARLIC CHIPS
  Slice 2 or 3 large cloves of garlic into thin flakes and fry them in a little olive oil until nutty brown on both sides, 2 minutes. Take care because they burn quickly once cooked, so cook a few at a time and remove them to drain on kitchen paper as soon as they are ready. Sprinkle the soup with garlic chips and serve.
- CHILLI CHIPS
  Remove the core and seeds from a red or green chilli. Blanch the chilli by dropping the slices into a cup of boiling water, drain immediately and dry on kitchen paper. Scatter the chilli chips on to the soup and serve.

# Pumpkin Soup ⓥ

Simple to make, simply delicious and so good for you.

Food category – M/A
Serves – 4

INGREDIENTS

- 1 tablespoon olive oil
- 1 small onion
- 1 lb/500 g pumpkin flesh, diced
- sea salt and white pepper, to taste
- 1¾ pints/1 litre Basic Vegetable Stock (see page 48)

- 1–2 tablespoons single cream
- zest of an orange, finely grated, as garnish
- freshly grated nutmeg

METHOD

Heat the oil in a large heavy based saucepan over a low heat and sauté the onion, stirring occasionally, until the onion is soft and clear, about 5–10 minutes. Add the pumpkin, season with salt and pepper, cover and cook, stirring occasionally for a further 10 minutes. Add all but half a cup of the vegetable stock, bring to a simmer, cover and cook for 15 – 20 minutes until the pumpkin is soft and well cooked. Transfer to a food processor or blender and blend until smooth. Add and blend in extra stock or water and as much cream as needed to bring to the texture you desire. Return to the saucepan, (through a fine sieve if you require a smoother soup), warm without boiling and adjust to taste with salt, pepper and nutmeg. Serve into warm bowls and garnish with a sprinkle of finely grated orange zest.

# Fish Soup
Food category – P
'1 in 5' – white fish, shellfish, oily fish
Serves – 4

INGREDIENTS

- 2 tablespoons olive oil
- 1 small onion, finely chopped
- 1–2 cloves garlic, finely crushed
- 1 leek, white part only, trimmed and finely chopped
- ½ fennel, trimmed and finely chopped
- 1 carrot, trimmed, peeled and finely chopped
- ½ medium celeriac, trimmed, peeled and finely chopped
- 2 pints/900 ml Fish Stock (see page 47)
- 8 oz/250 g cooked prawns, peeled and shells retained
- pinch cayenne pepper
- pinch saffron powder (or turmeric)
- ½ bottle dry white wine
- 2 medium ripe tomatoes, skinned, seeded and chopped (or use tinned)
- 1 teaspoon fresh tarragon, finely chopped (or ½ teaspoon dried)
- 8 oz/250 g firm white fish (cod, haddock) filleted, skinned and cut into ¾ inch/2 cm chunks
- sea salt and freshly ground black pepper, to taste
- lemon juice, to taste
- 2–3 anchovy fillets, drained and chopped
- 2 tablespoons tomato purée, for garnish
- 1–2 tablespoons single cream (optional)
- 2 tablespoons finely chopped fresh parsley, for garnish

METHOD

Heat the oil in a large heavy based saucepan over a low heat, sauté the onion, garlic, leek, fennel, carrot and celeriac together, and stirring occasionally until the onion is soft and clear, without browning, for 5–10 minutes. At the same time, in another saucepan, cover the prawn shells with most of the fish stock, retaining about a cup for later use. Bring to the boil, turn the heat down and simmer for 5–10 minutes. Add the cayenne and saffron to the main soup, cover and cook for 1–2 minutes. Add the white wine, tomatoes, tarragon, and the white fish, season with black pepper and bring to a simmer. Cook uncovered for 5–10 minutes.

Strain the fish stock through a clean cloth, discard the prawn shells and add the stock to the soup base. Simmer uncovered for a further 5–10 minutes until all the ingredients are cooked. The fish should separate easily into flakes and be white all the way through. Cool and transfer the soup to a food processor or blender, add the anchovies and purée until very smooth. While waiting for the soup to cool for processing, make the tomato purée garnish. In a small mixing bowl blend the concentrated tomato purée with 1–2 tablespoons fish stock from the quantity retained, until you have a rich red, smooth, quite thick, running liquid. Set aside for later.

Wipe the saucepan clean and return the processed soup to it through a fine sieve. Keep the soup warm without boiling while you adjust for flavour and texture to your taste with fish stock or water, lemon juice, cream if used, salt and freshly ground black pepper, mixed well in (an electric hand blender is perfect for this). The texture should be fairly thick and smooth. Keep the soup hot without boiling and add the prawns, stir once and allow the heat of the soup to warm them through, about 2–3 minutes. Serve immediately into warm bowls garnished with a drizzle of tomato purée and chopped fresh parsley.

## CHINESE-STYLE 'FIVE MORSELS' SOUPS

And now for something completely different! Soups made the Chinese way have to be the easiest, most healthy, lowest calorie and most fun to make. They taste good, look good and by following the basic method you'll keep coming up with new variations. It's with these soups that ready made stocks from the supermarket chill cabinet really can come into their own, though make your own stock if you prefer (see page 47).

The basic method is to boil and reduce the stock you're going to use – chicken, fish or vegetable – while you prepare the soup ingredients, which must be sliced, grated or shredded so thinly that the boiling stock will cook them instantly when it is poured over. There should be 5 different ingredients of substance in addition to the stock and any flavourings, hence 'five morsels' soups.

Whatever ingredients you're using are placed straight into the individual soup bowls and only a small amount of each is used: just enough to add their flavour to the stock and give an attractive appearance. These are not cluttered soups, they are art in a bowl and delicate flavours to savour. Don't be tempted to 'fill them up' – too much in the bowl will cool the stock too quickly and the ingredients won't cook. It's easier to make another bowl of soup if you want more, though you'll find it surprisingly filling.

When the bowls are ready with their ingredients, pour a portion of the simmering stock over, and serve immediately – with a caution about how hot it is of course.

Recipes for three very different soups follow. Other Five Morsel ingredients you can choose from include:

Food category – P
- Make a thin omelette with two eggs and slice into thin strips, (use chicken or vegetable stock).
- Any fish thinly sliced i.e. mackerel, tuna, sea bass etc. (use fish or vegetable stock).
- Pork fillet, treat as chicken by pre-cooking, (use chicken or vegetable stock).
- Cooked peeled prawns, (use fish or vegetable stock).

Food category – C
- Clear rice noodles (not egg)

Food category – M/A
- Watercress
- Courgette
- Cucumber
- Water chestnut

# Chinese Mushroom and Bean Curd Soup

Replace the chicken stock in this recipe with vegetable and it becomes a vegetarian dish, although still Protein because of the soya.

Food category – P
'1 in 5' – soya, chicken
Serves – 4

INGREDIENTS
- 30 fl oz/900 ml chicken (or vegetable) stock
- 4 pieces smooth tofu, each a 1 inch/2.5 cm cube

- 4 shiitake mushrooms, wiped clean, stems trimmed
- 4 tablespoons bean sprouts, blanched under boiling water in a sieve
- 4 inches leek, white part only
- 1 piece of fresh ginger root about 2 inches/5 cm
- sea salt for seasoning

METHOD

Bring the stock to the boil, reduce the heat and simmer uncovered while preparing and arranging into each of four soup bowls the five soup ingredients.

Per bowl:
- 1 cube bean curd cut into 8 small cubes or strips
- 1 shiitake mushroom, sliced very thin
- 1 tablespoon blanched bean sprouts
- 1 inch/2.5 cms white part of leek, very finely sliced or shredded into fine ribbons
- 4–5 'matchsticks' or slivers of fresh ginger root
- pinch salt

Pour a cupful of simmering stock over each bowl of ingredients and serve immediately.

# Chinese Chicken and Bamboo Shoot Soup
Food category – P
'1 in 5' – chicken
Serves – 4

INGREDIENTS
- 30 fl oz/900 ml chicken stock
- 4 pieces chicken breast meat, each 2 inches/5 cm × 1 inch/2.5 cm
- 4 pieces spring onion, green part only, 2 inches/5 cm long
- 4 pieces tinned bamboo shoot, about 1 inch/2.5 cm cube each
- 2 pieces of carrot, peeled and trimmed, about 2 inches/5 cm each
- 1 piece of fresh ginger root about 2 inches/5 cm
- sea salt to taste

METHOD

Bring the stock to the boil, reduce the heat and simmer uncovered while preparing and arranging into each of four soup bowls the five soup ingredients.

**Per bowl:**

- 1 piece of chicken, shred finely, seasoned with soy sauce and stir fried over a high heat to 'seal'. About 2–3 minutes. (Cook all chicken together and place a quarter in each bowl.)
- 1 piece spring onion, finely sliced
- 1 piece bamboo shoot, finely sliced
- Half a piece of carrot, split lengthwise and sliced into fine 'matchsticks'
- 4–5 'matchsticks' or slivers of fresh ginger root
- pinch salt

Pour a cupful of simmering stock over each bowl of ingredients and serve immediately.

# Chinese Salmon and Vegetables Soup

Food category – P
'1 in 5' – oily fish
Serves – 4

INGREDIENTS

- 30 fl oz/900 ml fish stock (see page 47)
- 4 pieces fresh salmon fillet, each 2 inches/5 cm × 1 inch/ 2.5 cm
- 4 inches leek, green part only
- 4 tablespoons very finely shredded cabbage leaves (i.e. Chinese leaves, spinach, spring greens)
- 2 pieces of daikon radish, peeled and trimmed, about 2 inches/ 5 cm long
- 1 piece of fresh ginger root about 2 inches/5 cm long
- 1/4 teaspoon finely chopped fresh tarragon
- sea salt for seasoning

METHOD

Bring the stock to the boil, reduce the heat and simmer uncovered while preparing and arranging into each of four soup bowls the five soup ingredients.

**Per bowl:**

- 1 piece of salmon, finely sliced
- 1 inch/2.5 cms green part of leek, very finely sliced or shredded into fine ribbons
- 1 tablespoon finely shredded cabbage leaves
- 1/2 piece of daikon radish, split lengthwise, sliced in to fine 'matchsticks'
- 4–5 'matchsticks' or slivers of fresh ginger root
- pinch tarragon
- pinch salt

Pour a cupful of simmering stock over each bowl of ingredients and serve immediately.

### SOUP ACCOMPANIMENTS

Various types of accompaniment can add a delicious counterpoint to soup and turn a snack into a substantial meal. Here are a few which you can use as your combining and rotation allows.

# Wheat Croutons ⓥ

Food category – C
'1 in 5' – wheat
Serves – 4

INGREDIENTS

• 2 slices white or wholewheat bread,      • 2 tablespoons olive oil
  thick sliced, crusts removed

METHOD

Heat the oven to 180 C/350 F/Gas Mark 4. Oil a baking sheet. Slice the bread into ½ inch/1 cm cubes. Drizzle the oil onto the cubes in a bowl and mix to coat as evenly as possible. Spread on the baking sheet and bake in the oven for 8–10 minutes until crisp and golden and ready to serve.

VARIATIONS

•   SEASONED CROUTONS
    Proceed as for plain croutons, when oiled toss the croutons in a
    bowl with sea salt and freshly ground black pepper to taste.
•   HERB CROUTONS
    Proceed as for plain croutons, when oiled toss the croutons in a
    bowl with a teaspoon of fresh chosen herb, finely chopped or half a
    teaspoon of the dried herb. Suggestions: sage, oregano, tarragon,
    marjoram, provençal mixed.
•   GARLIC CROUTONS
    Mix 1–2 cloves garlic, very finely crushed, with the oil, then
    proceed as for plain croutons.
•   SPICY CROUTONS
    Proceed as for plain croutons, when oiled toss croutons in a bowl
    with a pinch of chosen spice sprinkled over until all the cubes are

flavoured. Suggestions: cinnamon, paprika, curry powder, allspice (Pumpkin Soup).

● OLIVE CROUTONS

INGREDIENTS

• half a cup of olives (black or green), pitted
• olive oil

Proceed as for plain, but prepare a purée of the olives by processing them with enough olive oil in a blender (or mash through a sieve) to make a smooth, thin paste. Spread the olive purée thinly over each side of the bread, cut into cubes, place on the baking sheet, bake until crisp for 8–10 minutes and serve when ready.

# Polenta Croutons Ⓥ

The crouton variations mentioned so far are all made from wheat bread. KD style healthy eating recommends you reduce your wheat intake as much as possible and at the most to only one day in any five, '1 in 5'. So even if there is no protein in your meal and you have no concerns about combining, wheat croutons may still be out of bounds. Here are some alternatives to wheat croutons suitable for M/A and Carbohydrate soups.

Food category – C
'1 in 5' – maize corn

INGREDIENTS

• 4 oz/125 g pre-cooked or quick cook polenta
• 16 fl oz/500 ml boiling vegetable stock or lightly salted water
• 1 oz/30g unsalted butter or 1 tablespoon olive oil
• sea salt and freshly ground black pepper, to taste
• herbs or spices of your choice (see below)

METHOD

Pour the polenta slowly into the boiling stock in a non-stick saucepan over low heat, stirring continuously to avoid lumps. Continue to stir quite vigorously for 3–5 minutes until the polenta has thickened and forms a single mass.

Remove from the heat, add 1 oz/30 g unsalted butter or 1 tablespoon olive oil, plenty of salt and freshly ground black pepper (avoid extra salt if you have used stock made from cubes) and spices or herbs if desired. Beat vigorously to mix well and spread evenly, about ½ inch/1 cm thick, on the bottom of an oiled or buttered rectangular flan or casserole tray or dish. Leave to cool for 30–40 minutes, remove in one piece and cut into ½ inch/1 cm cubes. Bake on an oiled baking sheet at 180 C/350 F/Gas Mark 4 for 10 minutes, turning occasionally until browned. Serve as usual.

TIP

☞ Polenta does not take colour in the same way as bread when oven baked, so to get an attractive appearance you could pan fry the croutons in a little olive oil, turning occasionally until browned, or pop them under a hot grill for a few minutes before serving.

VARIATIONS

- Plain polenta croutons can be flavoured by adding ¼ teaspoon of spice such as freshly ground nutmeg, cinnamon or paprika, or ½ teaspoon dried herb such as sage, marjoram, thyme or even a herb mixture such as herbes provençal. Mix these additions with the oil before the polenta is set aside to cool and set.
- Onion can be used to flavour the croutons: include 1 tablespoon finely chopped onion with the oil, with or without a herb as well.
- Alternatively, after the polenta croutons have been browned, gently toss them in seasoning, spices or fresh herbs just before serving.

# SERVING SALADS

## EVERYTHING YOU NEED TO KNOW
## ABOUT SALADS

Salads are used frequently in The Kensington Diet way of eating as starters, main courses or even desserts. Like soups, salads can be used to blunt a sharp appetite and save you from overeating, but in a way that offers no compromise to the enjoyment of food you'll come to expect with KD eating. Salads are exciting eating if you use your imagination.

Salads offer the ultimate in versatility with high nutritional values and, in most cases, low calorie penalties for the weight conscious. The sheer variety of ingredients that can be used, raw or cooked, Mix With Any, Protein or Carbohydrate, provide a food combining and rotation dream. The textures, flavours and colours can be counterpoint, contrast or complete canvas on any dining table. My only problem is which salads to suggest to you.

What you actually choose to put in a salad will ultimately come down to your personal preferences so I'm going to stick to helping your imagination. I'll just give you some guidelines and examples of how combining works with salads and stir your creative and digestive juices a little, and then I'll leave the rest to your interpretation and creativity.

One thing people often do is forget just how many different things can go into a salad or dressing. You'll realise what I mean from the recipes which follow later in the book as main course accompaniments, or even as desserts. For too many people, though, salad still means lettuce, tomato and cucumber, and on a good day a spring onion or two. So here's a list of Mix With Any salad ingredients to choose from.

## BASIC SALAD INGREDIENTS
All the following salad ingredients are Mix With Any.

**Salad leaves**: Cos lettuce, lambs lettuce, lollo lettuce, oak leaf lettuce, frisee, rocket, spinach, watercress, mustard and cress, Chinese leaves, chicory, raddichio, dandelion, cabbage. Try to avoid iceberg lettuce which has little to recommend it in terms of flavour, texture or nutritional value.

**Fresh herbs** of all kinds can be used too. Try dill, mint, coriander, parsley, basil, chives, tarragon, sage or fennel, for the exquisite aromas and flavours they can provide.

**Unusual additions** add interest and make a salad different. Try thinly sliced fresh ginger root, capers, dill pickles, green or black olives, thinly sliced water chestnuts, raw mange tout or petit pois, and fine green beans plunged for three or four minutes into boiling water and then refreshed in cold water to stop them cooking.

**Raw vegetables** make excellent salad ingredients or crunchy crudités. If weight control is important to you, raw vegetables are filling, have plenty of fibre, few calories and no fat. They are the ideal way to stop you over eating from another course which has a bigger weight gain penalty. Use them at the start or finish of a meal in a whole variety of ways that make them anything but rabbit food.

These are just a few of the vegetables you can enjoy in their raw state. Always choose the youngest and freshest. In salads cut, slice, grate and chop them whatever way your fancy and creativity takes you. For crudités clean and trim your chosen vegetables well and refresh them in clean cold water, then cut them into pieces suitable for dipping or spreading with the accompaniment you've selected.

Try celery sticks, batons of carrot, slices or separate leaves of chicory, florettes of cauliflower or broccoli, slices of red, green or yellow peppers, whole mange tout, slices of sweet onion, batons or slices of courgettes, thin slices of fennel, slices or leaves of gem lettuce, radicchio, turnip sticks, red radish, sliced kohl rabi, batons of cucumber, whole cherry tomatoes. Are you getting the idea yet? And we haven't even considered how to put proteins or carbohydrates in salads or the opportunities for hot and cold combinations.

There are lots of ideas and recipes to come, some quite traditional, others might come as a surprise to you, but before I start giving you actual suggestions it's worth thinking about that other vital part of a good salad – the dressing. Dressings can make a simple salad into a gourmet event.

The easiest way to dress your starter and main course salads is with some variation on the simple and classic vinaigrette which can be made from oil, vinegar, salt and mustard. It has the advantage in that all the ingredients are Mix With Any so there is no combining considerations to take into account. There's a basic vinaigrette recipe below, and lots of ideas of how to transform and tweak it so it will complement other salad or meal ingredients. I have a personal preference I'd like to recommend to you. I prefer not to have a salad which is uniformly flavoured all over with the same dressing, so I like to add taste sensations. A few drops of a special oil, a pinch of a spice or herb or a touch of some other special flavouring dotted here and there, and a salad, after it is dressed, adds a whole different dimension of flavours in the mouth, no matter how excellent the main dressing may be. I'll make some suggestions as we go, but give your imagination free reign and you'll find your salads even more exciting and enjoyable.

There are, of course, many other types of dressing besides vinaigrettes and you'll find examples of these where food combining allows and where they enhance a particular salad. In the meantime here's a recipe for a basic vinaigrette which can form the foundation for many exquisite variations.

# Basic Vinaigrette ⓥ

Proportions are 1 part of vinegar to 4 parts of oil for a standard portion which can be multiplied according to need:

Food category – M/A

INGREDIENTS

- 1 tablespoon white wine vinegar or cider vinegar
- 4 tablespoons olive oil
- 1 level teaspoon smooth Dijon mustard
- ½ teaspoon fine sea salt
- ½ teaspoon clear honey or soft brown sugar, optional
- 1–2 fresh garlic cloves, finely crushed, optional
- 5 drops Tabasco sauce, optional

METHOD

Measure the ingredients into a large screw top jar. Screw down the top of the jar and shake vigorously until the ingredients blend and thicken into a smooth dressing. Alternatively mix all the ingredients except the oil in a large bowl, then whisk in the oil a little at a time to produce the same end result.

VARIATIONS

- Add finely chopped fresh herbs of your choice just before serving so the vinegar in the dressing will not affect the flavour of the herb. For instance, basil goes well with a tomato salad; dill with a cucumber salad; tarragon with a salad containing artichokes or mushrooms; a salad with lots of onion or olives benefits from finely chopped fennel leaf.
- Replace a proportion of the olive oil with a delicious nut oil such as walnut or hazelnut, or one of the herb flavoured olive oils now widely available in supermarkets and health food shops.
- Replace one or two tablespoons of oil with natural yogurt or single cream to make a yogurt- or mayonnaise-like dressing.
- Replace a proportion of the vinegar with any of the range of herb flavoured or speciality vinegars such as balsamic or sherry vinegar. Again, these are now available widely from supermarkets and health food stores. Just mixing a teaspoon of tomato purée into a portion of basic vinaigrette will give you a rich red and superb tomato vinaigrette. Experiment and be amazed by what you create.

**Storage**

Basic vinaigrette will keep for up to a week in an airtight container when made without garlic or herbs. When made with garlic it will keep for up to 36 hours.

There are many more recipes for special dressings throughout the book. Look out for them with side salads that are included with many main meal dishes. They'll be just as good with main course salads of course. For now, though, let's talk salads and dressings suitable for starters and light meals. Often the only difference between the two is the quantity you serve, so if you like the look of a salad which follows remember the quantities are for a light meal unless otherwise stated, and you can reduce the amounts used by up to half to make starters for four.

And that reminds me of a couple of other things about salads which make them so attractive. They're the perfect opportunity to make a small amount of an expensive ingredient go a *loooong* way and they are a chance to try some new, unusual ingredient or flavouring without great risk of waste. A small amount of unusual or expensive ingredient used successfully in a salad will enable you to use it confidently on a bigger scale at another time.

# Twice-Cooked Duck Salad

This salad has its inspiration in that popular Chinese dish, aromatic crispy duck, but it takes a fraction of the time for an equally wonderful result. Traditional crispy duck is first steamed for a couple of hours, then deep fried. Not many of us have the time or patience for that, even if we have a steamer big enough, and deep frying tends to make an already high fat food into a calorie calamity. So here's a twice-cooked alternative which starts with roasting as a way to reduce the fat content in a salad that contains crispy duck skin, moist meat and loads of oriental flavour. Try it as a lunch, with one of the 'five morsels' soups from the previous chapter served as a starter, and jasmine tea to finish.

Food category – P
'1 in 5' – duck
Serves – 4

INGREDIENTS

- 2 duck breasts, skin on, boneless if possible, but on the bone will do
- sea salt and freshly ground black pepper, to taste
- 1 teaspoon five spice powder
- mixed salad leaves for four, washed, dried, torn to suitable size and tossed (use varieties without too strong a flavour e.g. cos, little gem, lambs lettuce, oak leaf, round green lettuce)
- half a cucumber, peeled, seeded and shaved into ribbons
- 4 whole spring onions, finely chopped to garnish

FOR THE PLUM SAUCE DRESSING

- 2 tablespoons white wine vinegar
- 2 tablespoons sunflower or groundnut oil
- 2 tablespoons prepared plum sauce
- Tamari (non-wheat) soy sauce to taste

You'll need a wire rack or trivet on which to roast the duck over an oven tin to catch the drips of fat.

METHOD

Heat the oven to 220 C/425 F/Gas Mark 7. Wipe the duck breasts with a damp cloth, pat dry with kitchen paper and score the skin half a dozen times with a sharp knife without cutting through to the meat. Brush lightly with oil and rub salt and five spice powder well into the duck breasts on both sides. Roast skin-side up on the wire roasting rack over a roasting tin for 1 hour. Remove from the oven and allow to cool. Retain the duck fat. Don't turn the oven off yet and keep the roasting tin and wire rack available for further use. While roasting the duck prepare the rest of the salad ingredients and the dressing. For the dressing simply blend all the ingredients together in a bowl. You want a rich, thick but free-running dressing. The salad will only require a very small amount of dressing for the powerful plum and soy sauce flavours to come through and complement the duck and other ingredients. At this point, the duck meat should be left to rest for 5–10 minutes to become really tender.

When the duck breasts are cool enough to handle, remove the skin and then place them back on the wire rack or trivet in the hot oven or under a hot grill to become very crisp, about 5–10 minutes. Chop into pieces on kitchen paper to drain off excess fat. Mix the cucumber ribbons with the salad leaves and arrange a portion of this salad on four plates. If using duck breasts on the bone remove the meat from the bone now. Cut the duck meat into strips and flash fry over a high heat for 2–3 minutes in a wok or frying pan, using a little of the duck fat which has drained from the breasts during roasting. Divide and arrange on the salads, scatter the crispy duck skin over, sprinkle with finely chopped spring onion and drizzle each salad with about a tablespoon of the Plum Sauce Dressing. Serve.

VARIATIONS

• Aromatic crispy duck is traditionally served with pancakes which are used to wrap plum sauce, cucumber, spring onion, duck meat and crispy duck skin so it can be eaten like a small roll. Pancakes and duck are not a good food combination and this method of eating crispy duck won't work for combiners – but we don't have to be left out. A similar and equally enjoyable (to my mind *more* enjoyable) way of eating crispy duck 'pancake' is possible. Here's how: the ingredients are virtually the same as for the original recipe, though you won't need all the dressing ingredients – just the plum sauce. Sharwoods make a really good one and it's readily available in most supermarkets.

Cook the duck in the same way as described above. When ready arrange meat and skin on opposite sides of a plate in the middle of the table, so pieces of each can be selected separately.

Choose salad leaves of a type and size able to wrap around half a teaspoon of plum sauce, a few slivers of spring onion and cucumber, a strip of duck meat and a little crispy duck skin. About 4 or 5 leaves per person should do. Try large cos leaves, oak leaf lettuce (although the shape is a bit odd) or the outer leaves of a simple round lettuce. Place the washed and dried leaves in a large bowl from which everyone can help themselves.

Slice the spring onions into matchstick length ribbons, and the skinned and seeded cucumber into matchstick sized julienne. Put them into separate dishes on the table. Serve the plum sauce straight into a bowl on the table with a spoon – or two. Provide each person with a small plate and a pair of chopsticks or a spoon and fork.

Take a lettuce leaf, spread a little of the plum sauce on it, add cucumber julienne and ribbons of spring onion, a piece of duck meat and some crispy duck skin. Fold the combination of tasty ingredients into the leaf so nothing can fall out or drip on you when you eat it. Each person serves themselves from the bowls and makes and eats as many parcels of twice-cooked duck as they can manage before all the ingredients are gone. Delicious.

- If you don't want to use duck, try seasoning leg portions of chicken in the same way and roasting them until they are very well done and the skin is very crispy. Then serve them in the same way with all the trimmings.

# Chicken Liver Salad

I really enjoy hot ingredients on cold salad leaves. This is one of my favourites and it's so easy and quick too.

Food category – P
'1 in 5' – chicken
Serves – 4

FOR THE DRESSING
- 2 fl oz/60 ml sour cream
- 1 dessertspoon French mustard, (Dijon, herb etc.)
- 1 tablespoon white wine vinegar
- 2 tablespoons olive oil
- 2 tablespoons finely chopped fresh parsley
- 3 tablespoons vegetable stock or water
- sea salt and freshly ground black pepper, to taste

INGREDIENTS
- mixed salad leaves for four servings, washed, dried and torn to suitable size (use varieties with a mild flavour, e.g. cos, little gem, lambs lettuce, oak leaf, round green lettuce)
- 4 ripe tomatoes, skinned and seeded, cut into small dice
- 12 oz/375 g chicken livers, trimmed, washed and patted dry
- 1 tablespoon olive oil
- sea salt and freshly ground black pepper, to taste
- 1 tablespoon lemon juice
- 1 tablespoon fresh parsley, finely chopped

METHOD

Make the dressing first. Mix the ingredients together in a bowl or blender until smooth, set aside in a jug or bowl to pass around. Prepare the tomatoes and salad leaves. Arrange the salad leaves on four individual dinner plates. Set the tomato dice aside for later use. Sauté the chicken livers in hot oil in a non-stick pan for 2–3 minutes until lightly browned on all sides and pink (but not raw) in the middle. Season and sprinkle with lemon juice and chopped parsley. Toss together, arrange on the salad leaves, sprinkle over the diced tomatoes and serve immediately with the dressing separate.

# Spicy Quick Roast Chicken Salad with Salsa Dressing

Another hot one – in more ways than one.

Food category – P
'1 in 5' – chicken
Serves – 4

FOR THE CHICKEN

- 2 large chicken breasts, skinned, boned and trimmed
- 4 tablespoons olive oil
- 1 tablespoon balsamic vinegar
- 1 teaspoon dried oregano
- 1 teaspoon dried marjoram
- ½ teaspoon cayenne powder
- ½ teaspoon fine sea salt
- ½ teaspoon freshly ground black pepper

FOR THE SALSA DRESSING

- half a cucumber, peeled, seeded and roughly chopped
- 4 ripe tomatoes, seeded and roughly chopped
- ½ small red or Spanish onion, roughly chopped
- 1 small mild green chilli pepper
- 2 tablespoons olive oil
- 1 tablespoon lemon juice
- 3 tablespoons finely chopped coriander
- 1 tablespoon tomato juice
- sea salt and freshly ground black pepper, to taste

FOR THE SALAD

- mixed salad leaves for four servings, washed, dried and torn to suitable size (e.g. rocket, lambs lettuce, oak leaf, raddichio)
- juice and finely grated zest of a lemon
- sea salt to taste

METHOD

Pre-heat the oven to 200 C/400 F/Gas Mark 6. In a heavy based, non-stick oven proof frying pan (or place a heavy roasting tin to pre-heat in the oven if your frying pan is not oven proof) seal the chicken breasts on both sides over a high heat, about 2–3 minutes each side. Transfer to the oven and cook for 25–30 minutes. Remove, cover and allow to rest for 5 minutes before serving.

While roasting the chicken, mix the oil, vinegar, herbs and spices (for the chicken) together and spread over the chicken breasts in a shallow dish so they are well coated. Cover and set aside. Make the salsa dressing. Put all the ingredients into a food processor and blend to a coarse textured mixture. You do not want a smooth purée so pulse the machine a few times until the ingredients are chopped reasonably finely but still retain some texture and crunch, and are well mixed with enough juice to be able to spoon over the salad. Cover and set aside for the flavours to blend.

Place the salad leaves in a large mixing bowl ready for dressing. If desired, char and warm the chicken a little under a hot grill before serving. When ready sprinkle the salad leaves with lemon juice, zest and salt to taste, toss lightly and arrange a serving on each of four plates. Slice the chicken breasts into ½ inch/1 cm slices, divide between the four plates and arrange on the salad leaves. Stir the salsa dressing and season with salt and pepper, add more tomato juice if needed then drizzle spoonfuls of the salsa dressing over the chicken and salad. Serve immediately.

# Turkey, Bacon and Walnut Salad

A warm salad with many of the flavours of Christmas but you don't have to wait until then, it's just great all year round.

Food category – P
'1 in 5' – turkey, bacon, walnuts
Serves – 4

INGREDIENTS

- 2 oz/60 g walnut pieces
- mixed salad leaves for four servings, washed, dried and torn to suitable size (e.g. little gem hearts, frisee, lollo rosso, round lettuce)
- 2 turkey steaks
- 1 medium sized gammon steak
- 1 tablespoon olive oil
- sea salt and freshly ground black pepper, to taste

- 1 tablespoon finely grated zest of orange, optional
- 2 portions Basic Vinaigrette made with whole grain mustard, garlic, honey and Tabasco (see page 73)
- 12–16 ripe cherry tomatoes, halved

TASTE SENSATIONS
walnut oil, for garnish, optional
natural orange essential oil or flavouring, optional

METHOD

Pre-heat the oven to 180 C/350 F/Gas Mark 4. Spread the walnuts on a baking sheet and roast in oven until golden, about 10 minutes. Remove, cool until you can handle them and rub skins off with a cloth. Set aside. Prepare the salad leaves and mix together in a large mixing bowl ready for dressing. Put the turkey steaks between sheets of Clingfilm and beat out with the heel of your hand until they are about 1/4 inch/6 mm thick. Slice them into 1/2 inch/1 cm slices about 2 inches/5 cm long. Trim the gammon steak of all fat and slice into 1/2 inch/1 cm x 2 inch/5 cm pieces.

Sauté the turkey and bacon together in the olive oil, with a little salt and pepper seasoning in a heavy based non-stick frying pan over a fairly high heat, until just cooked through and browning at the edges. Add the orange zest if used, and mix quickly together then add to the salad leaves, dress with vinaigrette and serve onto four plates. Add a few roasted walnuts and halves of cherry tomatoes, and 3 or 4 drops of walnut oil and orange essence, if used, to each salad, and serve immediately.

# Smoked Salmon, Dill and Caper Salad

A starter dish really. It looks and tastes sensational, and with the availability of smoked salmon these days it's very economical for ordinary dining. The taste sensation and appearance of shiny pink salmon roe makes it spectacular for a special occasion.

Food category – P
'1 in 5' – salmon
Serves – 4

INGREDIENTS

- 8 oz/250 g smoked salmon
- 2 portions Basic Vinaigrette made with honey and garlic (see page 73)
- 1 tablespoon finely chopped fresh dill
- 1 small cucumber, peeled, seeded and chopped into small dice

- 2 tablespoons capers, drained
- 1 large ripe slicing (beef) tomato or 4 smaller ripe tomatoes
- 1 small mild onion (red or Spanish), very finely sliced

DILL PURÉE

- 1 cup fresh dill

- olive oil

- 2 little gem lettuce hearts or chicory hearts, washed and trimmed

- 1 tablespoon capers
- few sprigs fresh dill
- coarsely ground black pepper

TASTE SENSATIONS

Tabasco sauce, optional
salmon roe, optional

METHOD

Slice the smoked salmon into fine strips and mix with two teaspoons vinaigrette in a large bowl or dish. The salmon strips will tend to stick together so add them to the vinaigrette as you slice, then mix them with your fingers so they are well coated before adding the dill, cucumber and capers. Set aside to marinade. The salmon will lighten in colour as it marinades. Place a $\frac{1}{2}$ inch/1 cm slice of beef tomato in the centre of each of four plates, or use a mould to arrange a bed of slices from smaller tomatoes. Arrange slices of onion on the tomato and top with a teaspoon of vinaigrette.

Make a Dill Purée by blending the cup of fresh herb in a liquidiser with enough olive oil, added slowly, to make a smooth, green, runny purée. Pile a quarter of the marinated smoked salmon mixture onto each tomato slice. Cut each little gem, or chicory heart into six equal segments through the stalk and arrange three pieces together, on each plate, beside the salmon on tomato. Garnish the plate around the tomato and piled salmon with a drizzle of vinaigrette, overlaid with a drizzle of the Dill Purée. They will trickle over the lettuce or chicory on the way. Then add a few sprigs of dill, a scattering of capers and a few salmon roe if used. On top of the salmon mixture and a little coarsely ground black pepper, scatter 4 or 5 drops of Tabasco if used. Serve.

VARIATIONS

- If you don't like capers or don't have any available you can replace them with diced black or green olives or dill pickles.
- Try Olive Purée (see Page 61) for a purée garnish instead of the Dill.

# Prawn and Avocado Salsa Salad

The presentation of this dish is similar to the smoked salmon salad, above, but the flavours are completely different – see which you prefer.

## Food category – P
## '1 in 5' – prawns
## Serves – 4

INGREDIENTS

- 1 large ripe but firm avocado, peeled, stoned and cut into small dice
- ½ red pepper, cored and cut into small dice
- ½ yellow pepper, cored and cut into small dice
- 1 small red onion, finely chopped
- 1 mild green chilli pepper, finely chopped
- 1 tablespoon finely chopped fresh coriander (or parsley)
- juice of 1 lime
- 8 oz/250 g cooked prawns, peeled and large prawns cut in half (if frozen prawns are used, thaw and drain before use)

- 2 portions Basic Vinaigrette made with honey and garlic (see page 73)
- 1–2 tablespoons tomato purée, to taste
- 1 large ripe slicing (beef) tomato, or 4 small ripe tomatoes
- half a cucumber, peeled and thinly sliced

BASIL PURÉE

- 1 cup fresh basil leaves

- olive oil

GARNISH

- coarsely ground black pepper
- handful salad greens (lambs lettuce or watercress)

- 4 small dill pickles, finely chopped or made into fans

TASTE SENSATION

Harrissa hot sauce (from supermarkets) or Tabasco sauce

METHOD

In a large bowl, mix the avocado, peppers, onion, chilli pepper and chopped coriander or parsley with the lime juice, being careful not to break up the avocado. Carefully fold in the prawns until well mixed. Set aside to marinade while you prepare the rest of the dish. Mix the basic vinaigrette with tomato purée to make a Tomato Vinaigrette. Place a ½ inch/1 cm slice of beef tomato just off centre on each of four plates, or use a mould to arrange a bed of slices from smaller tomatoes. Arrange slices of cucumber on the tomato and top with a teaspoon of Tomato Vinaigrette.

Make a purée of basil by blending the cup of fresh herb in a liquidiser with enough olive oil added slowly to make a smooth, green, runny purée. Pile a quarter of the marinaded prawn and avocado mixture onto each tomato slice and top with a little of the juices – the rest can be discarded. Spoon a dessertspoon of Tomato Vinaigrette on top and scatter on a little coarsely ground black pepper. Arrange a small bunch of salad leaves on each plate, beside the prawn and avocado salsa on tomato. Garnish the plate (around the tomato and piled salsa) with a drizzle of tomato vinaigrette, overlaid with a drizzle of the basil purée. They will trickle over the salad leaves on the way. Add a scattering of chopped dill pickle or arrange a dill pickle 'fan' on each plate. If desired, add four or five drops of Harrissa or Tabasco sauce to each plate and serve.

---

To make a dill pickle fan, use a sharp knife to make five or six thin slices virtually the whole length of the pickle but leaving about a $\frac{1}{4}$ inch/6mm intact at the stalk end so the pickle can be spread like a fan.

---

## KD NIÇOISE SALADS

The accurate list of the ingredients for Niçoise salad seems to have been lost in the mists of time but it doesn't matter very much. The basic idea is still out there, alive and well and producing inspired variations which add up to wonderful light meal salads with tremendous colours, tastes and textures. Traditional Niçoise salads don't fit with combining rules: fish doesn't mix well with potatoes. That simply means combiners get two bites at the salad, so to speak. And here they are. Two salads developed from one famous original.

# Niçoise-Style Tuna Salad
Food category – P
'1 in 5' – tuna, anchovies, eggs
Serves – 4

INGREDIENTS

- 8 oz/250 g fine green or Kenya
  beans
- mixed salad leaves for four servings,
  washed, dried and torn to suitable
  size (e.g. little gem, lambs
  lettuce, round lettuce)
- 4 tuna steaks each about 3 oz/90 g
  (or two tins best tuna in olive
  oil, drained and flaked)

- olive oil, to brush
- 4 fresh eggs, hard boiled
- sea salt and freshly ground black
  pepper, to taste

FOR THE DRESSING

- 2 portions Basic Vinaigrette
  (made with garlic and Tabasco,
  see Page 73)
- yolk of a hard boiled egg

- 4 tinned anchovy fillets, drained
- small bunch fresh tarragon
- freshly ground black pepper,
  to taste

SALSA

- 8 large ripe plum tomatoes,
  seeded and chopped
- 2 oz/60 g black olives, stoned
  and finely chopped (try good
  quality olives marinated in oil
  and herbs, stone them yourself if
  necessary)

- 1 tablespoon capers, drained
  and chopped
- ½ cup fresh basil leaves, finely
  chopped

METHOD

Trim the fine beans and plunge them into lightly salted, boiling water for 4–5 minutes until cooked but still firm. Drain and plunge into cold water to cool rapidly and stop the cooking. Drain well before using. Prepare the salad by mixing the salad leaves with the cooked fine beans in a bowl, ready for dressing. If using fresh tuna, brush the steaks with olive oil, season with salt and pepper and put to one side until ready to cook. Peel and quarter the hard boiled eggs and put to one side until ready to serve. Make the salad dressing by first putting aside two tablespoons of the vinaigrette. Blend the hard boiled egg yolk, anchovies and tarragon, in a liquidiser or processor, adding the remaining vinaigrette a little at a time until smooth and creamy. Season with black pepper to taste. Make a salsa by mixing the tomatoes, olives and capers with the retained 2 tablespoons of vinaigrette. Mix the chopped basil into the salsa.

Fry the tuna steaks in a heavy based non-stick frying pan or on an oiled griddle pan for 1–1½ minutes each side, until just cooked to your taste. Dress the salad with the anchovy and tarragon dressing, toss to cover the leaves and beans and arrange a portion on each of four plates. Place a tuna steak, or use a mould to shape the flaked tinned tuna, in the centre of each plate. Arrange four quarters of hard boiled egg around the tuna and spoon the salsa onto the tuna. Serve.

# Niçoise-Style Potato Salad Ⓥ

OK I'm stretching things a bit here to call it Niçoise, but I don't want you to feel deprived of your potatoes if you really want them and this does use a lot of the Niçoise ingredients. More important, it's fine in combining terms and makes a great meal.

Food category – C
'1 in 5' – potato
Serves – 4

INGREDIENTS

- 8 oz/250 g fine green or Kenya beans
- 2 tablespoons finely chopped fresh basil leaves
- mixed salad leaves for four servings, washed, dried and torn to suitable size (e.g. little gem, lambs lettuce, round lettuce)
- 16–20 new potatoes, boiled and cut into large dice (skins on)
- olive oil for sauté
- sea salt and freshly ground black pepper, to taste
- 1–2 cloves garlic, finely chopped
- 2 oz/60 g black olives, stoned and finely chopped (try good quality olives marinated in oil and herbs, stone them yourself if necessary)
- 4 large ripe, firm plum tomatoes, seeded, chopped and allowed to drain
- 1 tablespoon capers, drained and chopped
- 2 portions Basic Vinaigrette made with garlic, honey and Tabasco (see page 73)
- 1 tablespoon finely chopped fresh tarragon
- 2 tablespoons finely chopped fresh flat leaf parsley (or chives)

METHOD

Trim the fine beans and plunge them into lightly salted, boiling water for 4–5 minutes until cooked but still firm. Drain and plunge into cold water to cool rapidly and stop the cooking. Drain well before using. Prepare the salad by mixing the basil and salad leaves with the cooked fine beans in a bowl ready for dressing. In a large heavy based frying pan, sauté the potatoes in olive oil with salt and pepper seasoning, mixing occasionally, until crisp and golden. Add the chopped garlic and olives, toss together and cook through. Add the chopped tomatoes and capers, mix and allow to cook until the tomato is just warm. One or two minutes only so the tomatoes stay firm.

While cooking the potatoes, mix the vinaigrette with the chopped tarragon and dress the salad, toss to cover the leaves and beans, then arrange a portion on each of four plates. Scatter the potato mixture with the chopped parsley or chives, mix once more and serve onto the centre of the dressed salad. Serve.

## Caesar-Style Salad

What we can do with one classic dish we can do with another. The only real problem with classic Caesar salad, in combining terms, is that it puts eggs and anchovies with croutons. So here's a version of this wonderful salad which will suit any KD combiner. You'll use crisp, golden nutty chips of fried garlic in place of the traditional garlic croutons.

Food category – P
'1 in 5' – eggs, anchovies
Serves – 4

INGREDIENTS

• 2 oz/60 g Parmesan cheese, in
  shavings
• lettuce leaves for four servings,
  (best leaves and hearts of cos,
  Romaine, or little gem), washed,
  dried and separated, large leaves
  torn, hearts quartered

• 4 anchovy fillets, chopped into
  small pieces

FOR THE DRESSING
- 2 anchovy fillets, chopped
- 1 tablespoon Parmesan cheese, finely grated
- 1 tablespoon Worcestershire sauce
- ½ tablespoon lemon juice
- 1 tablespoon mayonnaise (a good ready made mayonnaise such as Hellmans will be fine)

- freshly ground black pepper, to taste
- 2 portions Basic Vinaigrette (made with garlic and plenty of Tabasco, see p. 73)

FOR THE GARNISH
- 4 large cloves garlic, sliced into matchstick thick slices

- 1–2 tablespoons olive oil

METHOD

In a large salad bowl, gently toss the lettuce, chopped anchovies and Parmesan shavings. (Pare the Parmesan into fine shavings with a swivel type potato peeler.) Make the dressing by processing all but the vinaigrette briefly in a blender or food processor, then on a slow speed setting, gradually add the vinaigrette until you have a smooth, creamy dressing. Pour over the salad and gently toss. Fry the garlic slices a few at a time in olive oil until crisp and nutty brown on both sides but not burned. Don't try to fry all the garlic together as it browns quickly and can easily burn. By the time you get the first slices out the last will be charcoal, so give them all your attention, turning the slices as soon as they are coloured and removing them to kitchen paper to drain as soon as they are ready. Scatter garlic chips onto the salad and bring to the table immediately to serve.

# KD Waldorf Salad ⓥ

No reason to stop now. You have a food combiner's version of two of the three classic salads so I suppose I'd better give you the KD variation of the last. The problem, for combiners, with Waldorf salad is the mixing of apple with cheese and nuts. In this perfectly acceptable and just as delicious option, the sweet/tartness of apple gives way to the flavours of slightly under-ripe cherry tomatoes, otherwise it gives more than a passing nod to its famous traditional version.

Food category – P
'1 in 5' – walnuts, cheese (cow's milk or goat's milk, see below)
Serves – 4

INGREDIENTS

- 2 oz/60 g raw shelled walnuts
- 2 celery stalks, sliced into ½ inch/ 1 cm pieces
- 4 oz/125 g sweet cherry tomatoes, slightly under ripe, halved

- juice of half a lemon
- salad leaves for four servings (watercress, oak leaf lettuce, curly endive), washed, dried and torn into suitable sized pieces

FOR THE DRESSING

- ½ clove garlic, finely crushed
- 1 teaspoon Dijon mustard
- 2 tablespoons white wine or cider vinegar
- 1 tablespoon crème fraîche
- 1 oz/30 g blue cheese (use the same cheese as above)
- 3 tablespoons olive oil

3 tablespoons walnut oil (or replace with a further 2 table-spoons of olive oil)
- sea salt and freshly ground black pepper, to taste

GARNISH

- 1 oz/30 g blue cheese (e.g. Stilton) [cow's milk], Roquefort [sheep's milk] crumbled into small pieces

METHOD

Pre-heat the oven to 180 C/350 F/ Gas Mark 4. Place the walnuts in the top of the oven on a baking sheet and roast for 10 minutes until golden. When cool enough to handle, rub off the skins with a cloth, break nuts into pieces and set aside. Mix together three-quarters of each of the broken walnuts, celery and cherry tomato halves, season with salt and pepper and toss to coat in the lemon juice.

In a bowl, mix together the salad leaves and make the dressing. Beat the garlic, mustard, vinegar, crème fraîche and cheese to a smooth paste in a bowl or use a food processor or blender. Mix the olive and walnut oils together and add to the other ingredients a little at a time until you have a smooth creamy dressing. Use the slow or pulse setting on the blender or processor. Season to taste. Pour half the cheese dressing over the salad, toss gently and divide between 4 individual plates or bowls. On top of each serving of salad leaves add a quarter of the celery and walnut mixture. Spoon a little of the remaining cheese dressing over the top. Sprinkle with a scattering of the retained celery, walnut pieces, tomato halves and the crumbled blue cheese. Season with freshly grated black pepper and serve.

☞ The rules of '1 in 5' food rotation allow both cow's milk cheeses and goat's milk cheeses to be treated separately. That means, after you've eaten cow's milk cheeses you shouldn't eat them again in the next four days, but you can have goat's or sheep's milk cheeses within that period. The recipe above indicates either cow's milk or goat's/sheep's milk types of blue cheese.

# Cashew Nut Salad ⓥ

I always think of Chinese food when I think of cashews hence the oriental overtones to this salad. Raw grated vegetables, cooked cashews and spicy soy sauce dressing all blend together into a wonderful food experience.

Food category – P
'1 in 5' – cashew nuts
Serves – 4

INGREDIENTS
- 6 oz/175 g raw cashew nuts
- 4 oz/125 g mange tout
- 1 teaspoon toasted sesame oil
- 1 red chilli pepper very finely sliced
- ½ raw white radish (mouli), peeled and finely grated
- 2 medium raw courgettes, skin on, finely grated

- 3 raw carrots, peeled and finely grated
- 2 red peppers, finely sliced
- ½ cucumber
- 3 little gem lettuce, washed, trimmed and shredded
- 1 cup bean sprouts

FOR THE DRESSING
- 1 tablespoon Tamari (non-wheat) soy sauce
- 1 tablespoon rice vinegar (or white wine vinegar)
- pinch five spice powder
- ½ teaspoon clear honey
- 1–2 cloves garlic, finely crushed

- 1 dessertspoon finely grated fresh ginger
- 6–8 tablespoons sunflower or groundnut oil

FOR THE GARNISH
- 3 spring onions (green part only), finely chopped

METHOD

Pre-heat the oven to 180 C/350 F/Gas Mark 4. Spread the cashews on a baking sheet and roast in the top of the oven for 10–15 minutes until golden brown on both sides, mixing after a while to ensure even colouring. Set aside to cool. Make the dressing by mixing the soy sauce, vinegar, five spice powder, honey, garlic and ginger until the honey has dissolved. Add and whisk in the oil a little at a time until the ingredients are well blended. Set aside.

Plunge the mange tout into lightly salted boiling water for 4–5 minutes, until cooked but still with crunch. Transfer to cold water to cool and stop cooking. Drain well, pat dry in a clean towel then toss with the sesame oil until well coated. Set aside. Carefully split, deseed and slice the chilli pepper. Use a sharp knife and work on a piece of kitchen paper so you can discard the trimmings straight away. As soon as you've finished wash the utensils and your hands, and at all times avoid touching sensitive areas of skin such as your eyes.

In a large mixing bowl, mix all the grated raw vegetables, the red pepper, the bean sprouts and the chilli until they are well combined. Add enough soy sauce dressing to lightly coat all the vegetables when well mixed in. Set aside. Split the cucumber lengthwise and scoop out the seeds with a spoon. Slice into ribbons with a swivel type potato peeler, taking a thread of skin with each shaving. Mix the cucumber ribbons in a clean bowl with the mange tout and shredded lettuce. Season with salt and pepper.

Mix the roasted cashews with the grated vegetable mixture. Use a cup-shaped mould with the mixture well pressed down, to turn out a mound of cashews and vegetables in the middle of each of four plates. Arrange mange tout, cucumber and lettuce around each mound, garnish with chopped spring onions and soy sauce dressing if any remains. Serve.

## PASTA SALADS

Just a few general comments before a couple of tempting recipes.

Always use dried, non-egg pastas to avoid the bad combination of eggs and carbohydrate. Pasta shapes are best in salads because they mix more easily with salad ingredients, which are often chopped or sliced. Try penne (pen nib shaped), rigatoni (fat cylinders), fussili (twists, spirals), farfalle (bows), conchiglie (shell shaped) or gnocchi (similar to shell shapes).

Pasta shapes are available in wheat or corn pasta, which will help you keep to your '1 in 5' rotation of both, if you like to eat pasta often. (There's more advice about this later in the book.) Wheat and corn pasta are interchangeable in the recipes shown, it's up to you and what your diet allows which you use.

Cook your pasta in lightly salted boiling water until it is *al dente*, that is cooked through but still firm to the bite. The packet instructions should tell you how but test as you go until you feel happy, then take the pasta off the heat straightaway, drain it and wash it under cold running water to cool it and stop it cooking further, and to wash off starches which would make it stick together.

Adding a tablespoon of olive oil to the boiling water helps to stop the pasta sticking together in the pan, and helps to keep the water from boiling over too. Corn pasta makes more starch in the water and is quite prone to frothing up. It's a good idea to use a big saucepan with plenty of room when you cook any pasta. Tossing the cooked, cold pasta in a little olive oil will also stop it sticking and make it easier to mix with other salad ingredients, especially if you're going to set it aside for a while before using it.

# Pasta Salad with Herb Dressing ⓥ

Food category – C
'1 in 5' – wheat or corn
Serves – 4

INGREDIENTS

- 1 mild onion (red or Spanish), finely chopped
- 1 red pepper, finely chopped
- 1 yellow pepper, finely chopped
- 1 avocado, peeled, stoned and finely chopped
- 4 large ripe but firm plum tomatoes, seeded and cut into small dice

- ½ cup finely chopped fresh parsley
- 1–2 tablespoons lemon juice
- sea salt and freshly ground black pepper, to taste
- 8–10 oz/250–315 g pasta shapes (see page 91), cooked, drained and cooled

FOR THE DRESSING

- 2 cups finely chopped fresh basil
- 1 tablespoon capers, drained, optional
- 1 portion Basic Vinaigrette (see page 73)

- 1 tablespoon lemon juice
- olive oil to blend
- sea salt and freshly ground black pepper, to taste

FOR GARNISH
- 2 bunches rocket or watercress, washed and dried
- 1–2 tablespoons lemon juice
- pinch salt

METHOD

Mix the onion, peppers, avocado, tomatoes and parsley together in a large bowl with the lemon juice and season with salt and pepper. Turn the cooled pasta shapes into a large bowl. Make the dressing by processing or blending all the ingredients together except the oil, salt and pepper, then add olive oil in small amounts until you have a smooth, fairly thick, beautiful green dressing with which to dress the pasta. Season to taste with salt and pepper. Add the dressing to the cooled pasta and toss well to cover. Line four salad bowls with portions of rocket or watercress and lightly sprinkle with lemon juice and salt. Spoon the pasta salad onto the salad leaves and serve topped with the mixed vegetable salad. Garnish with wheat bread or polenta croutons (see page 68), or crusty bread if desired and suited to your diet.

# Pasta Salad with Sun Dried Tomato Dressing ⓥ

Food category – C
'1 in 5' – wheat or corn
Serves – 4

INGREDIENTS
- ½ bulb fennel, washed, trimmed and cut into ¼ inch/6 mm slices
- 8 oz/250 g fine asparagus, washed and trimmed
- 2 red peppers, washed, trimmed, cut into (1 inch/2.5 cm) dice
- 2 yellow peppers, washed, trimmed, cut into (1 inch/2.5 cm) dice

- 8 oz/250 g (4 cups) lamb's lettuce, washed and dried
- 1–2 tablespoons of lemon juice

- 1–2 tablespoons olive oil
- sea salt and freshly ground black pepper, to taste
- 8–10 oz/250–315 g pasta shapes (see page 91), cooked, drained and cooled
- sea salt and freshly ground black pepper to season
- 4 oz/100 g black olives, pitted

- 1 tablespoon finely chopped fresh tarragon
- pinch salt

FOR THE DRESSING
- 1 jar (6–8 oz/175–250 g) sun dried tomatoes marinated in oil, drained, oil retained
- 2 portions Basic Vinaigrette (see page 73) made with garlic
- ¼ teaspoon dried Provençal herb mixture
- 1 clove garlic, peeled and chopped
- 1 teaspoon red chilli pepper, chopped, optional
- sea salt and freshly ground black pepper, to taste
- retained oil from tomatoes, to blend

METHOD

Heat the grill to very hot. Lightly oil a grill pan or baking sheet suitable for grilling the vegetables. Blanch the fennel in boiling water for 5 minutes, transfer to cold water to cool and stop cooking, drain and pat dry. Blanch the asparagus in boiling water until just soft but still firm – 2 to 3 minutes – transfer to cold water to cool and stop cooking, drain, pat dry and cut into 1 inch/2.5 cm pieces. Blanch the red and yellow peppers separately in boiling water for 4–5 minutes until softening but still with some crunch. Transfer to cold water to cool and stop cooking, drain and pat dry.

Transfer all the partially cooked vegetables to the grill pan or baking sheet, sprinkle and turn in olive oil, season with salt and black pepper and grill under a high heat for 10–15 minutes. Stir occasionally so that all the vegetables collect a little charring and colour, but you don't want them to burn and they should retain some crunch. If you prefer, sauté the vegetables over a high heat in a large heavy based frying pan with the olive oil to achieve a similar result. Meanwhile, prepare the pasta and turn into a large bowl.

Make the dressing by processing or blending together all the ingredients except the oil, then gradually add oil in small amounts until you have a smooth, fairly thick, beautiful red dressing with which to dress the pasta. Set aside for the flavours to blend. Line four salad bowls with a portion of lambs lettuce, lightly sprinkled with lemon juice, chopped tarragon and seasoned with salt. Season the sun dried tomato dressing to taste with salt and pepper, add to the pasta and toss well to coat. Arrange the pasta salad beside the herbed leaves and serve topped with grilled vegetables and black olives and garnished with wheat bread or polenta croutons (see page 68), or crusty bread if desired and your diet allows.

# Tabbouleh ⓥ

Bulgur or cracked wheat and the alternative for tabbouleh, cous cous, are varieties of wheat. So if you're rotating wheat '1 in 5' in your diet, you need to take care to have tabbouleh only on a wheat day. If you're slimming, reduce or omit the olive oil in the tabbouleh mixture.

Food category – C
'1 in 5' – wheat
Serves – 4

INGREDIENTS

- 1 pint/600 ml Basic Vegetable Stock (see page 48)
- 10 oz/315 g bulgur (cracked wheat or cous cous, see below)
- 1 large aubergine
- 6 tablespoons olive oil
- sea salt and black pepper, to taste
- 4 tablespoons lemon juice
- 3 tablespoons finely chopped fresh mint
- 3 tablespoons fresh, finely chopped flat leaf parsley

- ½ red pepper, finely diced
- ½ yellow pepper, finely diced
- 1 onion (red, Spanish or same amount of shallots), finely chopped
- 1 clove garlic, finely chopped, optional
- 1 tablespoon finely chopped fresh coriander
- 3–4 whole ripe tomatoes per person

FOR GREEN LEAF SALAD AND GARNISH

- mixed salad leaves for four, washed and dried (e.g. rocket, lambs lettuce, oak leaf, round green lettuce)

- 1 portion Basic Vinaigrette (use Basic Vinaigrette recipe with half the oil replaced with walnut oil if desired)

METHOD

Pre-heat the oven to 200 C/400 F/Gas Mark 6. Oil and pre-heat a baking sheet or baking tray. Boil the stock and pour it over the bulgur wheat in a bowl, a little at a time, mixing as you go. Set aside for the bulgur wheat to absorb the stock and cool to room temperature – about 45 minutes – 1 hour. Remove the skin and about ½ inch/1 cm of flesh from the aubergine by taking four slices off the sides and trimming off the ends. This will leave you with an almost rectangular block of aubergine flesh and four thick slices. Take two tablespoons of the olive oil and lightly brush the slices and the block on all sides with oil. Season the aubergine block with salt and pepper and place on the baking sheet in the oven. Cut the slices into ½ inch/1 cm strips and lightly brush the newly cut edges with oil. Cut the strips into ½ inch/1 cm dice. Lightly season with salt and pepper and place with the aubergine block on the baking sheet in the oven. Turn the block and stir the aubergine dice every 5 minutes until you have a block of soft, cooked aubergine flesh well browned on all sides, and well coloured aubergine dice. The block will take about 30–40 minutes, the dice less. Set aside to cool.

Add the remainder of the olive oil, three tablespoons of the lemon juice, the chopped mint and parsley, the chopped peppers, onion and garlic if used, to the bulgur wheat and mix well, season to taste. Set aside for the flavours to blend. Chop up the aubergine block in a bowl until you have a coarse mash, mix with the chopped coriander and add salt, pepper and as much of the remaining lemon juice as you desire, to taste. Slice the stem ends from the tomatoes, scoop out and discard the cores, flesh and seeds using a small spoon or melon baller. Dress the salad leaves with the walnut oil vinaigrette and season to taste. Fill the tomatoes with tabbouleh.

Mix the roasted aubergine dice with the remainder of the tabbouleh, make a bed of the mixture on each of four plates using a ring mould to stop it spreading too much. Arrange three or four filled tomatoes on each bed and garnish with a few dressed salad leaves and a scoop of the aubergine and coriander mash. Serve with the remaining salad passed separately and crusty bread if desired.

VARIATION
• You can make tabbouleh with ordinary or quick-cook cous cous instead of bulgur wheat. Genuine bulgur or cracked wheat has slightly more chewiness and is an excellent unrefined carbohydrate with more fibre. All are readily available in supermarkets. Pour 1 pint/600 ml of boiling stock onto 10oz/315 g ordinary cous cous and leave to cool and absorb the stock as you would for bulgur wheat. Then proceed as before.

# Curry and Rice Salad ⓥ

This is a salad which uses plain boiled basmati rice as a foil for the zingy, spicy flavours in this recipe. You may be surprised that sultanas are used when you consider the 'fruit only with fruit' advice, but sultanas are a dried fruit very high in sugar carbohydrate, so there is no health or weight penalty here. Your KD healthy eating remains intact with this dish.

Food category – C
'1 in 5' – rice
Serves – 4

INGREDIENTS

- 10 oz/315 g uncooked basmati rice
- juice of 1 lemon
- 4 oz/125 g mange tout, washed, topped and tailed
- 5 fl oz/150 ml crème fraîche
- 1 tablespoon prepared 'cook in' curry sauce or paste (see tips below)
- sea salt and freshly grated black pepper, to taste
- 3–4 carrots, grated
- 3 courgettes, grated
- 2 sticks of celery, finely chopped
- 1 green pepper, finely chopped
- 3 oz/90 g sultanas
- 1 teaspoon very finely grated fresh ginger root
- 1 small clove garlic, finely crushed, optional
- ¼ teaspoon sugar
- 2 tablespoons prepared mango chutney
- 2–3 tablespoons water
- 4 ripe salad tomatoes, each cut into eight segments
- 1 mild onion (red, Spanish), finely sliced
- paprika powder, for garnish

You'll also need a ring mould or ring pastry cutter about 3 inches/8 cm diameter × 1 inch/ 2.5 cm deep, and a small tea cup, ramekin or similar as another mould.

METHOD

Cook the rice according to the packet instructions with a few drops of lemon juice added to the water, then cool to room temperature. Plunge the mange tout into boiling salted water for 3–4 minutes until just cooked but still crisp and crunchy, transfer to cold water to cool and stop further cooking. Drain and pat dry.

In a small bowl blend the crème fraîche with curry sauce or paste a little at a time until you have a good smooth, mild curry flavoured, cream dressing. You may not need all the curry sauce. You need a dressing that's thick and creamy not runny. Season to taste with a little of the lemon juice and salt. In a large bowl mix the carrot, courgette, celery, pepper, sultanas, ginger, the garlic if used, and the sugar. Mix the curry cream dressing with the raw vegetables a little at a time until the vegetables are well coated but not overpowered by the dressing. The dressing should make them hold together so the mixture can be moulded to shape.

Mix the mango chutney with enough water to make a thin runny sauce with small pieces of mango (chop up and add in some large pieces). Arrange the four plates. Press about a quarter of the basmati rice into a small lightly oiled mould (cup or ramekin) and place upside down on a plate. Tap and shake gently to release the shaped rice onto the plate. Place a ring mould to one side of the rice and fill with vegetables in curry cream dressing, pressing the mixture down into place and levelling the surface with the back of a teaspoon. Ease the mould away to leave the shaped curry dressed vegetables.

Arrange seven mange tout and eight tomato slices overlapping on the plate and drizzle with mango chutney. Mix the sliced onion with a little of the remaining lemon juice and pile some on top of the curry cream dressed vegetables. Garnish the onion and rice with a sprinkling of paprika. Serve with naan bread if your rotation requirements allow.

TIP

☞ Use a good brand of curry cook-in-sauce or paste with lots of natural spices and flavourings but without additives, which won't help you or your cooking. Check the labels carefully. Cook-in-sauces will usually have starch to thicken them, which is fine for Carbohydrate dishes like this but not if you want to use this salad with Protein dishes. In that case you should find a curry paste without starch in it, or a powder which you can cook in a little oil before mixing to taste with the crème fraîche.

VARIATIONS

- Basmati rice works well with this salad because it has a distinctive flavour and moulds into shape easily. Try mixing in a small amount of cooked wild rice to add a spectacular contrast to the snowy white of plain basmati. About a quarter of a cup (2 oz/60 g) will do. (Or replace 2 oz of the rice with pre-washed millet. Cooking the rice mixture in vegetable stock will also give it extra flavour.)
- You can also colour the basmati rice yellow by adding a pinch of turmeric or saffron powder to the water while it is cooking; or flavour it with cinnamon (stick or powder), cardamom pods and whole cloves or chopped fresh coriander, stirred in 5 minutes before the rice has cooked to add their flavour while the rice cools.

# Lentil Salad ⓥ

This dish has some similarities to the curry and rice salad (see page 96) in its preparation but tastes completely different. Puy lentils (a nutty flavoured small, dark green lentil) are used for this recipe because they stay whole and firm when cooked. You could use other types such as red or brown lentils, but you'll have to watch carefully and catch them when they are just tender and before they start to break up into mush.

Food category – C
'1 in 5' – pulses (lentils)
Serves – 4

INGREDIENTS

- 12 oz/385 g puy lentils
- 1 pint/600 ml Basic Vegetable Stock (see page 48) or salt water
- 1 tablespoon olive oil
- 1 small clove garlic, finely crushed, optional
- 8 oz/250 g fresh spinach, washed, coarse stems removed
- 3–4 carrots, grated
- 3 courgettes, grated
- 2 sticks of celery, finely chopped
- 1 green pepper, finely chopped
- 1 mild onion (red, Spanish, shallot), finely sliced
- 1 small carton 5 fl oz/150 ml sour cream

- 3 tablespoons fresh chives, very finely chopped (if using sour cream which already includes chives – 1 tablespoon will do)
- 6 ripe salad or plum tomatoes, seeded, roughly chopped and drained
- 1 tablespoon lemon juice
- freshly ground black pepper, to taste
- 2 portions of Basic Vinaigrette (see page 73) made with garlic and Tabasco sauce

TASTE SENSATION
4 teaspoons balsamic vinegar

FOR THE GARNISH
3–4 large cloves garlic, optional

A ring mould or circular pastry cutter about 3 inches/8 cm diameter × 1 inch/2.5 cm deep would be handy for this recipe but is not essential.

METHOD
Wash the lentils under cold running water and put in a large, heavy based saucepan. Add the stock and slowly bring to the boil over medium

heat. Simmer for 30–40 minutes until tender. They should have a pleasant nutty texture. The time puy lentils take to cook can depend on their freshness, they cook more quickly if less fresh, so check them after 30 minutes. Remove from the heat, drain off any excess liquid, wipe the saucepan and replace the lentils while still warm. Add salt, the tablespoon of olive oil, the crushed garlic if used and the spinach. Mix well, cover and set aside so that the remaining heat wilts the spinach while the lentils cool. Place in the refrigerator to cool further, ready for serving.

In a large bowl mix together the carrot, courgette, celery, pepper and onion. Mix the sour cream and chives together in a small bowl. Then fold into the raw vegetables a little at a time until there is enough to make them hold together so the mixture can be moulded to shape. Gently fold the chopped tomatoes and lemon juice with the lentils and spinach to mix them without breaking up the tomatoes. Season with black pepper and immediately spoon the mixture around the moulded vegetables in sour cream. Drizzle two spoonfuls of vinaigrette over the lentils followed by a teaspoon of balsamic vinegar.

Peel the cloves of garlic, cut them into matchstick-thin slices and fry in a little olive oil until nutty brown on both sides. Cook a few at a time to avoid burning the garlic chips which 'turn' very quickly and need careful attention. Set aside on kitchen paper to drain off excess oil. Garnish the lentils with garlic chips if used and the vegetables with the remaining chopped chives. Arrange the four plates. Place a ring mould in the centre and fill with vegetables in sour cream dressing, pressing the mixture down into place and levelling the surface with the back of a teaspoon. Ease the mould away to leave the shaped sour cream dressed vegetables. Serve with crusty bread or garnished with wheat bread or polenta croutons (see page 68), if your rotation requirements allow.

VARIATION
• Try using crème fraîche mixed with a teaspoon of grated or creamed horseradish in place of the sour cream with chives – the pungent horseradish is just sensational with the lentils.

# Bean Salad ⓥ

There are definite overtones of Greek food in this really simple recipe. Use whatever beans you like, dried or tinned kidney beans, black beans, white cannelloni beans, green flageolet beans, even butter beans or chickpeas will do. Or use fresh or frozen broad beans to make it a M/A dish.

While we're on the subject of beans I've always been curious about why flageolet beans were so called – according to my dictionary a flageolet is a wind instrument which may give us a clue. Yes, some people have a problem with beans and they avoid them because of it. So that the benefits of these delicious and nutritious foods are not lost to you here are some tips on preparation.

If you want to use dried beans this is how. For the 4 cups of cooked beans needed for this recipe use 2 cups dried beans. Soak them overnight in cold water. Rinse in several changes of cold water then, to cook, put them in plenty of fresh cold water, bring them to the boil slowly and simmer for 45–60 minutes, until they are tender. Add bay leaves, onion, or thyme for extra flavour while cooking. Drain and rinse under cold running water when cooked.

Don't eat a lot of beans at one time unless you are used to them – a small amount with plenty of accompaniment is best. Finally, in those countries that use beans frequently, they are served with lots of olive oil – I don't really *know* if that helps but I think it must be a factor in making them a pleasure without problems.

Food category – C
'1 in 5' – pulses (beans)
Serves – 4

INGREDIENTS

- 1 tablespoon olive oil
- 2 onions, sliced
- 1–2 cloves garlic
- 2 lbs/1 kg ripe plum tomatoes, skinned, seeded and roughly chopped (or use 2 tins chopped plum tomatoes, drained of excess liquor)
- 1 tablespoon tomato purée
- sea salt and freshly ground black pepper, to taste
- 1 tsp sugar

- 2 tablespoons finely chopped fresh herbs (coriander, mint or parsley)
- mixed salad leaves for four (e.g. spinach, green lettuce, rocket), washed, dried and finely shredded
- juice of 2 lemons
- 4 cups cooked beans, your choice
- 4 tablespoons best olive oil
- 1–2 extra cloves garlic, optional
- ½ cup black kalamata olives, pitted and chopped for garnish

METHOD

Heat the oil in a large heavy based saucepan, over a low heat, and sauté the onions and garlic until the onions are soft and clear, without browning, about 5–10 minutes. Add the tomatoes, tomato purée, salt and pepper and a pinch of sugar, mix well, bring to a simmer and cook uncovered over a low heat until the tomatoes reduce to a thick sauce with little liquid. Allow to cool to room temperature, season to taste with more sugar, salt and black pepper if desired. Mix in the chopped herbs.

Arrange a bed of shredded mixed salad leaves on each of four plates. Sprinkle with a little of the lemon juice and season with salt and black pepper. Mix the beans with the remaining lemon juice, olive oil, extra garlic if used and salt and pepper to taste. Arrange a quarter of the beans on each bed of leaves, spoon tomato dressing over and garnish with chopped black olives. Serve, with crusty bread or garnished with wheat bread or polenta croutons (see page 68), if your food rotation allows.

# Warm Vegetable Salads ⓥ

Vinaigrette is not just good for cold salads, it can make warm vegetables of all kinds feel like a feast or turn the simplest starter imaginable into a memorable classic. Visualise roasted or grilled Mediterranean vegetables such as courgette, peppers, tomatoes, fennel and aubergine, piled high on a plate smothered with basil vinaigrette, then garnished with olives and shavings of Parmesan cheese. You can give the same treatment to any vegetables in all seasons. This is not so much a fixed recipe as a collection of possibilities for you to mix and match.

Food category – M/A
Serves – 4

INGREDIENTS
mixed vegetables for 4 servings.
Choose from:

- cauliflower in approximately 1 inch/2.5 cm florettes
- broccoli in approximately 1½ inch/3.5 cm florettes
- carrots in ½ inch/1 cm slices
- fine green or Kenya beans, trimmed and cut in half
- leeks, trimmed and cut into ¾ inch/2 cm slices
- swede, peeled and cut into ¾ inch/2 cm slices
- small onions
- 2 portions of Basic Vinaigrette (see Tips below)
- sea salt and freshly ground black pepper, to taste
- garnish (see Tips below)

METHOD

Steam or poach your chosen selection of vegetables, (see Tips below). Arrange a portion in each of four warm bowls, dress with spoonful of your chosen dressing, season with salt and pepper and garnish with your chosen garnish. Serve.

TIPS AND TREATS TO CHOOSE FROM

Choose at least five different vegetables.

You can boil or poach each type on their own or all together, in the usual way, in water or vegetable stock or you can steam them (see page 226 for how to cook a medley of steamed vegetables). When cooked, keep the vegetables warm until ready to mix together and serve but don't try to keep them hot. They can be reheated in a microwave very quickly if necessary but this will cook them a little more so reduce the time you steam or boil them or they will become too soft and mushy. You want a collection of brightly coloured vegetables all cooked but each still retaining a good texture.

Your dressing can be the Basic Vinaigrette from page 73 with any of the host of variations possible. Here are some suggestions:

- Mix in 1 dessertspoon tomato purée per portion of Basic Vinaigrette for a scrumptious tomato vinaigrette.
- Replace half the olive oil with walnut or hazelnut oil to make a nut oil vinaigrette.
- Replace half of the wine vinegar with lemon juice to make a **Lemon Vinaigrette** and use the zest of the lemon, finely grated, sprinkled over as garnish.
- Add 2 tablespoons of finely chopped fresh herbs to the Basic Vinaigrette just before dressing the vegetables – try parsley, thyme, mint or basil.
- Replace the vinaigrette with a mixture of sour cream and chives or another fresh herb such as mint, coriander.

NOTE

So far all the ingredients mentioned are Mix With Any and present no questions regarding combining or rotation – many of the following suggestions, however, do include foods designated as Proteins or Carbohydrates, or as '1 in 5' foods, for which your combining and rotation requirements should be taken into account.

GARNISH SUGGESTIONS

Food category – M/A
- Pan fried garlic chips (see page 286)
- Chopped fresh herbs
- Sliced onion, crisply fried or raw

Food category – P
- Chopped bacon, crisply fried
- Parmesan cheese, grated or in shavings made with a swivel type potato peeler
- Roasted or toasted nuts

Food category – C
- Wheat bread or polenta croutons (see page 68)
- Sautéed potatoes

SERVING SUGGESTIONS

Food category – M/A
- Serve on a bed of spinach leaves which will partially cook from the warmth of the vegetables.

Food category – C
- Serve on a bed of warm new potatoes, steamed or boiled in their skins and sliced or quartered.

# Warm Salad of Mixed Mushrooms ⓥ

Sometimes the easiest and least complicated food turns out to be the most enjoyable and this is one of those occasions. Rapidly sautéed mushrooms on a bed of dressed salad leaves and an unusual taste sensation blend into a succulent starter or a light meal.

Food category – M/A
Serves – 4

INGREDIENTS
- mixed salad leaves for four (e.g. lamb's lettuce, spinach, rocket, oak leaf, frisée, lollo rosso) washed and dried, large leaves torn
- 1–2 cloves garlic, finely crushed, optional
- 2 tablespoons fresh, finely chopped flat leaf parsley
- ½ cup walnut kernels, roasted,

- 1 portion Basic Vinaigrette, made with half walnut oil and half olive oil, if preferred (see page 73)
- 2 tablespoons olive oil
- 1 oz/30 g unsalted butter
- 1 lb/500 g mixed mushrooms (e.g. chestnut, shiitake, oyster, chanterelle, cep) wiped clean, trimmed of hard stalks, larger ones cut or sliced
- skins removed, broken up (see page 89)
- sea salt and freshly ground black pepper, to taste

TASTE SENSATION
toasted sesame oil

METHOD
Prepare the mixed salad leaves in a large bowl. Prepare the dressing. Heat the olive oil and butter in a large, heavy based frying pan over a fairly high heat. Sauté the mushrooms and garlic together, omitting oyster mushrooms if used, for 3–4 minutes until well coloured. Stir frequently to assure sealing and browning the mushrooms and to avoid water seeping. Dress and toss the salad while cooking the mushrooms.

If oyster mushrooms are used, set the other cooked mushrooms aside on a warm plate and flash fry the oyster mushrooms separately in a hot pan over a high heat for 30–60 seconds, add the previously cooked mushrooms and stir together for 30 seconds. Remove from the heat, stir in the chopped parsley, the roasted walnuts and salt and pepper. Place the salad leaves on four plates, arrange the mushroom and walnut sauté amongst the leaves. Drizzle 5–6 drops of sesame oil onto each salad and serve immediately.

GARNISH VARIATIONS

Food category – P
- Parmesan cheese shavings taken with a swivel type potato peeler
- Crispy bacon pieces

Food category – C
- Wheat bread or polenta croutons (see page 68)

## CRUDITÉS
Turn to page 72. Refresh your memory about how to choose and prepare raw vegetables for crudités. For the purposes of The Kensington

Diet it's best to use all Mix With Any vegetables and to create accompaniments, dips or sauces to fit in with your combining and rotation needs. (Mix With Any, Protein or Carbohydrate.) Here are some suggestions for dips to be used with your choice of chunky crudités vegetables. If you choose to make your own dip rather than using a ready prepared one, make the dip before preparing the crudités or the cut vegetables will dry out and loose freshness, flavour and nutritional content.

Food category – M/A
- SOUR CREAM AND CHIVES (V)
  (mix plain sour cream with your choice of finely chopped fresh herbs e.g. parsley, tarragon, mint, coriander.)
- GUACAMOLE (V)
  (mash the flesh of ripe avocados with chopped red onions, chopped flesh of tomatoes, lemon juice and crushed garlic. Season with salt, black pepper and Tabasco sauce to your taste.)

Food category – C
- HUMMUS (V)
  (drizzle extra virgin olive oil and sprinkle chopped fresh herbs or paprika on a good quality, ready prepared version of this classic chickpea dip.)
- SPICY PEANUT DIP (V)
  (mix 2 cups of crunchy peanut butter with 4 tablespoons Tamari [non-wheat] soy sauce, juice of lemon, 2 tablespoons very finely grated fresh ginger root, 1 tablespoon clear honey and a little water if necessary until you have a dippable sauce to your taste. Mix in finely crushed garlic and/or finely chopped chilli peppers if desired and serve sprinkled with the grated zest of the lemon.)

Food category – P
- YOGURT RAITA (V)
  (mix about 2 cups of Greek yogurt with plenty of finely chopped, peeled and seeded cucumber [grating will make it too wet and soggy], finely chopped green pepper, finely chopped fresh mint and parsley or coriander, lots of black pepper and a little sea salt, until you have a thick, scoopable dip to your taste. Mix in finely crushed garlic and/or green chillis if desired and served sprinkled with paprika).

# Warm Walnut and Anchovy Dip

Here is a real 'Do Not Miss' recipe for anchovy lovers. The inspiration for it comes from one of the most famous restaurants in London, San Lorenzo in Beauchamp Place. I have no idea if it's even close to the original, because Mara wouldn't give me details of the secret ingredients she uses, but I think this is a pretty darn good version for all that. Certainly, I always feel it's worth the effort. This dip has very powerful flavours and needs lots of crudités to go with relatively little anchovy and walnut dip.

Food Category – P
'1 in 5' oily fish (anchovies), walnuts
Serves – 4 (with your choice of crudités)

INGREDIENTS
- 2 × 50 g tins best anchovy fillets in oil, drained and oil retained
- 8 oz/250 g walnut kernels
- 2 cloves garlic, finely crushed
- 6 oz/175 g crème fraîche
- pinch sugar
- Tabasco sauce, to taste

METHOD
In a food processor or with a pestle and mortar, blend the anchovies, walnuts and garlic to a coarse paste with about half of the oil from the tinned anchovies. I first use a coffee grinder to finely grind the walnuts. Transfer the mixture to a saucepan over a low heat and stir in the crème fraîche and sugar. Add a good shake of Tabasco sauce and adjust flavour with a little more crème fraîche and Tabasco to suit your taste. Serve in a dish over very low heat for communal dipping with fresh crudités.

SERVING TIPS
This may be the perfect dish for the umpteen unused fondue sets that must be lying around in the backs of cupboards. What you need is an earthenware bowl over a very low heat source, something like a large version of the essential oil burners you see around. Use the crudités to keep the dip well stirred to prevent scorching.

Other suggestions are to make an attractive centrepiece of a bowl of warm water kept heated on a table top food warmer; you know, one of those things with a night light candle in it. Put the serving dish with the dip into the bowl of warm water like a *bain-marie* but be careful not to use too much water or the dish will start to float as the dip is scooped out.

VARIATIONS
- This dip is virtually foolproof and you can add lemon juice, balsamic vinegar, the new green Tabasco, black pepper and so on to make subtle variations. Just experiment once you have the basic mixture warming in the saucepan.

# Shredded Vegetable Crudités with Classic Sauces

There can be more to crudités than chunks of vegetables with a dip-in sauce. Here are a couple of versions, each using finely grated raw vegetables, with a collection of pour-over sauces. Apart from the colours, textures and tastes the methods of serving enable each person to choose the dressing they want on each vegetable. As for the chunky crudités, it's best to make the sauces first. Here's my Classic Collection.

## Yogurt and Mint Sauce ⓥ
Food Category – P
Serves – 4

INGREDIENTS
- ½ medium cucumber
- 1 cup plain natural yogurt
- 1 clove garlic, finely crushed
- 2 teaspoons finely chopped fresh mint (or 1 teaspoon dried mint)

- sea salt and freshly ground black pepper
- pinch ground paprika, for garnish

METHOD
Peel the cucumber, halve it lengthways, scoop out the seeds with a spoon and chop the flesh into a fine dice (grating will make it watery). In a bowl mix the cucumber well with the yogurt, garlic and mint and pour the mixture into a serving bowl, cover and keep chilled until ready to serve. To serve, adjust the seasoning with salt and pepper and garnish with sprinkled paprika.

VARIATIONS
- Finely chopped parsley or chives instead of mint, or dill with grated fennel bulb in place of the mint and cucumber.

## Herb and Onion Vinaigrette (v)
Food category – M/A
Serves – 4

INGREDIENTS
- 1 cup Basic Vinaigrette (see page 73)
- 1 medium onion, very finely diced
- 1 large bunch fresh parsley, very finely chopped
- sea salt and freshly ground black pepper, to taste

METHOD
In a mixing bowl blend all the ingredients together to produce a thick but runny herb and onion vinaigrette. Remove to a serving bowl, cover and keep at room temperature until ready to serve.

## Blue Cheese Sauce (v)
Food Category – P
'1 in 5' – Blue Cheese, cow's or goat's milk
Serves – 4

INGREDIENTS
- 1 cup plain natural yogurt
- 1 teaspoon lemon juice
- 1 level teaspoon English mustard
- 1 clove garlic, crushed, optional
- 2 oz/50 g strong blue cheese (i.e. Stilton, Roquefort, Danish Blue)
- 2 tablespoons finely chopped fresh chives
- sea salt and freshly ground black pepper, to taste

METHOD
In a mixing bowl mix the yogurt, lemon juice, mustard and garlic if used, until all are well blended together. Mash three-quarters of the cheese until smooth and blend with the yogurt mix. Crumble the remainder of the cheese into small pieces with a fork and add to the mixture with all but half a teaspoon of the chopped chives which can be kept for garnish. Remove to a serving bowl, cover and keep cool. To serve, adjust the seasoning and serve garnished with freshly ground black pepper and the remaining chopped chives.

## Shredded Vegetable Crudités Ⓥ
Food Category – M/A
Serves – 4

INGREDIENTS
- 2 medium beetroot, finely grated
- 2 carrots, finely grated
- 4 courgettes, finely grated (skin and flesh, discard the pulp)
- 4 sticks of celery, very finely sliced
- 12 oz/350 g mange tout, very finely sliced
- 2 yellow peppers, very finely sliced
- 4 heads chicory, trimmed and washed
- 4 heads little gem or other small lettuce, trimmed and washed

METHOD
Prepare each vegetable as described above and store each separately in covered or airtight containers. Separate the larger outside leaves from the chicory and lettuce heads, retain the hearts for future use.

TO SERVE
Arrange piles of approximately half a cup of each crudités on individual plates. In a large central bowl from which all can help themselves place the chicory and lettuce leaves. Arrange the bowls of sauce, each with a serving spoon, around the leaves. Spoon a small amount of the crudités on a chicory or lettuce leaf and drizzle with a little of one of the sauces. Continue to mix and match the crudités and sauces on the leaves.

# Oriental-Style Shredded Vegetable Crudités

Here's my Oriental Collection. First the sauces:

## Tomato and Ginger Sauce Ⓥ
Food category – M/A
Serves – 4

INGREDIENTS
- 4 tablespoons very finely grated fresh ginger root
- 1 cup crushed tomatoes (passata)
- 1 teaspoon tomato paste or purée
- 1 tablespoon lemon juice
- sea salt and freshly ground black pepper
- Tabasco sauce, optional

METHOD
In a mixing bowl blend all but the salt, pepper and Tabasco together to

make a thickish running sauce. Adjust with a little extra tomato purée if necessary. Remove to a serving bowl, cover and set aside in a cool place. To serve, adjust seasoning with salt, pepper and Tabasco if used.

## Horseradish Mayonnaise ⓥ
Food category – M/A
Serves – 4

INGREDIENTS

- 1 cup sour cream
- 2 tablespoons creamed horseradish

- 2 tablespoons spring onion, very finely chopped
- sea salt and freshly ground black pepper

METHOD

In a mixing bowl blend together all but 1 teaspoon of the spring onions and the salt and pepper seasoning. Remove to a serving bowl, cover and keep in a cool place until ready to serve. To serve, adjust seasoning with salt and pepper and serve garnished with the remaining chopped spring onions.

## Black Bean Sauce ⓥ
Food category – P
'1 in 5' – Soya beans
Serves – 4

INGREDIENTS

- 1 jar black bean stir fry sauce

- water to dilute

METHOD

Simply mix one cup of the black bean sauce with enough water to make a thick running sauce suitable to spoon over the crudités.

## Oriental-Style Crudités ⓥ
Food category – M/A
Serves – 4

INGREDIENTS

- 1 small mooli (Japanese white radish), finely grated
- 2 cups bean sprouts
- 4 courgettes, (skin and flesh only, pulp discarded) finely grated

- 3 carrots, finely grated
- 1 celeriac, finely grated
- ½ red cabbage, very finely sliced

METHOD

Prepare the vegetables as described. The bean sprouts should be blanched. Place them in a colander and pour over a full kettle of boiling water then put them under cold running water to cool. Drain well and set aside in a cool place until ready to use.

TO SERVE

Place the bowls of sauce, with spoons, in the centre of the table. Arrange portions of about half a cup of each crudités on 4 plates with a small bowl and chopsticks to the side. Place a small serving of a crudités in the bowl, pour over a little of one of the sauces and eat with the chopsticks. Continue to mix and match the crudités and sauces.

# MORE STARTERS, LOVELY LUNCHES AND SUPPERS

## PÂTÉ

Pâté makes a great starter or even a pleasant light meal. In terms of your healthy eating, Kensington Diet style, the main problem with pâté is that traditionally it is served with toast. Here are a couple of recipes to show you how pâté can fit in with your KD eating, don't forget to watch your '1 in 5' rotation.

### CHICKEN LIVER PÂTÉ

Food category – P
'1 in 5' – chicken, bacon
Serves – 4

INGREDIENTS

- 1 onion, finely chopped
- 1 tablespoon olive oil
- 12 oz/350 g chicken livers (fully thawed if frozen), washed and trimmed
- ½ teaspoon dried marjoram
- ½ teaspoon dried rosemary
- 2 tablespoons wine
- 3 oz/90 g unsalted butter, at room temperature
- 4 oz/125 g lean bacon, cut into small dice
- 1 tablespoon green peppercorns, crushed
- 4 tablespoons vegetable stock
- sea salt and black pepper as seasoning
- crudités to serve (see below)

You'll find a food processor is best for this recipe.

METHOD

In a heavy based, non-stick, frying pan over a low heat, sauté the onion in the olive oil, without browning, until soft and clear, 5–10 minutes. Add the chicken livers and dried herbs to the onions and sauté until the livers are just cooked through, 8–10 minutes. Add the wine and cook for 2–3 minutes. Cool, transfer to a food processor and process just enough to produce an even though coarse pâté – it will not take very long, and you should avoid over processing.

In the same frying pan with a little of the butter, sauté the bacon over a low heat, without browning, until just cooked. Add the remaining butter, the peppercorns and the processed chicken livers and fold together with enough vegetable stock until you have an evenly mixed thick pâté. Season to taste with plenty of black pepper and a little salt. Spoon into four individual ramekins or dishes, and set aside in a refrigerator to cool and set. Bring to room temperature for serving and serve, garnished with celery leaves and accompanied with a selection of thinly sliced carrots, celery sticks, chicory leaves and scooped out halves of fresh plum tomatoes.

# Bean Pâté (v)

Make this with nearly any kind of tinned beans or pulses you like.

Food category – C
'1 in 5' – (beans/pulses) chickpeas
Serves – 4

INGREDIENTS
- 1 tablespoon olive oil
- 2 oz/60 g chestnut mushrooms, finely chopped into small dice
- ½ teaspoon cayenne pepper
- 1–2 cloves garlic, finely crushed
- 2 oz/60 g unsalted butter, at room temperature
- 15 oz/470 g cooked chickpeas (tinned chickpeas, drained and washed, are fine)

- ½ tablespoon lemon juice
- 1 teaspoon toasted sesame oil
- Basic Vegetable Stock, (see page 48) to taste
- sea salt and black pepper, to taste

TO GARNISH
- 2 tablespoons best olive oil
- 1 tablespoon finely chopped fresh parsley

You'll find a food processor will enable you to make this pâté more easily.

METHOD

Heat the oil in a heavy based frying pan over a low to medium heat and sauté the mushrooms with the cayenne pepper, until the moisture from the mushrooms has evaporated. Add the garlic and cook until the mushrooms are browned. Remove from the heat, add the butter to the pan so it will soften and set aside.

In the blender, process the chickpeas with the lemon juice and sesame oil, to a fine textured purée using a little vegetable stock if it is too dry. Add the chickpea purée to the mushrooms and beat together to obtain an evenly mixed pâté. Spoon into individual ramekins or dishes and set in the refrigerator to cool. Bring to room temperature to serve, garnished with a drizzle of olive oil and a little chopped parsley and accompanied by vegetable crudités and black olives, radishes and pickled green peppers.

VARIATION

- As your food rotation allows, this pâté can be served with any of a number of Carbohydrate accompaniments. Try warm pitta or crusty bread, rye bread or crackers or slices of fried or grilled polenta (see page 69 for how to prepare Polenta Croutons, then simply slice the cooked polenta into fingers or other shaped pieces before grilling or frying).

# Cheese and Herb Soufflé Omelette ⓥ

This dish is so perfect for a light meal, you just have to try it. But it's extra special with ratatouille. Make your ratatouille first and allow it to cool or make it well beforehand and warm up for serving (see page 238 for recipe). Prepare the soufflé omelette just moments before you are ready to sit at the table.

Food category – P
'1 in 5' – eggs, cheese
Serves – 1 (multiply total ingredients for the number of omelettes to be made)

INGREDIENTS

- 3 eggs, size 2
- 1 teaspoon butter
- 1 oz/30 g cheese, finely grated (use a strong cheese that's not too oily such as mature cheddar, Emmental or even Parmesan)
- 1 tablespoon finely chopped fresh herbs or half a tablespoon dried where fresh is not available (parsley, chives or tarragon or a mixture would be suitable)

- 1/2 teaspoon finely grated cheese, kept separately
- extra 1/2 teaspoon finely chopped fresh herbs, for garnish
- Cooked Ratatouille for four (see page 238)

You'll need a heavy based non-stick frying pan approximately 8 inches/ 20 cm in diameter with an ovenproof handle.

METHOD

Heat the oven to 200 C/400 F/Gas Mark 6. Bring the grill to a moderate heat. (If your grill is in the oven just be ready to switch from the oven setting to the grill when cooking the omelette). Separate the eggs for your omelette, whites in a large bowl with a whisk or hand blender, yolks in a smaller bowl with a fork for whisking them separately. OK, now you're ready.

On a medium hot hob heat the frying pan while you whisk the egg whites to a soft peak stage (it takes seconds with a hand held blender). Now whisk the egg yolks. With a metal spoon, fold the whites into the yolks until evenly mixed but don't be too rough. Add the butter to the hot pan. Fold the 1 oz/30 g grated cheese and chopped herbs into the omelette mixture. Again don't beat but *fold* in until all the ingredients are well dispersed. Tilt the pan to spread the butter, which should be foaming, and pour the omelette mixture in. When the mixture in the pan is quite well set on the bottom but still liquid in the surface, sprinkle on the extra half teaspoon of Parmesan and place the omelette in the top of the oven until it is well risen and starts to brown. It will come up to at least twice the original volume.

Finally place the omelette under the grill (or turn your cooker to the grill setting) until golden brown on top. If you're cooking only one omelette you may consider finishing it under the grill alone, but I find it gives a better result in the oven. It all moves rather quickly from here so if you're cooking more than one omelette, have everything you'll need to hand and set up for a production line approach so you can wash and wipe dry the large bowl and be whisking the eggs and making the mixture for the next omelette while its predecessor is cooking. It especially helps to have all the eggs separated in bowls containing three whites or three yolks each.

To serve, place the omelette on a warm plate with a generous serving of ratatouille overlapping one edge. Garnish with a scattering of chopped herbs and accompany with a bowl of green leaf salad, if desired.

## Scrambled Eggs with Ratatouille ⓥ

Almost any variety of cooked eggs have a natural affinity with the rich flavours of ratatouille. Here's an alternative to the Cheese and Herb Soufflé Omelette.

Food category – P
'1 in 5' – eggs
Serves – 4

INGREDIENTS

- 10 eggs, size 2
- 2 oz/60 g unsalted butter
- sea salt and freshly ground black pepper, to taste

- prepared Ratatouille for four (see page 238), warmed

TASTE SENSATION
Tabasco sauce

METHOD

Beat the eggs together in a bowl. Melt half the butter in a non-stick saucepan over a medium heat until it starts to foam. Add the egg mixture and stir continuously and vigorously while it heats and begins to thicken. When just over half the mixture has thickened into creamy scrambled egg continue to stir well while adding a small pinch of salt and the remaining butter. Stir vigorously until only a little of the liquid egg mix remains to be cooked. Be sure not to allow any of the mixture to remain unmixed with the butter or undisturbed in the pan where it can solidify. Remove from heat and spoon quickly onto four warm plates alongside warm ratatouille. Remember the eggs will continue to cook off the heat. Sprinkle the eggs with a little fresh, coarsely ground, black pepper and sprinkle 5–6 drops of Tabasco on the ratatouille. Serve immediately.

VARIATION
- A whole new dimension of flavours comes through when you mix herbs and cream cheese into the scrambled eggs. So if your food rotation allows, this is what to do. Reduce the amount of butter by half, to 1 oz/30 g, then proceed as before. Halfway through cooking, when you add the seasoning, also add 4 oz/125 g cream cheese such as Philadelphia with 2 tablespoons finely chopped fresh herbs of your choice (e.g. chives, parsley, marjoram, tarragon). Beat well over the heat until the eggs are just cooked through. The cheese will make the mixture creamier so there is no need to be so concerned about the eggs solidifying. Serve as before.

# Spanish-Style Omelette Ⓥ

A Spanish 'tortilla' omelette is easier than soufflé omelettes when feeding several people. Use M/A vegetables in place of the traditional potatoes and you have a feast of a meal which fits into your Kensington Diet eating plan.

Food category – P
'1 in 5' – eggs
Serves – 4

INGREDIENTS
- 4 tablespoons olive oil
- 2 small celeriac, peeled and diced
- 1 large onion, peeled and diced
- 2 small green peppers, cored and diced
- sea salt and freshly ground black pepper, to taste
- 8 eggs, beaten
- 2 tablespoons finely chopped fresh parsley
- 1 tablespoon finely chopped fresh thyme

METHOD
Heat the oil in a 8 inch/20 cm heavy based non-stick frying pan with a lid, over a medium heat. Mix the vegetables together and add them to the pan with the thyme and a good sprinkling of salt and freshly ground black pepper. Cover and cook slowly, mixing occasionally, until the vegetables are cooked through, about 10–15 minutes. With a slotted spoon transfer the vegetables to a dish lined with kitchen paper to remove as much oil as possible then add to the beaten egg mixture in a

large bowl. Add the chopped parsley and stir well. Pour off excess oil from the frying pan and place over a medium heat.

Pre-heat the grill to a high heat. Add the egg and vegetable mixture to the warm pan and spread evenly to the sides, cook gently without movement to allow the base of the tortilla to set, then carry on cooking, shaking the pan occasionally to prevent sticking and burning, until the eggs are almost set firm. Prepare a flat plate larger than the tortilla by lightly oiling the top surface all over. Put the frying pan under the grill and cook the top of the omelette until it is set, about 3 minutes.

Place the plate upside down on the frying pan, hold it in place with your hand in an oven glove or tea towel and flip the whole lot over so the omelette is on the plate. Slide it back into the pan upside down, return to the heat and cook until golden brown. Slide the tortilla onto a serving plate and serve in slices, hot or cold, with tomato salad and green salad leaves dressed with walnut oil vinaigrette.

If you feel nervous about flipping the tortilla over then finish cooking to a golden brown under the grill. In this case it won't have the classic shape of a tortilla and will actually be more of an Italian frittata-style omelette, but just as tasty.

VARIATION
• If your food rotation allows, add strips of cooked ham to the beaten egg mixture with the vegetables.

### RAREBITS

Welsh rarebit is a favourite winter snack, but of course, with its mixture of bread, eggs and cheese, it's a non-starter in food combining terms. Worry not, in Kensington Diet eating rarebit is still on the menu. The KD collection of rustic and sophisticated rarebits separate the extra fattening combination of bread and cheese and offers many tasty versions as healthier toppings for a range of grilled vegetables.

TIP
☞ The vegetable bases need to be just pre-cooked so they are hot but not breaking apart – they should still have some firm texture. Here's how to prepare and cook a selection.
**Slicing (beef) tomatoes** – use firm, large tomatoes cut into equal thick slices; discard the trimmings from top and bottom. Brush both sides of the slices with olive oil and season with salt and black pepper. Pan fry or grill until heated through but still

firm. Other vegetables may take longer to cook than tomatoes so keep these warm until ready to top with rarebit mixture and cook to a finish.

**Chicory hearts** – remove outside leaves and cut from top to bottom to give ½ inch/1 cm slices held together by the root. Brush both sides of the slices with olive oil and season with salt and black pepper. Pan or griddle fry, or grill the slices with high heat to brown both sides and leave the inside hot and crunchy. Spread the rarebit mixture on a cut surface.

**Fennel** – trim old outside leaves from the fennel bulb and retain the fennel fronds for garnish. Cut the bulb from top to bottom, to give ¼ inch/6 mm slices held together by the root. Blanch the slices in boiling water for 5 minutes, drain and transfer to cold water to stop them continuing to cook. Drain, dry and brush both sides of the slices with olive oil and season with salt and pepper. Pan or griddle fry, or grill the slices with high heat to brown both sides and leave the inside hot and crunchy. Spread the rarebit mixture on a cut surface.

**Onions** – choose large mild onions such as red or Spanish. Trim off the top and peel the skin back to the root. Carefully trim to leave the peeled onion held together by the root. Cut from top to bottom to give ½ inch/1 cm slices held together by the root. Brush both sides of the slices with olive oil and season with salt and black pepper. Pan or griddle fry, or grill the slices with high heat to brown both sides and leave the inside hot and crunchy. Spread the rarebit mixture on a cut surface.

**Mushrooms** – choose large flat/field mushrooms trimmed of tough stalk and wiped clean. Brush on both sides with olive oil and season with salt and black pepper. Pan or griddle fry, or grill the slices with high heat to just brown both sides and leave the inside hot and firm. Spread the rarebit mixture on the grilled surface.

The toppings need to cook quite slowly, 5–10 minutes under a medium grill, so the egg is fully cooked and the cheese melted. Test by breaking the crust on one piece to check if it is cooked underneath.

# Ploughman's Rarebit (v)

Food category – P
'1 in 5' – eggs, cow's milk, cheese
Serves – 4

INGREDIENTS

- 2 eggs
- 1 teaspoon prepared English mustard
- 2 tablespoons Worcestershire sauce
- 7 oz/220 g mixed British cheese (e.g. strong cheddar and double Gloucester) grated
- 4 slices mild onion, pre-cooked (see above)

- 4 slices tomato, pre-cooked (see above)
- sweet pickle (Branston, Piccalilli etc.)
- watercress
- 1 tablespoon lemon juice
- sea salt and freshly ground black pepper, to taste

METHOD

Pre-heat the grill to a medium heat, foil line and lightly oil a grill pan. Beat the eggs, mustard and Worcestershire sauce together, and mix in the cheese to form a thick mixture. Spread thickly over the slices of onion and tomato. Cook under the grill until the egg and cheese mixture sets right through, just before serving increase the heat to high, to brown and lightly crisp the topping, about 5–10 minutes in all. Arrange the hot rarebit slices on four plates with sweet pickle and watercress garnish. Dress the watercress with a sprinkle of lemon juice, salt and pepper. Serve immediately.


# Four Seasons Rarebit

A sophisticated collection suitable for lunch or supper.

Food category – P
'1 in 5' – eggs, cow's milk cheese, buffalo milk cheese, anchovies, pepperoni
Serves – 4

INGREDIENTS

- 10 fl oz/300 ml passata or chopped plum tomatoes, drained
- 1 teaspoon tomato purée

- 1 tablespoon finely chopped fresh oregano (or 1 teaspoon dried oregano)

- sea salt and freshly ground black pepper, to taste
- 2 eggs
- 1 tablespoon Dijon mustard
- 7 oz/220 g mature English cheddar, grated
- 4 large mushrooms, pre-cooked (see above)
- 4 slices chicory, pre-cooked (see above)
- 4 slices fennel, pre-cooked (see above)

- 2 oz/60g spicy pepperoni, finely chopped
- 2 oz/60 g black olives, pitted and chopped
- 2 tablespoons capers, drained and patted dry
- 2 tablespoons finely chopped tinned anchovy fillets
- 1–2 cloves garlic, finely crushed
- half cup mozzarella or Gruyère cheese, finely sliced or grated

TO GARNISH
- 2 bunches rocket leaves
- 1 tablespoon lemon juice

- 1 tablespoon balsamic vinegar

METHOD

Simmer the passata or chopped tomatoes with the tomato purée and oregano in a medium sized saucepan over a medium heat, until reduced to a thick sauce. Season with salt and pepper and set aside to cool a little. Pre-heat the grill to a medium heat, foil line and lightly oil a grill pan. Beat the eggs and mustard together, stir in the cheese to form a thick mixture. Spread a little tomato sauce over the mushrooms and slices of chicory and fennel. Spread the cheese and egg mixture thinly over the tomato sauce on the mushrooms and slices of chicory and fennel. Cook under the grill until the egg and cheese mixture sets right through, just before serving increase the heat to high, to brown and lightly crisp the topping, about 5–10 minutes in all.

Sprinkle the cooked cheese mixture with chopped pepperoni, olives, capers, anchovies and garlic. Top with mozzarella or Gruyère and return to a hot grill to heat the toppings and melt the extra cheese. Arrange the hot Four Seasons rarebit slices on four plates with rocket leaves as garnish. Dress the rocket with sprinklings of lemon juice, balsamic vinegar and salt. Serve immediately.

# Stuffed Leek Rarebit

A little bit different but still a rarebit in all the basics. For this recipe you'll need several large leeks. Trim and discard the coarse outer leaves and ends as usual, then split the good layers to obtain 16–20 'sheets' of leek suitable for eating. Retain the inner parts for another dish.

You'll need a steamer for this dish. A fan type steamer over shallow simmering water in a saucepan will do fine.

Food category – P
'1 in 5' – eggs, goat's milk cheese, bacon (optional)
Serves – 4

INGREDIENTS

- 16–20 sheets of leek leaf, (see above)
- 2–3 strips lean bacon, finely diced, optional
- 1 oz/30 g unsalted butter
- 1 medium onion, finely diced
- 1 clove garlic, finely crushed, optional
- 2–3 carrots, peeled and grated

- 2–3 courgettes, washed, trimmed and grated
- sea salt and black pepper, to taste
- 1 lb/500 g creamy goat's milk cheese
- 1 teaspoon Dijon mustard
- 2 eggs
- milk for mixing

TO GARNISH

- 2 medium onions, finely sliced
- 1 tablespoon olive oil

- 2 tablespoons finely chopped fresh parsley

METHOD

Blanch the 'sheets' of leek by placing them in a large saucepan and pouring over a kettle full of boiling water. Stand for 3 minutes until soft then transfer to cold water to stop further cooking. Drain, remove the very thin slippery layers between the leaves and pat dry. Set aside. In a large non-stick frying pan or saucepan, sauté the bacon, if used, until browned. Remove and keep warm. In the same pan, in the bacon juices and with a little butter if necessary, sauté the onion and garlic if used, over a low heat until the onion is soft and clear. Add the grated carrot and courgette, season with salt and pepper and cook, mixing well, until the vegetables soften and bind to form a good stuffing mixture. Remove from the heat, mix in the cooked bacon and set aside to cool.

Roll a few spoonfuls of stuffing in each sheet of blanched leek to give 16–20 stuffed leek rolls. Wrap each roll in kitchen foil, folding edges together to seal and twisting the ends to form 'Christmas crackers'. Trim off excess foil. Boil water in a saucepan for steaming, pre-heat the grill to a medium heat. Mix the cheese with the mustard and blend in the eggs to produce a smooth, egg and cheese sauce. Use a little milk if necessary to make a thick coating consistency sauce which will just about pour with a little help. Steam the stuffed, foil wrapped leeks for 10 minutes. Allow to cool for a few minutes then carefully unwrap the stuffed leeks and arrange in either a single heatproof dish or divide between four individual heatproof dishes. Cover the stuffed leeks with cheese and egg mix using a spatula. Grill for 5–10 minutes until the egg and cheese mixture cooks right through, just before serving increase the heat to high, to brown and lightly crisp the topping. While cooking the leek rarebit, sauté the sliced onions in olive oil over high heat until crisp and golden. Serve topped with crisp fried onion slices and sprinkled with chopped parsley.

### QUICHES

While we're on the subject of egg and cheesy things we really must mention quiches. The classic quiche is rather similar to the rarebits: a cheese and egg mixture baked in a pastry case that doesn't fit in with the good food combining of Kensington Diet eating. The trick is to cook and serve the various possible fillings separately from the pastry cases in which they would usually be found. Or to fill the pastry cases with any number of alternative fillings which *will* fit your combining needs. Of course, served without the pastry bases, rich and creamy quiche mixtures carry less of a weight penalty.

# Basic Quiche Filling ⓥ

The Basic Quiche Filling mixture of eggs, cheese and cream can be combined with many different added ingredients. Here's the recipe for a Basic Quiche Filling mixture. Two variations for you to try and follow – but your imagination will certainly come up with many more! For best results just pre-cook the additions before you mix them with the Basic Quiche Mixture and bake them.

This amount is suitable for an 8 inch/20 cm heavy based frying pan or 6 individual ramekins when mixed with other ingredients.

Food category – P
'1 in 5' – eggs, cheese
Serves – 4–6

INGREDIENTS
- 6 oz/175 g double cream
- 2 eggs
- 6 oz/175 g cheese (see variations below)
- sea salt and freshly ground black pepper, to taste

METHOD
Blend the cream, eggs and cheese together and season with salt and pepper: fold in your chosen added ingredients and use as described below.

# Bacon, Onion and Tomato Quiche
Food category – P
'1 in 5' – eggs, bacon, cow's milk cheeses
Serves – 4–6

INGREDIENTS
- 1 oz/30 g butter
- 1 small onion, finely diced
- 4–6 strips lean bacon chopped (or cooked ham)
- 1 fresh firm tomato, seeded and roughly chopped
- 1 portion Basic Quiche Filling mixture (made with 3 oz/90 g each of mature cheddar and Emmental cheeses)

You'll need an 8 inch/20 cm heavy based, non-stick frying pan with an ovenproof handle.

METHOD
Pre-heat the oven to 185 C/350 F/Gas Mark 4. Warm the butter over a moderate heat in the frying pan and sauté the onions until they are soft and clear, 5–10 minutes. Remove and set aside. Carefully cook the bacon in the same pan, without browning, until just cooked. Remove the pan from the heat. Return the cooked onions to the pan, add the chopped tomatoes and mix briefly together. Add the Basic Quiche Filling mixture to the pan and stir together.

Cook the Basic Quiche Filling in the oven for 30–35 minutes until completely cooked through. (The surface of the quiche will be firm and set, a sharp knifepoint pushed in will not encounter a liquid feel). Brown the top of the quiche under a hot grill for 1–2 minutes if desired before serving. Cool the base of the frying pan rapidly, to avoid too much further cooking, by resting it on a wet tea cloth. Transfer the pan to a heatproof surface at the table and slice the quiche onto plates from the pan. Serve with large dressed salad.

VARIATIONS

- For the quiche filling try using various blends of cheeses making sure to mix cow's milk cheeses together and goat's and sheep's milk cheeses together to maintain your '1 in 5' food rotation. For the additional pre-cooked ingredients try mushrooms (well cooked to reduce water content), courgettes (use flesh only, scoop out and discard the pulp), asparagus, broccoli florettes or spinach. Or try anchovies, smoked salmon or capers, and any of the various number of fresh herbs available.
- For accompaniment serve with your choice of salad, Ratatouille (see page 238) or a sauce such as Rich Tomato (page 272) or Sweet Pepper Coulis (page 276).
- There is another way of cooking these quiches and that's by putting a quarter of the mixture into each of four, individual, lightly greased ramekins or earthenware pots. Cook in the oven for 25–30 minutes then brown under the grill for a minute or two as before. Serve in the pots or cool and turn out onto a plate with your chosen accompaniment. To produce an even more delicious result put a teaspoon or two of Rich Tomato or Tomato and Herb Sauce (page 272) in the bottom of the ramekin before adding the quiche mixture.

# Goat's Cheese and Roquefort Quiche in a Pot Ⓥ

When I was test-cooking these quiche recipes I came up with this fantastic version in a pot. It is incredibly rich and you won't need much for each person, but it makes a fantastic hot or cold starter.

Food category – P
'1 in 5' – eggs, goat's milk cheese, sheep's milk cheese
Serves – 4

INGREDIENTS

- 1 cup mild onion (Spanish or shallots), finely sliced
- 1 oz unsalted butter
- 1 teaspoon sugar
- 5 oz/150 g creamy goat's milk cheese (I used Chavroux)
- 1 large egg

- 2 oz/60 g Roquefort (or fetta), crumbled into small pieces
- 2 tablespoons finely chopped fresh parsley
- freshly ground black pepper, to taste

You'll need four individual ramekins or small ovenproof earthenware pots

METHOD

Pre-heat the oven to 185 C/350 F/Gas Mark 4. In a small, heavy based frying pan, sauté the onions in the butter with the sugar over a low heat until the onions become soft, brown and caramelised, 30–40 minutes. Lightly grease the ramekins and spoon a portion of the onions into each. Mix the creamy goat's cheese with the egg until smooth, then fold in the Roquefort and parsley and season with plenty of black pepper. Spoon the mixture into the ramekins on top of the onions, sprinkle with black pepper. Cook in the oven for 25–30 minutes until firm, then brown under a hot grill for 3–4 minutes. Serve in ramekins or turned out onto individual plates, with a refreshing salad of mixed leaves.

### PASTRIES, PIZZAS, PANCAKES, CROSTINI AND RÖSTIS

The other half of the quiche equation, of course, is the pastry base. A simple pastry case can be part of a whole variety of fabulous dishes which will fit into your Kensington Diet eating far better than real quiches can. But pastry cases are usually wheat and part of the essence of KD healthy eating is to vary your food. That's the idea encompassed by '1 in 5' food rotation.

So I'd like to show you how to use the basic wheat pastry case to make some wonderful light meals, but I also want to show you some alternatives using replacements for wheat pastry. The result is an exciting selection of different bases and suitable toppings which you can confidently mix and match as part of your healthy Kensington Diet eating strategy.

# Shortcrust Pastry ⓥ

This recipe is sufficient for four 3 inch/8 cm flan or tart tins or one tin of 8 inches/20 cm diameter.

Food category – C
'1 in 5' – wheat

INGREDIENTS

- 6 oz/175 g plain flour
- pinch salt
- 3 oz/90 g unsalted butter, chilled and cut into small pieces

- 3–4 tablespoons tepid water

METHOD

Sift the flour and salt into a chilled mixing bowl and stir well. Working quickly, rub the butter in with fingertips or pastry cutter until the mixture is like fine breadcrumbs. Sprinkle on two tablespoons water and work in with a spatula or round edged knife then add as much extra water as is required to produce a ball of smooth dough. Wrap in Clingfilm and chill in the refrigerator for 30 minutes before use. Alternatively, you could buy some chilled or frozen shortcrust pastry from your supermarket.

# Mushroom Tartlets ⓥ

Food category – C
'1 in 5' – wheat
Serves – 4

INGREDIENTS

- 8 oz/250 g shortcrust pastry (see above, or use frozen as long as it's egg-free)
- 2 tablespoons olive oil
- 1 oz/30 g unsalted butter
- 1 lb/500 g mixed mushrooms (e.g. chestnut, shiitake, oyster, chanterelle, cep) wiped clean, trimmed of hard stalks, larger ones cut or sliced

- 1–2 cloves garlic, finely crushed, optional
- 2 tablespoons fresh, finely chopped flat leaf parsley
- sea salt and freshly ground black pepper, to taste
- 5 fl oz/150 ml crème fraîche

METHOD

Pre-heat the oven to 200 C/400 F/Gas Mark 6. Roll the pastry out to a thickness of $\frac{1}{4}$ – $\frac{1}{2}$ inch/6–10 mm and line four individual 3 inch/8 cm flan or tart tins. Prick the bases several times with a fork and bake blind (empty) for 10–15 minutes until just cooked and pale golden in colour.

Heat the olive oil and butter in a large, heavy based frying pan over a fairly high heat. Sauté the mushrooms and garlic together, omitting oyster mushrooms if used, for 3–4 minutes until well coloured. Shake or stir frequently to assure sealing and browning the mushrooms and to avoid water seeping out. If oyster mushrooms are used, set the cooked mushrooms aside on a warm plate and flash fry the oyster mushrooms separately in the hot pan over a high heat for 30–60 seconds, add the previously cooked mushrooms and stir together for 30 seconds. Remove from the heat, stir in the chopped parsley and season with salt and pepper.

Stir in the crème fraîche and cook for 2–3 minutes until the crème fraîche thickens. Spoon the mixture into the pastry cases and return to the oven for 5 minutes. Serve the tartlets onto individual plates with your choice of salad.

VARIATION

• Replace the shortcrust pastry case, above, with a blind pastry case made from puff pastry as follows:

Food category – C
'1 in 5' – wheat
Serves – 4

INGREDIENTS

• 8 oz/250 g frozen puff pastry, thawed
• 1 quantity of cooked mushroom and parsley mixture from recipe above

• melted butter to glaze

METHOD

Pre-heat the oven to 200 C/400 F/Gas Mark 6. Roll the puff pastry out into a sheet $\frac{1}{4}$ inch/6 mm thick. Use a round small plate about 4 inches/10 cm diameter as a template around which you can cut the pastry into eight disks. Place a smaller plate about 3 inches/8 cm diameter in the centre of four of the pastry disks as a guide and cut around it to give you four rings of pastry $\frac{1}{2}$ inch/1 cm wide. Discard the pastry from inside the rings you've just cut. Now you have 4 pastry rings and 4 disks.

Place the four pastry disks on a lightly oiled baking sheet. Brush one side of each pastry ring with water and sit each into place, moist side down, onto a pastry disk to form a lip around the edge. Press gently into place to seal. Prick the bases of the tartlets several times with a fork to prevent them rising on cooking. Brush with melted butter and bake for 5 minutes. Remove from the oven and spoon the mushroom mixture into the tartlets. Return the tartlets to the oven for a further 5–10 minutes until the pastry cases are cooked to a golden brown. Serve onto individual plates with your choice of salad.

## Tatin-Style Tart of Peppers and Onions with Sour Cream and Chives ⓥ

The sugar in the peppers and onions make it possible to adapt the famous apple tart into this very special savoury version. Served with a quenelle of sour cream and chives and accompanied by a green leaf salad with an unusual Fennel Vinaigrette dressing, this makes a splendid meal.

Food category – C
'1 in 5' – wheat
Serves – 4–6

INGREDIENTS

- 2 red peppers
- 2 yellow peppers
- 3 tablespoons olive oil
- 2 large Spanish or red onions
- 1 oz/30 g unsalted butter
- ¼ teaspoon ground cinnamon
- 1 teaspoon soft brown demerara sugar

- juice and zest of ½ a lemon
- fine sea salt and freshly ground black pepper, to taste
- 8 oz/250 g frozen puff pastry, thawed for use

METHOD

Pre-heat the oven to 200 C/400 F/Gas Mark 6. Wash the peppers, brush them with a tablespoon of the olive oil and place them in a foil lined tray. Roast or grill under a high heat, turning occasionally, until black charred spots and patches have appeared on all sides. Remove the tray, cover the peppers with a clean wet tea towel and leave to cool. While roasting the peppers, prepare the onions. Trim and peel off the outer skin. Quarter by slicing from top to bottom into four segments. Separate the layers.

In an 8 inch/20 cm heavy based, non-stick frying pan with an ovenproof handle (or use any frying pan and transfer to an 8 inch/20 cm pie tin later) sauté the onions in two tablespoons of the olive oil over a low heat, with the butter, cinnamon, sugar, lemon juice and zest and a pinch of salt. Cook uncovered, stirring occasionally, until the onions are soft and caramelised and there is a thick syrup. This will take 50–60 minutes, depending on whether you put it on a very low heat and leave it alone or use a higher heat to start with. When cooking onions in this way, it is important that you are prepared to watch carefully throughout the cooking time. Take care not to burn the onions, which is most likely to occur towards the end of the cooking when there is a lot of sugar and little water in the pan. That's the time to make sure the heat is very low. Add a little of the juices from the peppers or some water if they look like they are drying out too quickly and likely to scorch. The end result should be soft brown sweet onions in a caramelly syrup.

While cooking the onions, skin the peppers, but retain the juices to use with the onions as described. Discard the seeds and trimmings. Slice the flesh into quarters. When the onions are cooked spoon them into a dish to leave about 1 tablespoon caramel syrup in the frying pan for when you bake the tart. To create a little more syrup if you don't have that amount add a tablespoon of sugar and a little water to the pan before removing the onions. Keep on a low heat until the sugar has dissolved then transfer the onions as already described. Arrange the quarters of red and yellow pepper attractively on the caramel syrup, filling gaps with caramelised onions. When all the peppers are used add the remaining onions. Remember this is a tart that will be turned over and that your arrangement of the peppers in the base of the pan will show on the top of the tart, so take a little trouble at this point.

When the pan is filled with the peppers, onions and caramel syrup, season with freshly ground black pepper and put the pan over a very low heat to stay warm. Roll out the puff pastry to about ¼ inch/6 mm and cut a circle the same size as the pan using a plate as a guide. Fit the pastry circle over the filling and tuck the edges in all around so it is dome shaped. Pierce the pastry in 3 or 4 places with the tip of a sharp knife. Bake for 25–30 minutes until golden brown and crisp. Place a baking sheet under to catch any juices which may bubble out. While the tart is cooking, make the sour cream and salad accompaniments as described below. When cooked allow to cool for 10 minutes before putting a serving plate over the top of the pastry and carefully turn the whole thing, pan and plate, over. Make sure your hands are well protected from any caramel syrup which may escape around the edges. Serve slices of tart onto individual plates with quenelles of sour cream and chives (see below) and accompanied by a mixture of green leaves dressed with Fennel Vinaigrette (see page 277).

# Quenelles of Sour Cream and Chives ⓥ

This can be made well in advance. Store covered or in an airtight container until required.

Food category – M/A
Serves – 4–6

INGREDIENTS
- 5 fl oz/150 ml whipping cream
- 2 dessertspoons lemon juice
- 2 tablespoons finely chopped fresh chives
- 12 whole fresh chives, washed and dried as garnish
- paprika powder as garnish

METHOD
Mix the cream and lemon juice in a bowl and whip vigorously until stiff – a hand held blender does this job really well. With a metal spoon, fold in the chopped chives, cover and place in the refrigerator to cool and stiffen up. To serve, make egg-shaped quenelles between two dessert-spoons.

# Pizza KD style ⓥ
Food category – C
'1 in 5' – wheat
Serves – 4–6

INGREDIENTS
- 1 ready prepared pizza base (thawed if frozen)
- 1 large onion, finely sliced
- 1–2 cloves garlic, finely chopped
- 3 tablespoons olive oil
- 16 oz/500 g tin or jar of passata (crushed and drained tomatoes), or use chopped plum tomatoes
- 1 tablespoon tomato purée
- pinch sugar
- sea salt and freshly ground black pepper, to taste
- 1 tablespoon dried oregano
- 2 oz/60 g black olives, pitted and chopped
- 2 tablespoons capers, drained and patted dry

METHOD

Pre-heat the oven to 230 C/450 F/Gas Mark 7 or to the temperature instructed by the pizza base makers. Make a thick tomato sauce. In a large heavy based saucepan, over a medium heat, sauté the onions and garlic in one tablespoon of the olive oil, without browning, until the onions are soft and clear, 5–10 minutes. Add the passata, tomato purée, sugar and salt and pepper seasoning, bring to a simmer and cook uncovered until reduced to a thick tomato sauce, about 25–30 minutes. Spread the tomato sauce over the pizza base, sprinkle on the oregano, olives and capers, season with extra salt and pepper and drizzle with the remaining olive oil. Bake for 15 minutes or according to the maker's instructions. Serve in slices onto individual plates accompanied by your choice of salad and dressing.

VARIATION

• The same topping is equally delicious on polenta or wheat bread crostini.

# Polenta Crostini ⓥ

Food category – C
'1 in 5' – maize corn
Serves – 4

INGREDIENTS

• 4 oz/125 g pre-cooked or quick cook polenta
• 1 pt/500 ml boiling vegetable stock or lightly salted water
• 1 oz/30 g unsalted butter or 1 tablespoon olive oil
• herbs or spices of your choice (e.g. basil, parsley)

• 1 portion tomato sauce (see KD Pizza recipe above)
• pizza toppings (see KD Pizza recipe above)
• 2 tablespoons olive oil
• sea salt and freshly ground black pepper, to taste

METHOD

Pour the polenta slowly into the boiling stock in a non-stick saucepan, stirring continuously to avoid lumps. Continue to stir quite vigorously for 3–5 minutes until the polenta has thickened and forms a single mass. Remove from the heat, add the butter or olive oil, plenty of salt and freshly ground black pepper (avoiding adding salt if you have used stock cubes) and spices or herbs if desired. Beat vigorously to mix well and spread evenly, about ½ inch/1 cm thick on the bottom of an oiled or buttered rectangular tray or dish. Leave to cool for 30–40 minutes, remove in one piece and cut into 3 inch/8 cm × 4 inch/10 cm slices. Spread with tomato sauce, pizza toppings, olive oil and seasoning. Bake on an oiled baking sheet at 230 C/450 F/Gas Mark 7 for 15 minutes. Serve with salad.

## Wheat Bread Crostini (v)
Food category – C
'1 in 5' – wheat
Serves – 4

INGREDIENTS
- 4 large slices of good firm bread (e.g. ciabatta)
- 1 portion tomato sauce (see KD Pizza recipe above)
- pizza toppings (see KD pizza recipe above)
- 2 tablespoons olive oil
- sea salt and finely ground black pepper, to taste

METHOD
Toast the bread slices until golden brown on both sides. Spread the tomato sauce on one side of each slice, sprinkle with pizza toppings, olive oil and seasoning and replace under the grill until hot. Serve with your choice of salad.

## Socca with Mixed Roast Peppers (v)

Socca is like a pizza or pastry base made from gram (chickpea) flour available from many health food shops and supermarkets now.

FOR THE SOCCA

Food category – C
'1 in 5' – pulses (chickpeas)
Serves – 4

INGREDIENTS
- 4 oz/125 g gram (chickpea) flour
- 12 fl oz/400 ml tepid water
- 1 tablespoon olive oil
- 1 oz/30 g black olives, pitted and finely chopped
- ½ teaspoon dried thyme
- sea salt and freshly ground black pepper, to taste

For this recipe you'll need a heavy baking sheet or roasting tin about 8 inches/20 cm × 12 inches/28 cm and a pastry cutter or template for cutting about 4 inches/10 cm in diameter.

METHOD

Pre-heat the oven to 240 C/475 F/Gas Mark 8. Lightly oil the baking sheet. Sieve the gram flour into a mixing bowl, season with salt and pepper and gradually mix in the water a little at a time until you have a smooth thin batter. Beat in the oil and mix in the olives and thyme. Pour the batter onto the baking sheet until it is about $\frac{1}{4}$ inch/6 mm thick, and bake in the oven for 25–30 minutes, until the socca is firm. It may begin to blister on the surface, which is perfectly fine. Cool for a few minutes and cut into four rounds 4 inches/10 cm in diameter and set aside until ready to serve.

FOR THE ROAST PEPPERS

Food category – M/A
Serves – 4

INGREDIENTS

- 2 red peppers
- 2 yellow peppers
- 1–2 cloves garlic, thinly sliced

METHOD

Roast the peppers in the oven prepared for the socca, until they are well coloured with charring or black spots on all sides. Remove from the oven, cover with a damp tea cloth until cool enough to handle. Remove and discard the skins, cores and seeds, working over a plate to retain as much juice as possible. Slice the roasted peppers into $\frac{1}{2}$ inch/1 cm slices, mix together with the juices and sliced garlic. Set aside until ready to serve.

EXTRA INGREDIENTS FOR SERVING

- 1 tablespoon sun dried tomato paste (or tomato purée)
- 2 servings of Basic Vinaigrette (see page 73)
- 1 cup fresh basil leaves

METHOD

When ready to serve place the rounds of socca under a hot grill for 1–2 minutes to reheat and add colour. Arrange a round on each of four warm plates, spread each round with half a teaspoon of sun dried tomato paste and arrange a quarter of the roasted mixed peppers and garlic on top. Measure the Basic Vinaigrette into a food processor with the basil leaves and purée to make a luscious green sauce. Drizzle with a tablespoon of this Basil Vinaigrette and serve with side salads of green leaves dressed with lemon juice and a sprinkling of sea salt if desired.

VARIATION

• If your food rotation allows, try replacing the socca with rounds of short crust pastry made with whole wheat flour (use frozen or see the short crust pastry recipe above). Roll out the pastry to $\frac{1}{4}$ inch/6 mm thick, cut out four rounds 4 inches/10 cm in diameter and prick the surface all over with a fork. Bake on a lightly oiled baking sheet for 17–20 minutes at 200 C/400 F/Gas Mark 6 until golden. Serve as described for the socca (above) with sun dried tomato paste, roast peppers and garlic, and topped with basil vinaigrette.

# Rösti and Seasonal Vegetables ⓥ

FOR THE RÖSTI

Food category – C
'1 in 5' – potato
Serves – 4

INGREDIENTS

• 8 medium potatoes
• 2 teaspoons mixed dried herbs
• 2 oz/60 g butter, melted or 4 tablespoons olive oil

• 1 tablespoon Dijon mustard
• sea salt and freshly ground black pepper, to taste

A large baking tin or stiff metal baking sheet, preferably non-stick, and a metal ring mould or pastry cutter 3 inches/8 cm diameter will be needed for this recipe.

METHOD

Pre-heat the oven to 220 C/425 F/Gas Mark 7. Lightly oil the baking tin. Cut the potatoes to an even size to ensure they cook equally. Cover the potatoes in cold water in a large saucepan, bring to the boil in their skins for 10–12 minutes until almost cooked. Drain, cool by running under cold water if necessary, pat dry and peel the potatoes then grate them into a large mixing bowl, using a coarse grater. Add sprinklings of dried herbs, salt and pepper as you grate to make mixing them in easier. Mix in the melted butter and mustard using your fingers to prevent breaking the grated potatoes up too much.

Pre-heat the baking tin in the hot oven. Using the ring mould, lightly oiled each time, arrange eight rösti in the baking tin. Spoon enough grated potato mix into the mould to give a ½ inch/1 cm–¾ inch/2 cm thick cake when pressed down fairly firmly with a small spoon. Roast the rösti in the oven for about 12–15 minutes. To see that they are cooked golden brown on the bottom, lift one edge with a spatula. Turn the rösti carefully with a spatula or slice and return to the oven for a further 5–7 minutes. Serve with your chosen accompaniment. (see below).

FOR THE SEASONAL VEGETABLES
Choose whatever fresh vegetables are available and suitable for steaming or poaching. Here is an example of a selection you could use (see page 226 for steaming method).

Food category – M/A
Serves – 4

INGREDIENTS
- 4 medium or 8 baby carrots
- 4 medium or 8 baby courgettes
- 4 small leeks
- 8 small spears asparagus

METHOD
Prepare the vegetables by trimming, cleaning and cutting them into sizes that will look attractive together on the plate (e.g. baby carrots cut in half lengthways or larger ones cut into similar sized batons; split baby courgettes in half or cut larger courgettes into batons and scrape out the pulp; cut leeks into thick ribbons etc.) Separately, steam or poach the vegetables in vegetable stock or water, until they are just cooked but still have some bite or crunch. Keep warm without cooking further until ready to serve or set aside and microwave to reheat.

EXTRA INGREDIENTS FOR SERVING
- 1 quantity Basic Tomato Sauce (see page 271), warmed
- 2 tablespoons finely chopped fresh parsley
- sea salt and freshly ground black pepper, to taste

Place hot rösti onto four warm plates, arrange a selection of the seasonal vegetables around it, season with salt and pepper, top with some warm tomato sauce and sprinkle with chopped parsley. Serve.

- If you prefer, rösti are wonderful accompanied by a crisp freshly made salsa of chopped tomatoes, red onions and cucumber with fresh chopped basil mixed with lemon juice and olive oil then lightly seasoned with salt and pepper.

## STUFFED VEGETABLES

Wonderfully versatile as starters, light meals or as accompaniments to main course dishes. Stuffed vegetables are also colourful, tasty and can easily be filled with either Protein or Carbohydrate stuffing variations to fit your Kensington Diet and rotation needs. Here's how to prepare various vegetables for stuffing.

### Courgettes

Choose medium to large sized vegetables about 6 inches/15 cm long and quite fat. Trim off the stalk ends and wash. If you want a particularly attractive appearance, shave peelings off the courgettes lengthways at intervals so they have stripes of green skin and white flesh. Test to find out which long sides are the bottoms, that is the sides on which they will sit and be stable when cooking, then slice off the opposite, 'top', sides to about a quarter of the thickness of the courgettes. Retain what you've removed for later use. Scoop the pulp from the remaining three-quarters of each courgette to make room for the stuffing. When stuffed, bake at 200 C/400 F/Gas Mark 6 for about 30 minutes, in an oven pan or dish containing a small amount of water to prevent burning and drying out. Alternatively, poach in shallow, lightly salted water or stock for 12–15 minutes until the courgette is soft and the stuffing is cooked through and hot.

### Marrow

Choose a vegetable which will give you rings about 3–4 inches/8–10 cms in diameter, when sliced. Peel the marrow and either cut it into 2 inch/5 cm slices and remove and discard the core from each slice, or slice off the stem end of the marrow about 2 inch/5 cm from the end and hollow out both the main body and this 'cap'. You may also slice a quarter of the marrow off the top length of the marrow to create a 'lid'. As with the courgettes, remove the pulp from both sections, stuff and replace the 'lid'. Part cook the rings in lightly salted boiling water for 5 minutes before stuffing. When the marrow is stuffed, bake rings at 200 C/400 F/Gas Mark 6 for about 30 minutes, in an oven pan or dish containing a small amount of water to prevent burning and drying out. A complete, stuffed marrow, whether with cap or lid, can be roasted whole. Cover or wrap in foil, place in a roasting dish or tray containing half a cup of water, then bake for 50–60 minutes at 200 C/400 F/Gas Mark 6, until tender when tested with the sharp point of a knife.

### Onions
Choose large mild flavoured onions, Spanish or red are best. Boil in their skins for 12–15 minutes, cool under cold running water then remove the skins and trim the roots back. This will give the onions each a base to sit on while being further cooked. Take a 2 inch/3.5 cm slice from the top and remove the inside layers of each onion with a small sharp knife and a spoon or melon baller, to leave hollow vegetables with three or four onion layers forming their shells. Alternatively, slice the onions in half from top to bottom through the root end and scoop out the inner layers to leave two boat shaped shells three or four onion layers thick. Retain the removed parts for later use. Once stuffed, bake at 200 C/400 F/Gas Mark 6 for about 30 minutes, in an oven pan or dish containing a small amount of water to prevent burning and drying out. Alternatively, poach in shallow, lightly salted water or stock for 12–15 minutes until the onions are soft and their stuffing is cooked through and hot.

### Mushrooms
Choose large flat field mushrooms. Remove the stems and gills, but retain any useful trimmings for later use. Wipe the mushroom caps, brush with olive oil and part cook under a hot grill for five minutes before stuffing. Once stuffed, bake at 200 C/400 F/Gas Mark 6 for about 10–15 minutes, in a lightly greased dish or baking tray.

### Peppers
Choose large red or yellow peppers. For cooking on end when stuffed, select vegetables with a flat base, slice off the stem ends to create a cap but retain these to put onto the cooking peppers if desired. Remove the cores and seeds through the open tops. To cook the peppers in halves on their sides, choose peppers with flat sides, slice in half lengthways through the stem, remove the cores and seeds but leave the stems in place. Once stuffed, bake at 200 C/400 F/Gas Mark 6 for about 40–50 minutes in a lightly greased shallow dish or baking tray, to enable the edges of the peppers to become slightly charred.

### Kohlrabi and Turnips

Choose fresh, firm medium sized vegetables of similar size, without blemishes. Peel and boil in lightly salted water until just cooked, test with the sharp point of a knife – as you would a potato – but from the top if possible to avoid making holes in what will be the sides of the stuffed vegetables. Trim the base to enable the vegetables to sit securely during final cooking, when stuffed. Remove a slice ½–¾ inches/1–2 cm from the top and hollow out the vegetables with a spoon or melon baller to give you hollow spheres with walls about ½ inch/1 cm thick, don't be too adventurous. Retain the trimmings for later use. Once stuffed, bake at 200 C/400 F/Gas Mark 6 for about 20–30 minutes, in a deep sided oven dish or pan containing a small amount of water to prevent burning and drying out. Alternatively, poach in shallow, lightly salted water or stock for 12–15 minutes until the roots are soft and their stuffing is cooked through and hot.

# Autumn Medley of Stuffed Vegetables Ⓥ

Cooking instructions for stuffed courgettes, onions and turnips are given individually in case you want to cook them separately, but all the vegetables can be cooked in the same oven, albeit for different times for an attractive medley to be served together.

## Courgettes

Food category – M/A
Serves – 4

INGREDIENTS

- 2 large onions, finely sliced (include trimmings from onions for stuffing – below)
- 2 oz/60 g unsalted butter
- pinch sugar
- pinch ground cinnamon, optional
- 2 large parsnips, peeled, trimmed and diced

- 2 large carrots, peeled, trimmed and diced
- sea salt and white pepper powder, to taste
- 4 courgettes, prepared for stuffing (see above, page 138)

METHOD

Pre-heat the oven to 200 C/400 F/Gas Mark 6. In a heavy based, non-stick saucepan, sauté the onions in 1 oz/30 g of the butter, over a low heat, with the sugar, cinnamon, a pinch of salt and a little fresh black

pepper. Cook uncovered, stirring occasionally, until the onions are soft
and caramelised and there is a thick syrup, about 30–40 minutes. Take
care not to burn the onions, which is most likely to occur towards the
end of the cooking when there is a lot of sugar and little water in the
pan. That's the time to make sure the heat is very low. Add a little water
if they look like they are drying out too quickly and likely to scorch. The
end result should be soft brown sweet onions in a caramely syrup.

Cook the parsnips and carrots until soft in lightly salted boiling water
or vegetable stock. Drain and retain some of the liquor. Process or mash
the carrots and parsnips together with the remaining butter until you
have a smooth purée. Mashed vegetables may need to be pressed
through a fine sieve. Season to taste with salt and white pepper. Adjust
the purée so it is fairly dry, with the consistency of firm mashed
potatoes. You may require a spoonful or two of the cooking liquor if
the purée is too dry, or if it is too wet you may need to transfer the
purée to the saucepan and heat gently while stirring to drive off excess
water.

Spoon a little of the caramelised onion mixture into the bottom of the
prepared courgettes then top with the carrot and parsnip purée until
slightly overfilled. Drag a fork lightly over the purée in a criss-cross
pattern. Arrange the stuffed courgettes in a deep sided ovenproof dish or
baking tray, spoon two or three tablespoons of water into the dish
around them and bake for 25–30 minutes until the courgettes are wilted
and tender when pierced with the point of a sharp knife and the purée is
slightly crisp and browned. Place under a hot grill for 1 or 2 minutes for
an attractive finish to the topping. Serve with the stuffed vegetables, if
desired, with Onion and Sage Sauce made with vegetable stock (see
page 48) and with Horseradish Mayonnaise (see page 111).

## Onions
Food category – M/A
Serves – 4

INGREDIENTS
- 2 oz/60 g unsalted butter
- 2 tablespoons very finely chopped shallots
- 6 oz/175 g chestnut mushrooms, trimmed, wiped clean and very finely chopped
- freshly ground black pepper, to taste
- 1 tablespoon very finely chopped fresh parsley
- 1 tablespoon crème fraîche

- 1 large celeriac root, peeled, trimmed
  and cut into large dice
- sea salt and white pepper powder for
  seasoning
- 4 onions prepared for stuffing (see
  page 139)

METHOD

Pre-heat the oven to 200 C/400 F/Gas Mark 6. Heat the butter in a heavy based, non-stick saucepan over a low heat and sauté the shallots for 5 minutes until soft and clear. Add the mushrooms and a little black pepper, and cook uncovered, stirring occasionally, until the onions and mushrooms have softened and reduced to a concentrated mash-like consistency, about 30–40 minutes. Add the chopped parsley, and cook for 1–2 minutes, add the cream, stir well and remove from the heat. Cook the celeriac until soft in lightly salted boiling water or vegetable stock. Drain and retain some of the liquor. Process or mash the celeriac with the remaining butter until you have a smooth purée. Mashed vegetables may need to be pressed through a fine sieve. Season to taste with salt and white pepper. Adjust the purée so it is fairly dry with the consistency of firm mashed potatoes. You may require a spoonful or two of the cooking liquor if the purée is too dry or you may need to transfer the purée to the saucepan and heat gently while stirring to drive off excess water if it is too wet.

Spoon a little of the creamed mushroom mixture into the bottom of the onions then top with the celeriac purée until slightly overfilled. Drag a fork lightly over the purée in a criss-cross pattern. Arrange the stuffed onions in a deep sided ovenproof dish or baking tray, spoon two or three tablespoons of water into the dish around them and bake for 30 minutes until the onions are tender when pierced with the point of a sharp knife and the purée is slightly crisp and browned. Place under a hot grill for 1 or 2 minutes for an attractive finish to the topping. Serve with the other stuffed vegetables on Onion and Sage Sauce made with vegetable stock (see page 273) and with Horseradish Mayonnaise (see page 111).

# Turnips
Food category – M/A
Serves – 4

INGREDIENTS

- 2 oz/60 g unsalted butter
- 1 tablespoon olive oil
- 2 tablespoons finely chopped shallots
- 2 medium carrots, trimmed, peeled and grated
- 1 large parsnip, trimmed, peeled and grated
- 1 small celeriac, trimmed, peeled and grated
- 6 oz/175 g frozen leaf spinach, thawed
- small pinch nutmeg
- sea salt and freshly ground black pepper, to taste
- 1 tablespoon crème fraîche
- 4 turnips or kohlrabi, prepared for stuffing (see page 140)

METHOD

Pre-heat the oven to 200 C/400 F/Gas Mark 6. Heat 1 oz/30 g of the butter and the olive oil over a low heat in a large heavy based, non-stick saucepan, and sauté the shallots for 5 minutes until soft and clear. Add the grated root vegetables, season with salt and black pepper, and cook uncovered, stirring occasionally, until all the vegetables are well mixed and just softened. This will take about 5–10 minutes, by which time the vegetables will have combined to form a stuffing mixture.

Heat the spinach in a tablespoon of boiling water or vegetable stock until soft. Drain well, pressing in a colander to remove excess water if necessary. Retain a little of the liquor. Gently process or mash the spinach and season to taste with the nutmeg, salt and freshly ground black pepper. Adjust the purée so it is fairly dry. You may require a spoonful or two of the cooking liquor if the purée is too dry, or transfer the purée to the saucepan and heat gently while stirring to drive off excess water if it is too wet. Mix in the crème fraîche.

Spoon a little of the creamed spinach mixture into the bottom of the turnips then top with the sautéed vegetables until slightly overfilled. Arrange the stuffed turnips in a deep sided ovenproof dish or baking tray, spoon two or three tablespoons of water into the dish around them and bake for 20–30 minutes until tender when pierced with the point of a sharp knife and the topping is slightly crisp and browned. Place under a hot grill for 1 or 2 minutes for an attractive finish to the topping. Serve with the other stuffed vegetables with Onion and Sage Sauce (made with vegetable stock, see page 48) and with Horseradish Mayonnaise (see page 111).

VARIATIONS

Food category – P
- Add creamy goat's milk cheese in place of the crème fraîche
- Add crisply fried bacon to the filling
- Add roasted nuts or seeds to the filling (not peanuts)
- Top with any kind of cheese

Food category – C
- Top with creamy mashed potatoes or a herby rösti mixture (see page 136) or
- Top with herb stuffing (see page 206)

# Spring Medley of Stuffed Vegetables ⓥ

This recipe is given for a serving of one stuffed courgette, one stuffed onion and one half stuffed pepper per person.

Food category – M/A
Serves – 4

INGREDIENTS
- 2 medium aubergines, washed and trimmed
- 1 large red pepper, washed, seeded and trimmed and cut into ½ inch/1 cm dice
- 6–8 tablespoons olive oil
- 2 medium courgettes, washed, trimmed and cut into ½ inch/1 cm dice
- 8–10 tablespoons passata (tin or jar of crushed and strained plum tomatoes)
- 4 onions prepared for stuffing, trimmings retained (see page 139)
- 4 courgettes prepared for stuffing, trimmings retained (see page 138)
- 2 large yellow peppers prepared for stuffing (see page 139)
- 3 firm ripe tomatoes, skinned and quartered
- 16 black olives
- 3 cloves garlic, finely sliced
- 1 teaspoon dried marjoram

FOR FENNEL PURÉE
- 2 fennel bulbs, trimmed and cut
  into medium dice
- 8 fl oz/250 ml Basic Vegetable
  Stock (see page 48)
- 1 oz/30 g unsalted butter, chilled
  and diced

- ½ cup fresh basil leaves
- sea salt and freshly ground black
  pepper, to taste

You will require a deep sided oven dish or pan for the courgettes and onions and a shallow sided oven tray for the peppers.

METHOD

Pre-heat the oven to 200 C/400 F/Gas Mark 6. Remove four × ½ inch/1 cm slices from the aubergines and trim off the ends. Cut the aubergine slices and ends into ½ inch/1 cm dice for the ratatouille. Cook the aubergine block in the hot oven to make Aubeᵣ ᵢ ᴺe Purée (see page 146) for topping Stuffed Vegetables.

Prepare a Quick Sauté Ratatouille (see page 239). In a large, heavy based frying pan, sauté the red pepper dice in a tablespoon of olive oil over a gentle heat, without browning, until just soft. Transfer to a large saucepan then sauté the courgette dice and chopped trimmings from the courgettes prepared for stuffing in the frying pan in a tablespoon of olive oil until they are soft as well. Transfer to the saucepan with the peppers then sauté the aubergine dice in the frying pan in another two tablespoons of olive oil until soft. Add to the peppers and courgettes in the saucepan. Add two tablespoons of passata and season with salt and freshly ground black pepper. Simmer gently, uncovered, for 15–20 minutes to blend the flavours and reduce to a fairly dry ratatouille.

Brush the onions, courgettes and peppers with olive oil. To each pepper half add 3 tomato quarters, 4 black olives, a sprinkling of garlic slivers (retain about a third for later use), a pinch of dried marjoram and salt and pepper seasoning. Place the peppers on the lightly oiled, shallow baking sheet in the top of the oven for 40–50 minutes until soft and slightly charred around the edges. Fill the onions with ratatouille until just overfilled, spoon a little ratatouille into the bottom of the courgettes. Add a tablespoon of passata to the onions and a teaspoon of passata to the courgettes. Top the courgettes with Aubergine Purée until just overfilled. Place the onions and courgettes in the deep sided oven dish with one half cup of water around them. Bake in the middle of the oven for 20–30 minutes, until tender when tested with the sharp point of a knife.

Prepare the fennel purée for serving. In a saucepan, sweat the remaining garlic and the finely chopped trimmings from the onions prepared for stuffing in a tablespoon of olive oil, over a low heat until the onion is soft and clear, 5–10 minutes. Add the fennel and cook for a further 5 minutes. Add half the vegetable stock and simmer for 20–25 minutes until the fennel is tender. Process until smooth, adding a little extra stock to produce a thickish purée which will pour. Season to taste with salt and pepper and return to the pan. When the stuffed vegetables are ready to serve, tear or chop the basil leaves finely. Warm the fennel purée until almost simmering, add the butter a little at a time, mixing it in rapidly to form a smooth buttery fennel purée. Spoon onto four warm plates. Serve the cooked stuffed vegetables onto the beds of fennel purée. Scatter the finely chopped or torn basil over and serve immediately.

# Aubergine Purée Ⓥ

Make this purée whenever you prepare a dish that requires only the outer portion of the aubergine.

Food category – M/A
Serves – 4

Pre-heat the oven to 200 C/400 F/Gas Mark 6 and lightly oil a baking sheet or shallow tray. Lightly brush the block of aubergine flesh on all sides and the ends with olive oil then season with sea salt and freshly ground black pepper and any other flavourings you would like (e.g. chilli powder, ground ginger and cinnamon, dried herbs). Place the aubergine on the baking sheet and roast in the oven for 30–40 minutes, until browned and soft throughout. Turn every 10 minutes during cooking to ensure even cooking and browning. Allow the aubergine to cool a little then chop roughly and mash with a fork to produce a chunky purée or mash. Mix in finely chopped fresh herbs of your choice (e.g. parsley, coriander, mint) and check the seasoning. Your aubergine purée is now ready to be used as a stuffing, spread or side dish.

# PROTEIN MAIN COURSES

## EVERYTHING YOU NEED TO KNOW ABOUT MAIN COURSES WITH PROTEINS

Let me just remind you which foods the Proteins are so you'll know what I'm talking about.

### PROTEINS – A MEMORY AID

### *'Proteins Are Nuts That Eat Seeds'*

(Proteins are mainly animal products, plus nuts, seeds and soya)

*Animal Products*          Fish, Game, Meats, Offal, Poultry, Shellfish, Cheeses, Eggs

*Non-animal Products*      Coconut, Nuts, Seeds, Soya, Soya products

*Special Cases*            Milk: use milk in small amounts only, Yogurt: easy to digest and can be combined with any other food including fruits

If you're still not sure then check with the alphabetical list of foods at the back of the book. Proteins are marked P.

With The Kensington Diet way of eating there are two things to take note of when eating Proteins. First, they must not be eaten in the same meal with Carbohydrates. Second, all Proteins are designated '1 in 5' foods because they shouldn't be eaten too often. There are only a few

Proteins to which the second rule is likely to apply, after all you're not likely to eat chicken or pork or any single type of fish, on a daily basis, are you? You should, however, take care not to eat eggs, cheese, soya or large quantities of milk too often so the '1 in 5' should be applied to them.

The real point is, vary your Protein intake as much as possible. If you eat a lot of fish, have a different type of fish each day. If you like cheese a lot, have cow's milk cheeses '1 in 5' and goat's and sheep's milk cheeses on other '1 in 5' days.

The recipes here make '1 in 5' rotation easy for you. Often they use only one or two Proteins at a time, and they usually keep similar foods, such as the two groups of cheeses mentioned above, separated too. So you'll never run out of a Protein because you've used up all your options. And of course, in no recipe is a Protein ever combined with a Carbohydrate. The result is a fantastic range of Protein recipes which are easy to fit into '1 in 5' food rotation.

When you look through these main course recipes you'll find exciting and delicious ways of creating many popular dishes you might think wouldn't fit into KD eating. You'll also discover some new ideas to expand your repertoire of favourites dishes in the direction of healthier eating. But most of all, I hope you'll get some really brilliant ideas about how you can alter any poor food combining habits you might have, without having to sacrifice any enjoyment of what you eat.

## Spaghetti Bolognese KD Style

And you thought 'Spag Bog' was a thing of the past just because you're a food combiner now! The trick with the sauce, by the way, is to make sure it reduces until virtually all of the water that comes out of the ingredients is evaporated off and the sauce becomes very rich and thick, so it coats the 'pasta' well. I think the best thing about cooking Bolognese sauce is the 'cook's perk' of checking at frequent intervals while cooking, that the wine is up to scratch – I'm glad to be able to make it possible for you to continue this fine tradition.

Food category – P
'1 in 5' – beef, pork (bacon), cow's milk cheese (Parmesan)
Serves – 4

INGREDIENTS

- 1 medium onion, finely chopped
- 1 large clove garlic, finely crushed
- 1–2 tablespoons olive oil
- 4 oz/125 g chestnut mushrooms, trimmed, wiped and medium sliced
- 2 rashers unsmoked streaky bacon, finely sliced
- 1lb/500 g best ground beef
- 14 oz/440 g (approximately) tin chopped plum tomatoes, drained juice retained
- 2 tablespoons tomato purée
- 1 glass red wine
- 1 large bay leaf, torn in half
- 1 tablespoon finely chopped fresh marjoram (or 1 teaspoon dried)
- sea salt and freshly ground black pepper, to taste

TASTE SENSATIONS

1 tablespoon best olive oil
3 large cloves garlic, peeled and sliced into thin chips (about 1mm)

TO SERVE

- Carrot and Courgette Noodle 'Pasta' for four (see Page 214)

TO GARNISH

- 1 tablespoon finely chopped fresh parsley
- Parmesan cheese, grated or shaved (see below), for garnish

Use a large heavy based, preferably non-stick saucepan for this sauce so it can simmer uncovered for quite a while and reduce to the necessary thick consistency without splashing.

METHOD

In a large, heavy based, non-stick saucepan, sauté the onions and garlic in a tablespoon of olive oil over a medium heat, stirring occasionally, for 10 minutes, until the onion is soft and slightly browned. Add the sliced mushrooms and bacon and cook for a further 5–10 minutes until the bacon is slightly browned. Transfer to a bowl, leaving as much oil in the pan as possible, cover and set aside. Increase the heat under the saucepan, add a little more of the olive oil if necessary and add the ground beef. Stir fry rapidly for 5–8 minutes using a wooden spoon to break up the meat. When no raw meat remains add the tomatoes, the onion and bacon mix, the tomato purée, wine, bay leaf halves and marjoram. Season with plenty of salt and freshly ground black pepper, stir well together and bring to a simmer. Simmer uncovered for 40–50 minutes or until the sauce is a thick and rich liquid with no sign of separated watery juices around the edges. Add a little extra tomato juice if it appears to be reducing too quickly.

While cooking the sauce make the garlic chips. In a small frying pan fry the garlic slices in the tablespoon of olive oil until just browned on both sides. Take great care not to overcook as they 'turn' very quickly. Fry a few at a time on both sides until light brown, remove to drain on kitchen paper. When the sauce is cooked set it aside to cool a little while you cook the vegetable 'pasta' (see page 211.) Toss the pasta with the chopped parsley and the garlic chips along with the garlic flavoured oil they were cooked in. Serve into warm bowls, topped with your Bolognese sauce, with grated or shaved Parmesan cheese handed around. Oh yes, and with some wine if there's any left. Alternatively return the vegetable 'pasta' to the saucepan it was cooked in, add Bolognese sauce and stir gently until the 'pasta' is well coated. Serve into warm bowls sprinkled with chopped parsley and garlic chips.

TIP

☞ To make Parmesan shavings take a block of the cheese and 'shave' slivers from it with a swivel type potato peeler.

VARIATION

• Replace the carrot and courgette 'pasta' with 'spaghetti' from a spaghetti squash. For four people you'll need 2 × 1 lb/500 g squashes, or equivalent. Halve the squashes lengthways, remove the seeds and fibrous centre and boil or microwave until tender. You can do this in advance and reheat the spaghetti in the microwave before serving. Take care not to overcook though. Drain the cooked squashes and fork the 'spaghetti' flesh from inside the halves, toss gently with chopped parsley, garlic chips and garlic oil and serve topped with the Bolognese sauce.

# Beef Stroganoff

An old favourite that can be ready to eat in about 25 minutes. Served on any variation of vegetable 'pasta' (see page 211) instead of the usual rice or noodles, it's nowhere near as fattening as the traditional Stroganoff. Good food doesn't have to be long in cooking and heavy on the waistline. This KD version leans towards pepper steak for its inspiration and gives a series of nice surprises with the 'taste sensation' ingredient.

Food category – P
'1 in 5' – beef
Serves – 4

INGREDIENTS

- carrot, courgette and leek ribbon 'pasta' for four (see page 212)
- ½ oz/15 g unsalted butter
- 2 dessertspoons olive oil
- 1 medium onion thinly sliced
- 1 lb/500 g best rump steak, trimmed of any fat or sinew, beaten out fairly thin and sliced into strips 2 ins/5 cm x ½ inch/ 1 cm
- 6 oz/175 g chestnut mushrooms thinly sliced
- sea salt and black pepper powder, to taste

TASTE SENSATIONS

1 heaped tablespoon green peppercorns, drained
1 large carton, ½ pt/250 ml, crème fraîche
1 teaspoon Dijon mustard

TO GARNISH

- 2 tablespoons finely chopped fresh parsley, for garnish
- paprika for garnish, optional

METHOD

Cook the 'pasta' ribbons first, ready for the Stroganoff which will take about 15–20 minutes to cook. You can keep the noodles warm or reheat them in the microwave as long as you take care not to overcook them. In a large frying pan heat the butter and half the oil over a fairly high heat, until the butter stops sizzling, then fry the beef rapidly with frequent turning, to seal and brown it on all sides. Remove to a warm plate leaving as much oil and butter in the pan as possible. Add the remaining oil and sauté the onions over a medium heat, without browning, until soft and clear, about 5 minutes. Add the mushrooms and cook, stirring frequently until the juices are sweated off to concentrate the flavours. Another 3–5 minutes. Season with a little salt and plenty of black pepper powder and mix. Replace the meat in the pan, add the green peppercorns for a taste sensation, and stir all the ingredients together over a medium heat for 2–3 minutes. Stir in the crème fraîche and mustard and bring just to the point of simmering. Serve straightaway over warm vegetable noodle 'pasta' on warm plates and garnished with chopped parsley and a good pinch of paprika if desired.

VARIATION

• Substitute trimmed and sliced pork fillet for the beef.

# Roast French Rack of Lamb

This cut of lamb is quick and easy to cook but the preparation and marinading can be done well beforehand, so it's just perfect for modern lifestyles. Try it served on parsnip mash with purées of mint and garlic drizzled over and accompanied by a pressed terrine of vegetables, the preparation of which can also be done well before you eat.

Food category – P
'1 in 5' – lamb
Serves – 4

INGREDIENTS

FOR THE MARINADE

• 1 tablespoon lemon juice
• 1 tablespoon olive oil
• 1 teaspoon crushed cumin seeds
• sea salt and freshly ground black pepper, to taste

FOR THE LAMB

• 2 best end racks of lamb, 6–8 cutlets each, French trimmed
• olive oil
• large bunch fresh rosemary
• 5 fl oz/140 ml Basic Vegetable Stock (see page 48)

FOR SERVING

• Pressed Vegetable Terrine for four (see page 236)
• Parsnip Mash for four (see page 222)

TASTE SENSATIONS

Mint and Garlic Purées for four (see pages 285–6)

METHOD

Mix all the marinade ingredients together and pour over the lamb joints. Rub well in, cover and leave in the refrigerator, basting occasionally, for at least 2 hours. Remove to room temperature at least half an hour before cooking. When ready to cook, pre-heat the oven to 230 C/450 F/ Gas Mark 7. Brush a roasting tin with olive oil and heat it on the hob, seal the lamb joints on all sides in the hot tin. Remove from the heat. Make two beds of the rosemary for the joints to lie on, without touching, bone sides up. Pour any remaining marinade over the joints and roast in the oven for 20–25 minutes, depending on how well cooked you like your lamb, turning the joints bone sides down after 15 minutes. Remove from the oven to a warm plate and cover loosely with foil to retain heat and set aside to rest the meat for at least 10 minutes before cutting.

Remove the herbs and any excess fat from the pan and deglaze it of juices, over a medium heat on the hob, with half a cup of vegetable stock, stirring often to release the caramelised juices from the pan – about 5 minutes. Strain into a bowl and keep. To serve, arrange a slice of terrine on each of four warm plates and microwave to warm through if not preheated in the oven. Slice the lamb between the rib bones into 3 or 4 cutlets per person. Make a bed of mashed parsnips for the lamb cutlets, and sprinkle with a little of the meat juices. Arrange the cutlets on the mash. Drizzle the plate with purées of mint and garlic and serve.


# Lamb Kebabs

Marinading does add flavour and succulence to lamb. These kebabs are wonderful grilled or barbecued, but here they are cooked in the oven and served on aubergine noodles with tomato sauce. Make a crisp green salad of mixed leaves and green beans with a refreshing Lemon Vinaigrette (see page 103) served onto the plate after you've eaten the lamb to take up the tomato sauce that's left. You don't need bread to mop up the juices with KD food.

Food category – P
'1 in 5' – lamb
Serves – 4

INGREDIENTS

• 1 lb/500 g lamb leg steak, trimmed and sliced into strips the thickness of the steak, 2 inches/ 5 cm long and ¼ inch/6 mm wide

• 2 cloves garlic, finely crushed and mashed to a paste
• 1 teaspoon dried rosemary, powdered

- 1 teaspoon dried marjoram
- 2 tablespoons white wine vinegar (or cider vinegar)

- 1 tablespoon olive oil, for marinade
- sea salt and freshly ground black pepper, to taste

TASTE SENSATION

sesame seeds

FOR SERVING

- Aubergine Noodles for four (see page 216)
- Rich Tomato Sauce for four (see page 272)

- Green Salad for four (see page 247)
- Lemon Vinaigrette for four (see page 103)

FOR GARNISH

- 1 tablespoon finely chopped fresh mint

- 1 tablespoon finely grated lemon zest

You'll need 8–12 wooden or bamboo skewers about 8 inches long. The kind used for satay and sold in most supermarkets now are fine. Cooking requires a wire mesh over a roasting tin.

METHOD

Mix the lamb strips with the garlic and dried herbs, add the vinegar and olive oil and season with a little salt and plenty of freshly ground black pepper. Mix, cover and set aside in a cool place to marinade for at least half an hour, but several hours or overnight is better. While marinading, soak the wooden skewers in water and prepare the aubergine noodles, tomato sauce, salad and salad dressing. When ready to cook, pre-heat the oven to 200 C/400 F/Gas Mark 4 and begin cooking the aubergine noodles as they will be ready with the lamb kebabs.

Push the marinaded lamb strips onto the soaked wooden skewers. Sprinkle each kebab with sesame seeds and cook in the oven, on a wire mesh over a roasting tin, for 12–15 minutes, turning occasionally, until cooked. Alternatively grill under a high heat for 8–10 minutes, turning occasionally to ensure even cooking. Arrange aubergine noodles in the centre of four warm plates, spoon thick tomato sauce around the noodles and arrange lamb kebabs on top. Sprinkle with chopped mint and lemon zest, and serve accompanied by green salad with lemony dressing to hand around.

VARIATIONS

- This has to be one of my favourite ways of cooking, and almost any meat protein is suitable in place of the lamb. Chicken, turkey, pork, beef all work well and all you need to do is alter the herbs you use in the marinade and as a garnish. Try:

- Chicken with thyme and tarragon marinade and garnished with parsley.
- Pork fillet with sage and thyme marinade and garnished with parsley.

# Stuffed Pork Fillets

A vegetable stuffing with whole chestnuts and a variety of side vegetables make pork fillets into a roast meal to satisfy anyone. The fillets are tied together to make one joint and can be prepared in advance, covered and set aside in the refrigerator for several hours until you are ready to cook. Just remember to bring the joint to room temperature about half an hour before you start cooking. The Quick Braised Red Cabbage can be cooked at the same time as the pork.

Food category – P
'1 in 5' – pork, chestnuts (optional)
Serves – 4

INGREDIENTS

- 1 shallot, finely chopped
- 4 tablespoons sunflower or groundnut oil
- 2 carrots, peeled, trimmed and finely grated
- 2 medium courgettes, washed, trimmed and finely grated
- sea salt and freshly ground black pepper, to taste
- 2 pork fillets, each 12–14 oz/ 375–440 g, of equal weight and shape

- 1 teaspoon dried mixed herbs
- 8 oz/250 g tinned whole chestnuts, washed and drained, optional
- 1 tablespoon cider vinegar
- 1 teaspoon clear honey
- 10 fl oz/300 ml vegetable stock (see page 48)
- 6 oz/175 g fine green or Kenya beans
- 3–4 oz/90–125 g unsalted butter, at room temperature
- 1 tablespoon wholegrain mustard

FOR SERVING

- Purée of Swede for four (see page 222)
- Quick Braised Red Cabbage, see page 237, lines 1–10

You'll require a roasting tin or metal dish for this recipe. I use a 10 inch/ 25 cm Le Creuset non-stick frying pan with an ovenproof handle.

METHOD

Pre-heat the oven to 190 C/375 F/Gas Mark 5. In a heavy based frying pan over a low heat, sauté the shallot without browning, in one tablespoon of the oil, stirring occasionally until the shallot is soft. Add the carrot and courgette, mix, season with salt and freshly ground black pepper and cook together until all the ingredients are softened and the mixture has combined so it can be used to stuff the pork fillet. Set aside to cool.

Slice the pork fillets lengthways about halfway though their thickness, open out flat, cut side down, cover with Clingfilm and beat out to around twice the original size. Uncover and turn cut sides up, season with salt and freshly ground black pepper and a sprinkling of dried mixed herbs. Spread the stuffing mixture along the centre of both fillets, embed whole chestnuts down the middle of one 'stuffed' fillet and put the stuffed cut sides of the two fillets together to enclose the stuffing and chestnuts. Because the fillets taper at one end, put the narrow end of one to the wider end of the other. Tie firmly but not tightly around the fillets with string at 1 inch/2.5 cm intervals, to produce a well stuffed joint of even size. Season well with salt and pepper on all sides. Mix two tablespoons of sunflower oil with the vinegar and honey to produce a basting mixture. Brush the fillets on all sides with the mixture. (If you're not yet ready to cook you can now set the stuffed fillets aside in the refrigerator.) Heat the remaining tablespoon of oil in a metal roasting dish or tray on the hob of your cooker, then sear the stuffed fillets on all sides until well browned – about 5–8 minutes.

Add half the vegetable stock to this roasting pan and cook in the oven for 25–35 minutes, depending on how you like your pork, brushing occasionally with the basting mixture. When cooked remove from the oven and set aside for at least 10 minutes to rest before carving. Strain the cooking juices into a small saucepan with the remaining vegetable stock. Cook the fine beans by plunging them into boiling salted water for 4–6 minutes until softened but still with some crunch, to your own taste. Drain, return to the pan over the heat and toss with a small knob of butter and some freshly ground black pepper. Set aside and keep warm without further cooking until ready to serve.

When ready to serve, warm the vegetable stock over a low heat until it just simmers. Cut the stuffed pork fillets into slices and arrange on portions of red cabbage to one side of each of four warm plates, add scoops of swede purée and a pile of fine beans. Add half the remaining butter and the wholegrain mustard to the simmering stock and whisk in vigorously to combine them into a silky smooth mustard butter sauce. A hand held electric blender is perfect for this. If the sauce is too thin blend in a little more butter and when ready spoon over the pork. Serve immediately.

VARIATION
● Try stuffing breast fillets of turkey in the same way.


# Pork Steaks with Onion and Garlic Sauce

Here's a twist on delicious onion confit that goes so well with pork. In this version the confit does not use heaps of butter and it's puréed to make a rich sauce for the pork and roasted Mediterranean vegetables. Superb.

Food category – P
'1 in 5' – pork
Serves – 4

INGREDIENTS

- 2 dessertspoons dried provençal herb mix
- 4 boneless pork steaks each 5–6 oz/155–185 g (or pork chops)
- 2 large Spanish (or 4 red onions), peeled and thinly sliced
- 1 oz/30 g unsalted butter
- 1 clove garlic, finely crushed, optional

- 1 teaspoon sugar
- sea salt and freshly ground black pepper, to taste
- 10 fl oz/300 ml Basic Vegetable Stock (see page 48)
- 5 fl oz/150 ml red wine
- 1 tablespoon olive oil

FOR SERVING
- Roast Mediterranean Vegetables for four (see page 233)

TASTE SENSATION
2 tablespoons fresh Basil Leaf Purée (see page 84)

METHOD
Rub the dried herb mixture well into both sides of the pork steaks. Cover and set aside until needed. Place a large, heavy based casserole or oven dish over a medium heat, sauté the onions in the butter until they are soft and lightly coloured, about 5 minutes. Lower the heat and add the garlic, sugar and a light seasoning of salt and pepper, mix and cook for a

further 2 minutes, then add half the vegetable stock and the wine. Bring to a simmer, cover and cook, for 15–20 minutes. Uncover the onions, stir and allow to simmer for a further 10 minutes or until the onions are well browned and caramelised in a thick syrup. If they appear to be drying out, add a little extra stock. While cooking the onions, season the pork steaks with a little salt and pepper and fry in the olive oil on a hot griddle pan or in a frying pan, for about 4 minutes each side, depending on thickness, until cooked through. Alternatively grill under high heat, turning several times, until browned and cooked through. Cover with foil and set aside to rest for 5 minutes.

When the caramelised onions are ready, transfer to a blender or processor and purée with as much extra stock as is needed to produce a thick caramel onion sauce. Spoon the sauce over the pork steaks on four warm plates and add the Roasted Mediterranean Vegetables. Drizzle with Basil Leaf Purée (see page 84) and serve.

# Salmon Fillet with a Charred Oriental Spice Crust

This dish is great served with stir fried vegetables and cashews and together they make a wonderful – and healthy – combination of cultures, flavours and colours. The salmon and vegetables take about the same time to cook – 10 minutes or so. So prepare the salmon with its spicy crust and have all the vegetables cleaned and cut up ready for stir frying before you start to cook anything. Then it's just a matter of a little fast action to get it all onto the plates together.

Food category – P
'1 in 5' – salmon
Serves – 4

INGREDIENTS

- 4 salmon tail fillets, about 4 oz/ 125 g each (skin on and descaled)
- 2 tablespoons Tamari (non-wheat) soy sauce
- 2 tablespoons lemon juice
- 1 rounded teaspoon Chinese five spice powder

- 1 rounded teaspoon ginger powder
- 1 rounded teaspoon garlic powder
- 1 rounded teaspoon chilli powder or cayenne pepper
- 1 rounded teaspoon fine sea salt
- sunflower or groundnut oil, for brushing

FOR SERVING
• Stir Fried Vegetables with Cashews       • small bunch of whole chives,
  for four (see page 228–30)                   washed and dried for garnish

TASTE SENSATION
Fresh ginger root cut into 12–16 very fine julienne batons

METHOD
Heat the grill to hot. Line a grill pan with foil and oil the wire grill mesh ready for the fish. Trim and wash the salmon fillets and pat dry with kitchen paper. Mix the soy sauce and lemon juice together in a bowl. Brush both sides of the salmon fillets liberally with the soy sauce and lemon juice and set aside on the wire mesh to dry. Meanwhile, mix the five spice powder, ginger, garlic, chilli and sea salt together (if possible grind them together using a pestle and mortar). Brush the salmon fillets both sides with oil, sprinkle with the spice mixture and rub well in on both sides of each fillet. Make sure each fillet has plenty of the mixture rubbed into each side. Set the fillets aside on the wire mesh to await cooking. (Now's the time to prepare your vegetables for stir frying).

When ready to start cooking, grill the salmon for 4–5 minutes on each side (skin side first) until crisp and charred on the outside and pink and just cooked in the centre. Test one fillet at the thickest part by parting the flakes with a knife to make sure it is just cooked through. Alternatively, shallow fry the salmon fillets in a little sunflower or groundnut oil for 3–4 minutes each side (skin side first) until crisp and slightly charred. Set aside on a wire mesh to drain off excess oil.

To serve, arrange a serving of stir fry vegetables and cashews in a semicircle on one side of each of four warm plates and moisten with a spoonful of cooking liquor. Place a salmon fillet garnished with a few whole chives and fine ginger batons on each plate opposite the vegetables. Serve.


# Grilled Haddock

White fish like haddock or cod have a lovely clean flavour to them. Here it's very briefly marinated and quickly grilled to maintain the moist texture. With a non-egg, Mix-With-Any herb mayonnaise and steamed vegetables lightly dressed with butter, salt and pepper, this is a simple, light fish dish suitable for any time of year.

Food category – P
'1 in 5' – white fish, haddock or cod
Serves – 4

INGREDIENTS

- juice of lemon
- 2 tablespoons olive oil
- 2 tablespoons very finely chopped spring onions
- 1 tablespoon finely chopped fresh tarragon (or 1 teaspoon dried)

- sea salt and freshly ground black pepper, to taste
- 4 haddock or cod fillets each 5–6 oz/155–185 g, skin on

FOR SERVING

- Medley of Steamed Seasonal Vegetables for four (see page 226)
- 2 oz/60 g unsalted butter

- handful of green leaves (lambs lettuce, rocket, watercress) for garnish

TASTE SENSATION

2 portions Dill or Parsley Mustard Mayonnaise (see page 278)

METHOD

Pre-heat the grill to a moderate heat. Mix the lemon juice, olive oil, finely chopped onions and tarragon in a bowl, add salt and freshly ground black pepper. Leave to stand for 10 minutes if dried tarragon is being used. Place the fish in a shallow dish and pour the mixture over, turn the fish once or twice to cover and leave flesh side down for 5 minutes.

Pre-heat a well oiled grill pan or ovenproof dish under the grill for 2–3 minutes. Arrange the fish, skin side down in the hot pan or dish and pour a tablespoon of the marinade over each fillet. Grill for 10–12 minutes until the fish is cooked through and browned on top. Check by separating the flakes of a thick part of one fillet to make sure it is white and cooked right through. Gently turn the steamed vegetables with the butter and plenty of freshly ground black pepper and a little salt. Remove the fillets to four warm plates, add steamed vegetables in butter, green leaves to garnish and a scoop of herb mustard mayonnaise beside the fish. Serve.

Shredded vegetable crudités with classic sauces

Cheese and herb soufflé omelette

Tatin-style tart of peppers
and onions, served with sour
cream and chives

Roast French rack of lamb, served with parsnip mash, mint and garlic purées and pressed terrine of vegetables

Chicken breast stuffed with goat's cheese and sage,
with griddled chicory hearts, layered spinach and carrots,
and a sage and onion sauce

Spaghetti with herbs and olives

Vegetable paella

Roast of crispy potatoes and onions

# Griddle Fried Tuna

The firm texture of tuna and swordfish, makes them perfect for quick griddle pan frying or grilling, like good steak. Here I suggest Oven Cooked Ratatouille as an accompaniment. The flavour of tuna is strong enough to accommodate the rich tomato and Mediterranean vegetables. You can serve the ratatouille hot in the usual way but it really does make a superb cold dish as well when served on a selection of green salad leaves, so do try it. A warm vinaigrette, powerfully flavoured with anchovies and capers adds a Taste Sensation to make this dish memorable to eat yet easy to cook.

Food category – P
'1 in 5' – tuna, anchovies (optional)
Serves – 4

INGREDIENTS
- 1 lemon, quartered
- 4 tuna or swordfish steaks about
  5–6 oz/155–185 g each
- olive oil, for brushing
- sea salt and freshly ground black
  pepper, to taste

FOR SERVING
- Oven Cooked Ratatouille for four
  (see page 238)

TASTE SENSATIONS
2 servings of Basic Vinaigrette, see p. 73, made with Tabasco and garlic but not with honey
1 tablespoon finely chopped fresh parsley
1 tablespoon capers, drained and patted dry
4 anchovies fillets, drained and finely chopped, optional

METHOD
Your ratatouille should be prepared and warmed through if it is to be served hot, before you start cooking the tuna. Pre-heat a well oiled griddle pan. If using a grill, oil a wire mesh over a grill pan ready for grilling and pre-heat the grill to a high heat. Squeeze lemon juice on both sides of each tuna steak, brush with olive oil and season with a little salt and freshly ground black pepper. Set aside while you prepare the vinaigrette.

Mix the Basic Vinaigrette with the parsley, capers and anchovies, if used. Warm through, over a low heat, without boiling, in a non-stick or enamel saucepan. Cook the tuna on the hot griddle pan or under the grill, for 3–5 minutes each side, until done to your taste. Like steak, tuna is best slightly pink and rare in the middle but you may prefer to cook it more. Serve with warm vinaigrette spooned over and accompanied by ratatouille.

# Hot and Sour Fish

This is fast food the Far-East way. I haven't mentioned any particular fish in the title because this recipe is suitable for many kinds. Instead, I've listed some suggestions after the recipe. Served in bowls with stir fried vegetables on a bed of vegetable 'rice' this makes a perfect Kensington Diet dish.

Food category – P
'1 in 5' – fish, various
Serves – 4

INGREDIENTS

- 1 lb/500 g fish, your choice, thinly sliced (see below)
- sea salt and white pepper powder, to taste
- sunflower or groundnut oil for shallow frying
- 1 tablespoon finely shredded fresh root ginger
- 1 small red pepper, cored, seeded and finely sliced
- 1 small yellow pepper, cored, seeded and finely sliced
- 3 fl oz/100 ml vegetable or chicken stock (see page 48–50)

- 2 tablespoons dry sherry or rice wine
- 1 tablespoon rice vinegar or cider vinegar
- 1 tablespoon Tamari (non-wheat) soy sauce
- 1 tablespoon chilli sauce
- 2 teaspoons tomato purée
- 1 teaspoon sugar
- 2 tablespoons finely chopped spring onion, for garnish

FOR SERVING

- Stir Fried Spinach and Bean Sprouts for four (see page 232)
- Fried vegetable 'rice' for four (see page 217)

METHOD

Season your chosen sliced fish or shellfish with salt and white pepper. Heat one or two tablespoons of oil in a large non-stick frying pan until it is hazy. Carefully fry the slices of fish, on both sides, in batches, taking care not to break the fish. Set the fish aside on kitchen paper to drain. When all the fish is cooked, prepare the basic hot and sour sauce. Heat a tablespoon of oil in a wok until it is hazy. Stir fry the fresh ginger for 1–2 minutes, add and stir fry the red and yellow pepper slices until just softened. Add the stock, rice wine or sherry, vinegar, soy sauce, chilli sauce, tomato purée and sugar. Stir together and bring to a simmer. Cook for 4–5 minutes. Add the fried fish, cover carefully in the sauce and simmer for a further 2–3 minutes without stirring to avoid breaking the fish. Serve in warm soup bowls on Stir Fried Vegetable 'Rice' and Stir Fried Spinach with Beansprout, garnished with the chopped spring onions.

Various types of fish can be used for this dish, here's how to prepare and cook them:

- HADDOCK, COD
  Skinless fillets cut into slices 2 inches/5 cm long × $\frac{1}{4}$ inch/6mm is best. With most white fish, to avoid breaking it up you need to take care not to move the fish around too much when simmering in the sauce.
- MONKFISH, SEA BASS
  Skinless fillets cut into slices 2 inches/5 cm long × $\frac{1}{2}$ inch/1 cm work best. These fish are more robust and can be moved around a bit more.
- SALMON, TROUT
  Skinless fillets cut into slices 2 inches/5 cm long × $\frac{1}{2}$ inch/1 cm work best. These fish are also likely to break up if disturbed too much. Handle with care.
- PRAWNS
  Raw prawns work best, peeled and washed. If large prawns are used slice along the back and remove the black intestine after peeling, then slice in half. Thaw frozen prawns completely before using and with all shellfish take care not to overcook. If cooked prawns are used leave in the hot and sour sauce just long enough to reheat before serving.

# Chicken Breast Stuffed with Goat's Cheese and Sage

I really enjoy chicken breast cooked this way. With Sage and Onion Sauce, Griddled Chicory Hearts and Layered Carrots and Spinach it looks superb as well.

Food category – P
'1 in 5' – chicken, goat's cheese
Serves – 4

INGREDIENTS

- 4 dessertspoons creamy goat's cheese, (I use Chavroux)
- 1 teaspoon finely chopped fresh sage (or ½ teaspoon dried sage)
- 4 chicken supreme breast joints (each 4–5 oz/125–155 g) skin on, wing bone cleaned and all other bones removed
- olive oil
- sea salt and freshly ground black pepper, to taste

FOR SERVING

- Griddled Chicory Hearts (see page 243)
- Layered Spinach and Carrots (see page 224)
- Sage and Onion Sauce (see page 273)

TASTE SENSATIONS

2 tablespoons olive oil
1 onion, finely sliced
1 tablespoon finely chopped fresh sage

METHOD

Pre-heat the oven to 200 C/400 F/Gas Mark 6. Mix the goat's cheese with the chopped or dried sage and set aside. Push one finger carefully between the meat and skin of the chicken pieces then move the end of your finger around to make a pocket for the stuffing, taking care to leave the edges of the skin still attached to the breast meat. The pocket doesn't have to be very big. With the blunt handle end of a dessertspoon, fill each pocket with about a quarter of the goat's cheese and herb mixture. Scrape up a little at a time and insert it through the tunnel made by your finger and massage it into place in the pocket from outside the skin. Don't overfill and make sure that you wipe clean where you introduced the stuffing and press the skin back in place.

When all the breasts are stuffed, brush them lightly both sides with olive oil and season with salt and freshly ground black pepper. Place on a shallow oiled baking sheet and cook in the middle of the oven for 30–35 minutes. Set aside in a warm place for at least 5 minutes to rest before carving. Crisp the skin under a hot grill for 1–2 minutes before carving if desired. Meanwhile, heat 2 tablespoons of oil and fry the onion until crispy. To serve, make a bed of sage and onion sauce for the chicken breasts, to the side of each of four warm plates. Slice the breasts once, diagonally down across the length, to show the stuffing under the skin and arrange each sliced breast on a pool of sauce. Arrange the Layered Carrots and Spinach alongside the chicken breasts. Place two halves of Griddled Chicory on each plate cut side up, one laying across the other. Sprinkle the chicory with a pinch of chopped fresh sage leaves and garnish the layered vegetables with crisp fried sliced onions.

# Roast Chicken with Rich Chicken and Vegetable Sauce

Sometimes I think the most basic and traditional food is best. So here's roast chicken and vegetables KD style, to fit in with your food combining needs. I like my roast chicken well cooked with very crispy skin.

Food category – P
'1 in 5' – chicken, chicken livers
Serves – 4

INGREDIENTS

- 1 roasting chicken 3–3½ lbs/ 1.5–1.75 kg
- 2 oz/60 g unsalted butter
- 8 oz/250 g chicken livers, trimmed and washed (thawed if frozen), and cut to even size
- 1 onion, finely chopped

- 8 oz/250 g chestnut mushrooms, trimmed, wiped clean and finely chopped
- 1 carrot, trimmed, peeled and finely grated
- 1 parsnip, trimmed, peeled and finely grated

- 1 courgette, trimmed and finely grated
- 1 dessertspoon finely chopped fresh thyme (or 1 teaspoon dried)
- 1 dessertspoon finely chopped fresh parsley
- sea salt and freshly ground black pepper, to taste

- 1 onion, peeled and quartered
- 1 parsnip, trimmed and peeled and cut into large dice
- 1 carrot, trimmed and peeled and cut into large dice
- small bunch fresh rosemary
- 15 fl oz/450 ml chicken or vegetable stock (see page 48)

FOR SERVING

Vegetable selection of your choice (see Mix With Any vegetables from page 208). I suggest:

- Roasted Winter Vegetables (see page 235)
- Poached Carrots, see page 237, lines 14–16

- Purée of Brussels Sprouts (see page 224)

METHOD

Pre-heat the oven to 200 C/400 F/Gas Mark 6. Wash the chicken inside and out and remove excess fat from inside the carcass, pat dry with kitchen paper and leave to dry. Make the stuffing by heating half the butter in a frying pan. Sauté the chicken livers over a medium heat, until browned on all sides and just pink in the middle, about 8 minutes. Spoon into a bowl leaving as much butter in the pan as possible, and set aside. In the same pan sauté the onion over a low to medium heat until soft and clear, 5–10 minutes. Add the mushrooms and continue to cook until the mushrooms soften and release their juices. Add the grated vegetables, thyme and parsley and season with salt and pepper. Mix well and continue to cook until all the vegetables are soft and well combined.

In a large mixing bowl, mash the cooked chicken livers well, incorporating any juices which they may have produced while set aside. Add the cooked vegetables and mushroom mixture and mix together. This is your stuffing for the chicken. Cool until you can handle it comfortably and stuff the neck end of the chicken with the mixture. Sew the skin to hold it over the stuffing or fix it with wooden skewers or cocktail sticks. It must hold firmly. Heat the remaining butter over a medium heat, in a roasting tin large enough for the chicken. Seal the chicken in the hot butter by lying it alternately on each breast, the legs and the back, for 2–3 minutes each, until slightly browned all over and well basted in melted butter. Brush butter into areas not basted such as between the carcass and the legs and wings. Remove from heat. Sprinkle liberally with salt and freshly ground black pepper and rub in all over the skin on all sides.

Place the quartered onion, large diced parsnip and carrot and the rosemary inside the cavity, the opening not yet stuffed. Roast in the oven. Twenty minutes per 1 lb/500 g plus 20–25 minutes will give you a well done bird with crisp skin. For a less crispy bird loosely cover the breast of the chicken with a piece of foil and remove for the last 45 minutes of cooking. Test with a sharp knife or skewer in the thickest part of the thigh. The juices should run clear with no trace of pink.

Remove the chicken to a separate plate. Remove the stuffing to a dish and drain the juices back into the roasting tin by inserting a large fork into the cavity and upending the bird. You could also nick the fold of skin between the thighs and the breasts to drain juices held there. Remove the vegetables from the cavity and retain for later use, discard the rosemary. Cover the chicken and leave to rest in a warm place for at least 10 minutes before carving. Pour all the cooking juices from the pan into a jug and remove the fat which rises to the top with a spoon and then absorbent kitchen paper. In a saucepan warm the vegetables from the cavity with the cooking juices and half the stock, until just simmering. Test the vegetables with a sharp pointed knife to make sure they are well cooked and soft. If necessary simmer until the vegetables are thoroughly cooked. Purée the mixture with a hand held blender in the pan or in a processor, using as much extra stock as necessary to produce a sauce to the consistency you like. Pass the sauce through a fine sieve to make sure the thickening vegetables are as fine as possible. Season to your taste with salt and pepper. Carve and serve the chicken in the usual way with the stuffing and vegetables of your choice and the rich chicken and vegetable sauce poured over.

# Turkey Satay

Lovers of spicy meat satay may not have noticed yet that peanuts are designated as Carbohydrate in food combining. So, while the traditional peanut based satay sauce is still OK for vegetables, it's a no go for Proteins such as beef, chicken or pork. There's no need to worry though, because the Kensington Diet makes all things possible. Here's a satay variation using cashew nuts for the sauce, this time on turkey, but of course it's suitable for most Proteins. Serve with mixed stir fried vegetables for a touch of Thailand.

Food category – P
'1 in 5' – turkey, cashews, coconut
Serves – 4

INGREDIENTS

- 12–16 wooden or bamboo satay skewers, about 8 inches/20 cm long
- 2 cups raw cashews
- 4 tablespoons Tamari (non-wheat) soy sauce
- 2 tablespoons coconut milk
- 2 tablespoons lime juice (or lemon)
- 1 tablespoon clear honey
- $\frac{1}{2}$ teaspoon chilli sauce or chilli powder
- 1 tablespoon very finely grated fresh ginger root
- 1 clove garlic, finely crushed and pulped, optional
- $\frac{1}{4}$ teaspoon salt
- $1\frac{1}{4}$–$1\frac{1}{2}$ lbs/625–750 g turkey breast steak
- 2 tablespoons groundnut or sunflower oil

TASTE SENSATIONS

2 tablespoons finely chopped or desiccated coconut
Tabasco sauce

FOR SERVING

- Mixed Stir Fried Vegetables, Thai variation, for four (see page 230)
- 1 tablespoon finely chopped fresh coriander, for garnish

The turkey can be cooked in the oven or under a hot grill. Either way you require a well oiled wire mesh over a foil lined tray to catch drips of marinade. You'll also need a food processor or coffee grinder to grind the cashews.

METHOD

Pre-heat the oven to its hottest. Put the satay skewers to soak in cold water. Scatter the cashews on a baking sheet and roast in the top of the oven for 10–15 minutes until golden brown. Shake occasionally to ensure even colouring on all sides and pay attention as the cashews can colour quickly and burn. Alternatively, place under a hot grill to achieve the same result. Remove from heat and set aside to cool. Reduce the oven temperature to 200 C/400 F/Gas Mark 6.

Mix the soy sauce, coconut milk, lime juice, honey, chilli sauce, ginger, garlic if used and salt. Grind the cashews to a fine powder, then in a mixing bowl add the soy sauce mixture a little at a time until you have a thick coating of satay sauce. If necessary beat the turkey out between sheets of Clingfilm to about $\frac{1}{4}$ inch/6 mm thick then cut into thin strips 2 inches/5 cm × $\frac{1}{2}$ inch/1 cm. Place in a glass or other non-reactive dish and mix well with 2 tablespoons of the satay sauce mixture and the groundnut oil to coat the strips. Set aside to marinade for 15–30 minutes.

Press the turkey onto the skewers until you have 3 or 4 per person. Don't pack the meat too tightly and leave about $1\frac{1}{2}$ inches/3.5 cm free at the end of each skewer. Sprinkle some of the skewers with coconut and drizzle a very few drops of Tabasco on others, leave some without coconut or Tabasco. Cook in the oven for 10–12 minutes, or grill for 8–10 minutes, turning occasionally to ensure even cooking, until golden brown and cooked through.

Warm the remaining satay sauce in a small saucepan, to almost simmering. Stir in a little more coconut milk if the sauce thickens too much. Pour into a serving dish that will include a spoon. The sauce is very rich and you won't require much. Arrange skewers of turkey satay on top of stir fried vegetables. Garnish with chopped coriander and serve with the remaining Warm Satay Sauce passed round.

# Liver in Tomato Sauce

No more dry, overcooked liver with this dish. And if you serve it with Purées of Root Vegetables as I suggest, you'll be able to soak up all the delicious sauce too.

Food category – P
'1 in 5' – lamb's liver
Serves – 4

INGREDIENTS

- 1 marrow, about 3–4 inches/8–10 cm in diameter
- 6 oz/175 g chestnut mushrooms, quartered
- 2 tablespoons olive oil
- 2 oz/60 g unsalted butter
- 1 lb/500 g lamb's liver, trimmed and cut into $\frac{1}{2}$ inch/1 cm cubes

- 2 tablespoons finely chopped fresh thyme or parsley
- Warm Basic Tomato Sauce for four, not puréed smooth (see page 271)
- sea salt and freshly ground black pepper, to taste

FOR SERVING
- Carrot and Parsnip Purée for four (see page 223)
- 2 tablespoons finely chopped fresh parsley, for garnish

METHOD

Cut four slices 2 inches/5 cm thick across the marrow. Peel the slices and remove the pulp to leave four marrow rings. Season the rings with salt and pepper and poach or microwave them in water or vegetable stock, or steam them, until they are just cooked through but still quite firm. Test with the point of a sharp knife. You don't want squashy marrow. Keep the rings warm if they are ready before the liver. In a large frying pan, over a medium to high heat, sauté the mushrooms in the oil until browned, about 5 minutes. Transfer to a warm plate and set aside.

Add the butter to the pan and allow it to foam, then sauté the liver, turning and tossing all the time until the cubes are browned on all sides without over cooking – they should still be pink in the middle, about 3–4 minutes according to how you prefer your liver cooked. Add the chopped thyme and season well with salt and pepper, cook for a further 1–2 minutes to allow the thyme to flavour the liver. Replace the cooked mushrooms in the pan, add the tomato sauce and mix all the ingredients together, warming the dish through until it just begins to simmer. Arrange the marrow rings on four warm plates, fill with puréed carrots and parsnips and spoon the liver in tomato sauce alongside. Sprinkle with chopped parsley and serve.

# Liver with Oregano

I couldn't resist another liver dish because they are so quick to cook and easy to make. The liver this time is served with griddle fried chicory and cauliflower in a rarebit sauce with a little horseradish added to give it a wonderful flavour.

Food category – P
'1 in 5' – calves' liver (or lamb's), eggs, cow's milk cheeses
Serves – 4

INGREDIENTS
- 2 eggs
- 1 tablespoon grated horseradish
- 2 tablespoons finely chopped fresh chives

- 7 oz/220 g mixed British cheese (e.g. strong cheddar and double Gloucester) grated
- 1 head cauliflower, cut into large florettes
- 1 lb/500 g calves' liver, trimmed and thinly sliced (or lamb's liver)
- 4 tablespoons finely chopped fresh oregano

- sea salt and freshly ground black pepper, to taste
- 3 cloves garlic, peeled and quartered
- 2 tablespoons olive oil
- 3 oz/90 g unsalted butter

TASTE SENSATION
balsamic vinegar

FOR SERVING
- 4 halves Griddled Chicory Hearts (see page 243)
- 4 halves tomato, grilled

METHOD

Pre-heat the grill to a medium heat. Beat the eggs and mix with the horseradish, chives and cheese until you have a thick sauce of coating consistency. Poach or microwave the cauliflower florettes in water or vegetable stock, or steam them, until they are just cooked through but still quite firm. Test the stems with the point of a sharp knife. Arrange in a heatproof dish and spread the rarebit sauce over. Sprinkle the liver with half the chopped oregano and salt and pepper seasoning. Cook the rarebit sauce under the grill until well browned and cooked right through. When the accompanying vegetables are ready and the cauliflower in rarebit sauce is nearly done, start cooking the liver.

In a large frying pan over a medium to high heat, sauté the garlic in the olive oil, stirring all the time to flavour the oil. About 1 minute. Discard the garlic. Add half the butter to the pan, allow to foam and settle then fry the slices of liver quickly, about 2–4 minutes on each side, depending on how you like it. It is best when browned on the outside and still pink in the middle. You may have to fry the liver in two lots and keep the first slices warm while cooking the remainder. Arrange slices of liver on four warm plates. Add the remaining butter to the pan and while still foaming add the remaining oregano and mix well. Spoon cauliflower in rarebit sauce alongside the liver. Spoon juices from the pan over the liver. Arrange chicory and tomato halves alongside the liver and cauliflower. Drizzle a few drops of balsamic vinegar onto the liver and serve.

# Frittata-Style Omelette Ⓥ

After Soufflé Omelette for one and Spanish-Style Omelette as a light lunch or supper, here's a big meal of an omelette. The basic method is the same for all frittata, you just have to get your imagination going to decide which vegetables you'll put in yours. Make sure they are all Mix With Any varieties; remember, no Carbohydrates. Frittata goes well with heaps of ratatouille and a crisp side salad or a huge mixed and dressed salad. Here are some favourite frittata versions of mine.

Food category – P
'1 in 5' – eggs, anchovies (optional)
Serves – 4–6

INGREDIENTS
- 3 medium courgettes, washed and trimmed
- 2 tablespoons olive oil
- sea salt and freshly ground black pepper, to taste
- 10 eggs, size 2

- 1 cup petit pois, cooked fresh or thawed frozen
- 1 oz/30 g unsalted butter
- 2 tablespoons finely sliced sun dried tomatoes in oil

TASTE SENSATION
2 tablespoons anchovy fillets, drained and finely chopped, optional

METHOD
Cut the courgettes lengthways into quarters and remove the central pulp with a sharp knife. Cut the remaining flesh into $\frac{1}{2}$ inch/1 cm dice. Heat the oil in a large heavy based, non-stick frying pan and sauté the courgettes with salt and pepper seasoning over a medium heat, stirring often, until softened and lightly browned. Remove from the heat and cool. In a large mixing bowl beat the eggs together until just light and frothy. Mix the courgettes and petit pois into the egg mixture. Wipe the pan clean, replace over the heat with the butter, and when it is foaming add the egg mixture and turn the heat to low immediately. Scatter the sun dried tomatoes, and anchovies if used, over the egg mixture and gently rearrange the mixture until they are well mixed into the omelette.

Pre-heat the grill. Allow the omelette to cook on the low heat without further disturbance until it is almost cooked through and a peek underneath shows it is golden brown. Too high a heat will burn the frittata so don't try to rush it. Place the pan under the grill and cook the top of the frittata until golden brown and set. Serve slices of the frittata straight from the pan onto warm plates with your chosen accompaniment.

VARIATIONS

If your food rotation allows, try these alternatives.

- ONION, CHEESE AND HERB
  Sauté a finely chopped, medium red onion until soft. Mix with a cup of grated Gruyère or cheddar and two tablespoons of fresh herbs (try parsley or chives). Stir into the beaten eggs and cook as above.

- SPINACH, PETIT POIS AND CRUMBLY GOAT'S CHEESE
  Cook, cool and chop 1 lb/500 g of whole leaf fresh or frozen spinach. Mix with cooked fresh or thawed frozen petit pois and fold into the beaten eggs. Scatter and mix into the pan the goat's cheese and cook as above.

# CARBOHYDRATE MAIN COURSES

## EVERYTHING YOU NEED TO KNOW
## ABOUT MAIN COURSES WITH CARBOHYDRATES

Here's your reminder about which foods are Carbohydrates.

### CARBOHYDRATES – A MEMORY AID

**'Carbohydrates Can Be Starchy Or Sweet But Are Never Stuffy'**

(Carbohydrates are mainly foods that are starchy or sweet. If you can mash it like potatoes or make it into a flour, it's a carbohydrate. You mustn't use them as stuffing for proteins though, because proteins and carbohydrates shouldn't be mixed.)

| | |
|---|---|
| *Gluten Cereals* | Barley, Oats, Rye, Wheat |
| *Non-gluten Grains* | Buckwheat, Millet, Rice |
| *Beans/Pulses* | Beans/pulses (dried), Chickpeas, Lentils (all), Peanuts |
| *Vegetables* | Maize/corn, Potatoes |
| *Special Cases* | Flours made from any of the above |
| *Sugars* | All sugars, honey, molasses, maple syrup etc. |

Check any food item with the alphabetical list of foods at the back of the book if you need to make sure. Carbohydrates are marked C.

What you need to consider when dealing with Carbohydrates in your

Kensington Diet is similar, in principle, to what you've just learned about proteins. First, and foremost of course, Carbohydrates must not be eaten in the same meal with Proteins. Second, all the Carbohydrates are designated '1 in 5' foods for the same reason as the Proteins, so they shouldn't be eaten too often. In fact, you're probably eating some of the Carbohydrates too much or too often, so varying your Carbohydrate intake is very important for your health and weight management.

To help you, these recipes and other suggestions for how to use Carbohydrates in your main course meals, feature only one or two Carbohydrates each. You may be able to think of many recipes or meals in which you could use two, three or even more Carbohydrates together but I wouldn't recommend this to you. In my experience, meals which contain several Carbohydrates together, even if there is no Protein in the meal, stress the digestion and cause bloating and fluid retention. These can become long term problems if you make multi-Carbohydrate meals your normal practice.

Try to keep your meals simple with only one or two Carbohydrates per meal. Choosing only one Carbohydrate will also help you keep on track with your '1 in 5' rotation. There are so many Carbohydrates to choose from, you'll never run out of exciting meal options if you use them separately.

Carbohydrates are frequently used as a 'filler up' in meals containing Proteins and vegetables. Usually they don't feature strongly as a main part of the meal but appear as an accompaniment to the star turn, the Protein. In The Kensington Diet, it's important to realise that Carbohydrates are served as the main item on the menu.

You already have quite a few wonderful Carbohydrate Light Meal recipes, and many of those can be adapted to become main courses. You'll also find advice as you go on how to use each Carbohydrate as an appropriate accompaniment in your KD eating. But what I really want to show you here is how to make Carbohydrate meals so irresistible that no-one who sits down to one will even notice there's not a Protein in sight.

Because there are no Proteins involved, KD Carbohydrate dishes are naturally vegetarian. And if you avoid those with cream and swap butter for oil where it appears, there are many which are vegan too.

A quick health note you might find useful is that putting spices like mustard with Carbohydrates stimulates an essential part of their pre-digestion which occurs in the mouth during chewing. The result can be of dramatic help to your health and weight management, since poor pre-digestion can cause many problems later on.

One last thing about Carbohydrates and weight management. Fats and oils are Mix With Any foods which can be combined with Carbohydrates but the combination of these two groups leads to easy fat accumulation on the body. So if you're trying to reduce or control your weight or shape, be sparing in the amount of fats and oils you put with your Carbohydrates. Go easy on the garlic or herb bread and don't dip your ciabatta into the olive oil too often!

Right now, let's get right into the recipes and get your imagination going.

## WHEAT AND GLUTEN GRAINS

Wheat, perhaps the most overused of all the carbohydrates, is a grain which is part of the same 'family' as oats, barley and rye because they all contain gluten. The *entire family* should be used only '1 in 5'. It's not correct, for instance, to replace a daily wheat intake with one day of wheat, the next with oats, the next rye and so on. For proper '1 in 5' rotation, eat **any** of the family on **1 day** and **none** of them on the next **4 days**. The good thing is you can eat any of them as often as you like on that one day – subject, of course, to your own weight control requirements.

Wheat turns up in breads, pastry, batters for coating and pancakes, pasta, cracked (bulgur) wheat and cous cous. As an accompaniment or component in meals it has to be the one that features more than any other Carbohydrate, being served as bread, croutons, blinis, pancakes, coatings, crumbs for gratins, thickener for sauces and who knows what else in processed foods. In KD eating, it's important that when you use wheat, you combine it only with Mix With Any foods such as salads, vegetables and herbs, and with other Carbohydrates.

So salad sandwiches are great and crusty bread with roast vegetables or garlic bread with vegetable casseroles are fine too. Pasta will go with tomato sauces but don't forget to always use dried, non-egg pasta. If you make pies or tarts use pastry that doesn't contain eggs and fill it with vegetables and Mix With Any sauces – not meat, eggs or cheeses.

Buckwheat, by the way, is from a different non-gluten grain, more about that later.

Here are some of my favourite ways of serving wheat as a main course dish.

# Spaghetti with Herbs and Olives ⓥ

Here is a quick and robust pasta dish that can be made in minutes and you'll be amazed by the result, especially if you put it with a refreshing side salad. Because it's so quick, it's a good idea to make the salad first. I suggest the Tomato and Onion Salad you'll find on page 246.

Food category – C
'1 in 5' – wheat (pasta)
Serves – 4

INGREDIENTS

- 2 full cups fresh basil leaves and tops, thick stalks discarded
- good quality olive oil
- 12 oz/375 g dried spaghetti (non-egg)
- 4 large cloves garlic, peeled and sliced into thin chips
- 2 small red chilli peppers, deseeded and thinly sliced

- 2 oz/60 g black olives, small oil marinated kind
- 2 oz/60g green olives, small oil marinated kind
- ½ cup finely chopped fresh oregano
- sea salt and freshly ground black pepper, to taste

FOR SERVING

- Tomato and Onion Side Salad with vinaigrette, for four (see page 246)

METHOD

Make a Basil Purée as follows: in a food processor or blender, purée the fresh basil leaves with olive oil. Add oil gradually until you have a smooth runny green purée. You may have to use a spatula between puréeing bursts to bring the leaves to the blades until you've added enough oil. Pour the purée into a bowl, cover and set aside.

In a very large saucepan bring about 4 pints/2.5 litres lightly salted water to a good rolling boil. Add 2 tablespoons olive oil and the spaghetti. Bring back to a gentle boil and cook for 8 minutes or according to the maker's instructions and to your taste. Pasta is best when cooked through but still firm to the bite in the centre, though not dry and powdery. While cooking the spaghetti, carefully fry the garlic chips in a little olive oil. Take great care not to overcook as they 'turn' very quickly. Fry a few at a time on both sides until lightly browned, then remove to drain on kitchen paper. In the same oil fry the chilli chips for a few seconds, then remove and allow to drain on paper. Make the oil up to about 2–3 tablespoons and warm all the olives together in the oil over a low heat.

Drain the spaghetti and return it to the warm pan. Pour over the warm olives in oil, add the garlic and chilli chips and scatter on the oregano while mixing until everything is evenly distributed. Divide the spaghetti into four warm pasta bowls, pour on some Basil Purée and season with freshly ground black pepper. Serve immediately with the side salads of Tomato and Mild Onion dressed with vinaigrette

# Pasta Stroganoff ⓥ

When it comes to pasta sauces, cheese won't work for you in The Kensington Diet, but you can use cream. Try this creamy pasta sauce adapted from the famous stroganoff.

Food category – C
'1 in 5' – wheat
Serves – 4

INGREDIENTS

- 1 oz/30 g unsalted butter
- 3 tablespoons olive oil
- 1 medium onion, thinly sliced lengthways
- 12 oz/375 g mixed mushrooms (chestnut, cep, shiitake, chanterelle) trimmed, wiped clean and cut into ½ inch/1 cm dice
- 12 oz/375 g dried (non-egg) tagliatelle pasta
- 1 heaped tablespoon green peppercorns, drained

- 8 oz/250 g ripe plum or salad tomatoes, seeded and finely chopped
- ½ cup fresh basil leaves, torn into small pieces
- sea salt and black pepper powder, to taste
- 1 large carton, ½ pt/250 ml, crème fraîche
- 1 teaspoon Dijon mustard

FOR SERVING

- large green salad for four (I suggest mixed leaves of lollo and lamb's lettuce with finely sliced celery and green peppers and lightly cooked fine green or Kenya beans)

- 2 servings of Lemon Vinaigrette (see page 103)

METHOD

Put a large pan of lightly salted water on to boil for the pasta. In a large frying pan over a medium heat, warm half the butter and two tablespoons of olive oil and sauté the onions without browning until soft and clear, 5 minutes. Add the mushrooms and cook, stirring frequently, until any escaped juices are sweated off to concentrate the flavours, another 3–5 minutes. Season with a little salt and freshly ground black pepper and mix well. Add the remaining tablespoon of olive oil to the boiling water, add the pasta and boil for 8 minutes or until cooked to your taste. It is best when soft but still retaining a definite firmness when bitten. Drain and toss with the remaining butter and some black pepper seasoning. Add the green peppercorns to the onions and mushrooms and, still over a medium heat, stir all the ingredients together until they are warmed, about 2–3 minutes.

In a mixing bowl, mix the chopped tomatoes with the torn basil and season to taste with salt and pepper. Stir crème fraîche and mustard into the mushroom mixture and bring just to the point of simmering. Serve straight away over the pasta in warm bowls, topped with a heap of tomatoes and basil and accompanied by a large green salad dressed with lemon vinaigrette.

VARIATION

- Mixing a proportion of vegetable 'pasta' ribbons made from leeks, courgettes or carrot with tagliatelle will reduce the wheat content of the dish and calories from the Carbohydrate pasta. It will also add interesting texture and colour to the dish. Reduce the real pasta content by one third and prepare enough vegetable 'pasta' ribbons (see page 211) to replace that amount. Simmer the vegetable 'pasta' in stock or lightly salted boiling water until soft but still with a little crunch. Mix the tagliatelle and vegetable 'pasta' when both are cooked before tossing them in the butter.

# Summer Vegetable Cous Cous ⓥ

Watch out for the harissa hot sauce that goes with this cous cous, it's fiery stuff.

Food category – C
'1 in 5' – wheat
Serves – 4

INGREDIENTS
- ½ teaspoon ground paprika
- ½ teaspoon ground turmeric
- ½ teaspoon ground cumin
- ½ teaspoon ground ginger
- ½ teaspoon ground cinnamon
- 2 tablespoons olive oil
- 1 medium onion, thinly sliced
- 2 cloves garlic, finely crushed
- 1 teaspoon chopped, fresh red chilli pepper, deseeded
- 3 carrots, in ½ inch/1 cm dice
- 4 sticks of celery, in ½ inch/1 cm slices
- 2 pints/1.2 litres Basic Vegetable Stock (see page 48)
- 3 medium courgettes, in 1 inch/2.5 cm slices
- 1 large red pepper, cored, seeded, in ¾ inch/2 cm dice
- 1 large green pepper, cored, seeded, in ¾ inch/2 cm dice
- 15 oz/470 g tin chickpeas, drained and well washed in cold water
- 12 oz/375 g quick-cook cous cous
- 1¾ pints/1 litre boiling water or extra vegetable stock
- 3 ripe plum tomatoes, skinned, deseeded and roughly chopped
- 2 tablespoons finely chopped fresh coriander, for garnish
- sea salt and freshly ground black pepper, to taste

TASTE SENSATION
Harissa hot sauce, to taste (available from most supermarkets)

METHOD
Put all the dried spices together in a bowl and mix well. Heat the olive oil in a large saucepan, over a low heat and sauté the onion, garlic and chilli with the dried spice mixture, stirring occasionally, until the onion is soft but not browned, about 5–10 minutes. Add the carrots and celery, stir and cook for 1–2 minutes then add three-quarters of the vegetable stock. Bring to a simmer, cover and cook for 10 minutes. Add the courgettes, red and green pepper and chickpeas, stir to mix, return to the simmer and cook for a further 10–15 minutes, until all the vegetables are just tender. Meanwhile, measure the cous cous into a large bowl or saucepan, sprinkle with salt and pour on the boiling water. If using vegetable stock omit the salt. Stir well, cover and leave to stand for at least 5 minutes until all the water has been absorbed. To the vegetables in liquor, add the chopped tomatoes and remaining stock and simmer rapidly for 2 minutes. Adjust to taste with salt and pepper. There should be plenty of quite thin liquor in which the vegetables have cooked, for pouring over the cous cous.

Turn the cous cous into a large warm serving bowl and fluff up with a fork to separate the grains. Add a large knob of butter or 2–3 tablespoons of olive oil if desired, before mixing. Turn the vegetables and liquor into another warm serving bowl, scatter the chopped coriander over. Place the harissa hot sauce in a small bowl or provide Tabasco sauce. Let each person help themselves to cous cous with vegetables and liquor, into individual bowls. Hot sauce can be added as desired.

## RICE

When using rice as an accompaniment be sure to put it only with vegetables or other Carbohydrates. Add a few drops of lemon juice during cooking to whiten and help grain separation. For attractive preparation, pack the rice fairly firmly into individual, lightly oiled ramekins or tea cups and tip out onto the plate, press the rice into a ring mould or ring pastry cutter on the plate.

**Long grain rice** is the standard easy-to-cook variety we're most used to. Serve with any vegetables cooked in or with a sauce, or with vegetable stir fries. Try mixing two parts of rice with one part of vegetable 'rice' (page 217) to reduce calories and the Carbohydrate content of a meal and to add flavour, colour and interest. Cook separately and mix before serving.

**Brown rice** gives good fibre content, a chewier texture and more flavour than plain white rice. It's also better in terms of sustained release of available energy if you undertake a lot of physical activity.

**Basmati rice**, an Indian variety, has a delicious flavour well suited to spicy vegetable curries. Rinse well in several changes of cold water before cooking to remove starch. Colour with a sparing use of saffron or turmeric during cooking to create the distinctive yellow of Indian cuisine.

**Chinese rice noodles** are an interesting variation to rice available from many supermarkets now. These are the fine, clear noodles or vermicelli and not the egg noodles that are more common. Serve with anything you'd put with ordinary grain rice, especially vegetable stir fries. Rice noodles can also be fried after cooking and draining. Either stir fry until crisped or use a ring mould to pack handfuls of noodles onto a little hot oil in a frying pan, fry on both sides to form a crispy rice noodle rösti then drizzle with soy sauce and sesame oil and serve with stir fried vegetables.

**Wild rice** is from a different variety of grass than the rices we see most often in the supermarket. It's more expensive and takes longer to cook than ordinary rice and cooking times vary according to the product. Cook separately and add to regular cooked rice for flavour, texture and attractive appearance, or use on its own.

# Paella Ⓥ

A vegetarian version of a timeless, all in one, rice dish which means it fits in with The Kensington Diet, but this version is special. You'll get the taste of the sea to mirror the seafood flavours of the traditional dish if you choose to use the Arame seaweed as I recommend. Serve the paella on its own or with side salad and even garlic bread if your food rotation allows.

Food category – C
'1 in 5' – rice
Serves – 4

INGREDIENTS

- ¼ cup dried Arame seaweed, optional
- olive oil
- 1 large onion, medium diced
- 1 clove garlic, finely chopped
- 1 small red pepper, in ½ inch/1 cm strips
- 1 small green pepper, in ½ inch/1 cm strips
- 2 oz/60 g mange tout
- 10 oz/375 g (raw) long grain rice
- ½ teaspoon saffron powder (or turmeric)
- 4 whole bay leaves, torn in half
- 26 fl oz/800 ml Basic Vegetable Stock (see page 48)

- 2 small heads chicory, outside leaves discarded
- pinch paprika powder
- 4 artichoke hearts (drained of brine or oil and halved)
- 2 oz/60 g (raw) wild rice, cooked and cooled
- 4 ripe tomatoes (preferably plum type), skinned, deseeded and roughly chopped
- 2 oz/60g frozen petit pois
- sea salt and freshly ground black pepper, to taste
- 2 lemons, cut in wedges
- 2 tablespoons finely chopped fresh parsley, for garnish

METHOD

Place the dried Arame seaweed, if used, into a saucepan and cover with plenty of boiling water, set aside to soften. Heat 4 tablespoons of olive oil in a large frying pan or paella dish over a low heat and sweat the onion and garlic until soft but not brown, about 5 minutes. Add the pepper strips and mange tout and cook, stirring occasionally, for a further 5 minutes. Add the rice, stir to mix well with the vegetables and to coat with oil. Add the saffron powder and torn bay leaves, stir well and add the vegetable stock. Season with salt and pepper but be careful not to add too much salt if stock cubes have been used. Simmer for about 20 minutes.

While the paella is simmering, cook the Arame seaweed, if used, and prepare the chicory and artichokes. Lift the seaweed from the soaking water to be sure not to take any of the fine sand which is sometimes on it. Rinse the saucepan, replace the seaweed, cover with boiling water and simmer for 5–7 minutes. Then lift from the cooking water and set aside in a colander to drain. Halve the chicory hearts lengthways through the core and split the leafy end down to the core to form a 'brush' effect. Brush each half with olive oil and season with salt and a pinch of paprika, pan fry in a little olive oil or on a hot griddle pan until just softened and attractively browned, about 2–3 minutes each side should do. Set aside to keep warm. Halves of artichoke hearts from a tin should be patted dry of brine with kitchen paper and brushed with oil both sides. Artichokes in oil from a jar can simply be drained. Pan or griddle fry the artichoke halves in the same way as the chicory and set aside.

Pre-heat the grill. When the rice is virtually cooked and the stock almost absorbed add the cooked wild rice and stir in. Add the chopped tomatoes, Arame seaweed strands if used and petit pois and stir gently to mix. Finish cooking for approximately 5 minutes, until the peas are cooked through, the rice is cooked completely and all the stock has been absorbed. Reheat the chicory brushes and artichokes under a hot grill for 1–2 minutes which will also add a bit more colour. Serve into individual dishes with halves of fried chicory and artichoke arranged into each serving. Garnish with wedges of lemon and a sprinkling of chopped parsley.

# Vegetable Rice Curry ⓥ

Serve this colourful and delicious basmati rice dish with mixed vegetable curry and look in your supermarket for Indian style chutneys to put with it.

Food category – C
'1 in 5' – rice
Serves – 4

INGREDIENTS

- 1 small onion, finely sliced
- 2 oz/60 g butter
- 1 clove garlic, crushed
- 6 whole green cardamoms
- 6 whole cloves
- 1 bay leaf, torn in half
- 1 teaspoon ground cinnamon (or a 1 inch/2.5 cm stick)
- 1 teaspoon ground cumin
- 1 teaspoon ground ginger
- 1 teaspoon chilli powder
- ½ teaspoon turmeric

- 8 oz/250 g fresh peas (or frozen)
- ¼ cauliflower, cut into florettes
- 1 green pepper, in 1 inch/2.5 cm dice
- 2½ cups basmati rice
- ½ teaspoon fine sea salt
- 5 cups water
- 4 small ripe tomatoes, quartered from top, for garnish
- 2 tablespoons finely chopped fresh coriander, for garnish

FOR SERVING

- Mixed Vegetable Curry for four (see page 248)
- ready prepared Indian chutneys of your choice

You'll need a large, heavy based frying pan, or saucepan with a lid for this recipe.

METHOD

Fry the onions in the butter over a medium heat until golden brown. Add the garlic, cardamoms, cloves, bay leaf, cinnamon, cumin, ginger, chilli and turmeric. Stir together and cook for 1 minute. Reduce the heat. Add the peas (if fresh are used), the cauliflower florettes and green pepper and fry gently for 4–5 minutes. Add the rice and salt and stir together then add the water. Stir and bring to a very gentle simmer, then cover and cook for 10–15 minutes until all the water is absorbed. If using frozen peas, add to the rice about 4–5 minutes before the end of cooking. Remove from the heat and allow to stand for at least 5 minutes. Just before serving add the tomato quarters and gently fold in so they are warmed through by the heat of the rice. Serve onto warm plates, with chopped coriander scattered over. Accompany with mixed vegetable curry and your choice of Indian chutneys.

## POTATOES

When eating the KD way, potatoes are combined only with Mix With Any foods or other Carbohydrates. Potatoes creamed or mashed with butter or cream (no milk), or puréed with olive oil then flavoured with roasted garlic or herbs like parsley and chives can be served with stewed, roasted or casseroled vegetables to make a wonderful dish.

Vegetables, oven cooked in savoury sauce, can be topped with sliced or creamy mashed potatoes, or even with bubble and squeak. Baked jacket potatoes can be topped with butter or sour cream and herbs if you're not concerned about your weight, or try tomato sauce with herb purée drizzled over and served with salad. Salad, and I mean a big mixed salad, is also a great combination with French fries or new potatoes which have been tossed in butter with handfuls of chopped chives.

Sweet potatoes are not the same botanical family as the more common varieties we use. Treat them as a separate '1 in 5' Carbohydrate, which means you can have regular potatoes on '1 in 5' and sweet potatoes on another day in the same five. The sweet variety of potatoes can be cooked in many of the same ways as regular potatoes. Deep fried chips (a favourite in New Zealand), baked in their skins and mashed with butter and flavourings will all work well, as will variations of the recipes which follow.

# Roast of Crispy Potatoes and Onions Ⓥ

You'll want for nothing with KD eating. Here's a delicious roast dinner with all the trimmings and properly combined too. Serve your roast potatoes with a medley of steamed vegetables, wedges of Herb Stuffing (see page 206) and Onion Gravy (see page 275).

Food category – C
'1 in 5' – potatoes, wheat (stuffing and gravy)
Serves – 4

INGREDIENTS
- 5 tablespoons olive oil
- 5 tablespoons sunflower or groundnut oil
- 4–6 large potatoes, peeled and cut into 2 inch/5 cm dice

- 2–3 large onions trimmed, peeled and quartered
- sea salt and freshly ground black pepper, to taste

FOR SERVING
- Medley of Steamed Vegetables for four (see page 226)

- 2 tablespoons finely chopped fresh parsley, for garnish

- Onion Gravy for four (see page        • Herb Stuffing for four (see page
  275)                                     206)

You'll need two roasting tins for this recipe, one for the potatoes and one for the onions.

METHOD

Pre-heat the oven to 200 C/400 F/Gas Mark 6. Mix the oils and divide them between two roasting tins, place these in the oven to pre-heat. Parboil the potatoes by bringing them to the boil in plenty of lightly salted water and boiling for 10 minutes until the outside of the potatoes are becoming soft and floury. Drain into a colander and, using a tea towel or oven gloves, hold a plate on top of the colander and shake the potatoes to break up the surfaces and corners where they are softened. These are the areas which will become crispy when roasted. With oven gloves on, remove a hot roasting tin from the oven and tip the warm potatoes in. Move them around until all the surfaces are well basted in hot oil and place in the top of the oven for 50–60 minutes, until golden brown. Turn occasionally to keep the potatoes basted with oil and ensure even cooking.

When you put the potatoes in, remove the second roasting tin for the onions. Tip the onion quarters in and mix until they are well coated in oil, season with plenty of salt and freshly ground black pepper. Place in the middle of the oven for 45–55 minutes until soft and slightly browned – or even charred at the edges where the onions have caramelised. Turn the onions occasionally during cooking to ensure they are cooked completely and well coloured. On each of four warm plates, arrange a serving of crispy roast potatoes mixed with roast onions. Add a slice of baked stuffing and a selection of mixed steamed vegetables sprinkled with chopped parsley. Pour a measure of gravy over the stuffing and serve with the remaining gravy in a separate sauce boat on the side.

# Spicy Potatoes in Tomato Sauce ⓥ

This is one of my favourite ways of cooking potatoes. I use just one large frying pan or saucepan with a lid, add potatoes, tomatoes and whatever other ingredients I find at hand and simmer until the potatoes are cooked and the tomatoes reduced to a superb thick sauce. Lovely, especially as I don't lose a single drop of the sauce: I serve the potatoes in bowls into which a side salad can be placed afterwards to mop up any sauce that's left.

Food category – C
'1 in 5' – potatoes
Serves – 4

INGREDIENTS

- 4 tablespoons olive oil
- 1 small onion, thinly sliced
- 1 teaspoon paprika
- ½ teaspoon cayenne
- 1½ lbs/750 g smooth skinned new potatoes, scrubbed and, if necessary, cut into even chunks about 1–1½ inches/2.5–3.5 cms
- 8 oz/250 g small black olives
- 4 oz/125 g artichoke halves in brine, drained, washed and cut in half

- 1 small sprig fresh rosemary
- sea salt and freshly ground black pepper, to taste
- 2 × 16 oz/500 g tins Italian plum tomatoes
- 16 oz/500 g tin chopped tomatoes
- 2 tablespoons tomato purée
- 10 oz/315 g broad beans (fresh or frozen)

FOR SERVING

- Green Leaf Salad for four (e.g. round lettuce, lollo rosso, watercress)

- Vinaigrette Dressing made with Tabasco and garlic (see page 73)

If you don't have a large enough heavy based, non-stick frying pan or saucepan with a lid, make the recipe in a smaller pan in two equal amounts, each with half the ingredients, then combine them for four people.

METHOD

In a very large, heavy based, non-stick frying pan, heat the olive oil over a medium heat and sauté the onion with the paprika and cayenne for 2–3 minutes. Add the potatoes, olives, artichokes and rosemary, season with plenty of salt and black pepper and mix the ingredients until they are well distributed and coated with oil. Tip the tinned whole tomatoes into a bowl, remove and discard the seeds and core ends of the tomatoes and roughly chop the flesh. Add the chopped flesh and tomato juice, half the tin of chopped tomatoes and the tomato purée, to the pan with the potatoes. Mix well and bring to a simmer. Cover and simmer for 25 minutes, stirring occasionally, until the tomatoes have reduced to a thick sauce and the potatoes are almost cooked through. If using fresh broad beans, mix them into the contents of the pan after 15 minutes simmering. If using frozen, add them after 20 minutes. They need sufficient time in the simmering mixture to be properly cooked.

Test the potatoes with the sharp point of a knife to see if the dish is cooked. The sauce should be really thick and coating all the vegetables. If it's too thin, increase the heat for a minute or two and boil off any excess juice. If the juice is thickening too much during cooking, add a little more of the chopped tomatoes you've retained. Check and adjust the seasoning with salt and pepper. Serve into individual warm bowls. Pass the salad and dressing separately as a follow on course.

# Potatoes and Root Vegetables Boulangère Style Ⓥ

This is another favourite of mine. I've varied the traditional all potato dish to include other root vegetables and suggest you serve it with a butter sauté of Savoy cabbage with caraway seeds and petit pois. A vegetable slicer really comes into its own in this type of recipe.

Food category – C
'1 in 5' – potatoes
Serves – 4–6

INGREDIENTS FOR THE BOULANGÈRE:

- 2 tablespoons olive oil
- 3 medium onions, finely sliced
- 1 lb/500 g large potatoes, peeled and thinly sliced
- 2 large carrots, finely sliced
- 1 large parsnip, finely sliced
- 1 turnip finely sliced

- 1–2 cloves garlic, finely sliced
- ½ teaspoon mixed herbs
- sea salt and freshly ground black pepper, to taste
- 18 fl oz/560 ml Basic Vegetable Stock (see page 48)
- 1 oz/30 g unsalted butter

FOR THE CABBAGE AND CARAWAY SEEDS

- 2 oz/60 g unsalted butter
- 1 teaspoon caraway seeds
- 1 small Savoy cabbage, trimmed and shredded
- sea salt and ground white pepper, to taste

- 1 lb/500 g frozen petit pois
- ½ pt/300 ml Basic Vegetable Stock, optional

METHOD

FOR THE BOULANGÈRE POTATOES AND ROOT VEGETABLES

Pre-heat the oven to 230 C/450 F/Gas Mark 7. Lightly oil the inside of an ovenproof dish large enough to contain all the sliced vegetables. In a very large pan over a medium heat, sauté the onions in the olive oil, without browning, until they are soft and clear, about 5–10 minutes. Set aside enough potato slices to cover the top of the dish when they are overlapped a little. Add the remaining potatoes to the pan with the carrots, parsnips, turnips and garlic. Sprinkle with the mixed dried herbs and plenty of salt and black pepper. Turn and mix until all the ingredients are well combined.

Tip the mixture into the ovenproof dish. Ladle over as much of the vegetable stock as you need to come about three-quarters of the way up the side of the vegetables. You may not need all the stock. Finish with the slices of potato you kept aside, arranging them to overlap until the top of the dish is covered. Season with salt and freshly ground pepper and top with the butter in 6–8 small knobs evenly spaced on the potato slices. Cook in the oven at 230 C/450 F/Gas Mark 7 for 20 minutes then reduce the heat to 200 C/400 F/Gas Mark 6 and cook for a further 50–55 minutes. During cooking, occasionally press the vegetables down with a flat slice or spatula to make sure they absorb all the stock. When cooked the top of the dish should be golden brown and crisped at the edges, while all the stock underneath should have been absorbed. Test with the sharp point of a knife to make sure the vegetables are cooked through. Finish under a hot grill to crisp and colour more if necessary. Serve at the table with the butter sauté of Savoy cabbage and caraway seeds.

FOR THE SAUTÉ OF SAVOY CABBAGE AND CARAWAY SEEDS

A wok with a lid is best for this recipe but any large lidded pan able to take the shredded cabbage will do.

Heat the butter in the wok over a medium heat until it stops foaming, being careful not to overheat and burn it. Sauté the caraway seeds, stirring continuously, for 1–2 minutes, then add the cabbage, in two lots if necessary. Turn and toss the cabbage in the butter until softened and reduced in volume, seasoning with salt and white pepper as you go. When the cabbage is softened but still quite crunchy (this will only take a few minutes), add the peas, cover and cook for 3–4 minutes until the peas are cooked and the cabbage is soft but still retaining a little bite. If you want more buttery liquor with your meal add as much vegetable

stock as you require to the cabbage, bring to a rapid boil for 1 minute
and transfer to a serving dish to accompany the boulangère potatoes and
root vegetables.

## CORN

Maize or corn is available as polenta (corn meal), corn pasta in various
shapes, tacos (corn pancakes) and corn chips in addition to the usual
corn kernels on the cob and off it. All these forms of corn can be fitted
successfully into your Kensington Diet if you combine them only with
other Carbohydrates and Mix With Any foods.

Corn pasta, from health food shops and good supermarkets, can
replace wheat pasta in any KD dish in which it is used. Olive oil, tomato
sauce, grilled vegetables, herbs, olives and garlic are just a few options
with which to serve it. Corn tacos and corn chips are traditional
accompaniments to many dishes in Mexican cooking. Try them with
guacamole, sour cream, salsa and bean dishes such as frijoles. Corn on
the cob can be grilled or barbecued with spices rubbed over or simply
boiled and served with butter. The corn kernels themselves add colour as
well as flavour and nutrition to Carbohydrate salads and cooked
vegetable dishes.

Here's a more sophisticated recipe using one of the staple corn foods
of Italy – polenta.

# Polenta Stacked with Ratatouille Vegetables ⓥ

Cooked and cooled polenta can be sliced and fried or grilled to give a
crisp counterpoint to rich vegetables and lots of herbs as in this dish.
There are a number of layers to this dish so ingredients and instructions
are given for each separately. Serve with a mixed green salad dressed
with vinaigrette.

Food category – C
'1 in 5' – corn
Serves – 4

INGREDIENTS

FOR THE ROASTED PEPPERS
- 2 large red peppers
- 1 large green pepper
- 1 large yellow pepper
- 2 cloves garlic, finely sliced
- 1 teaspoon finely chopped fresh oregano (or half teaspoon dried)
- 1 teaspoon finely chopped fresh marjoram (or half teaspoon dried)
- 1 tablespoon olive oil
- sea salt and freshly ground black pepper, to taste

FOR THE POLENTA
- 1 medium onion, finely chopped
- 1 oz/60 g unsalted butter
- 3 tablespoons olive oil
- 25 fl oz/750 ml water
- 7 oz/220 g pre-cooked (quick) polenta
- 2 tablespoons finely chopped fresh parsley
- sea salt and freshly ground black pepper, to taste

FOR THE OLIVE PASTE
- 4 oz/125 g green olives, pitted
- olive oil for blending

FOR THE VEGETABLES
- 8 slices of large aubergines, $\frac{1}{2}$ inch/1 cm thick
- 8 slices of large firm beef tomatoes, $\frac{1}{4}$ inch/6 mm thick
- olive oil for pan frying
- sea salt and freshly ground black pepper, to taste

FOR SERVING
- Rich Tomato Sauce, puréed, sieved and warmed (see page 272)
- 2 tablespoons fresh basil leaves, torn into small pieces

METHOD

FOR THE PEPPERS

Pre-heat the oven to 230 C/450 F/Gas Mark 7. Roast the peppers in the oven, turning occasionally, until they are well blackened on all sides. Place in a bowl, cover with a clean damp cloth and set aside to cool. Reduce the oven temperature to 180 C/350 F/Gas Mark 4. When the peppers are cool enough to handle, remove and discard the cores, seeds and skin, retaining as much of the juice as possible by working over a bowl or plate. Cut the flesh into $\frac{1}{2}$ inch/1 cm slices lengthways and mix together in an ovenproof dish with the sliced garlic, herbs, olive oil, salt and pepper seasoning and the retained pepper juices. Cover with a lid or kitchen foil and cook in the lower part of the oven for 20 minutes. Allow to cool to room temperature.

FOR THE POLENTA

In a large, non-stick saucepan, over a medium heat, sauté the onions in the butter, 1 tablespoon of olive oil and salt and pepper seasoning, until soft but not browned. Add the water and bring to a gentle boil then add the polenta a little at a time, stirring continuously. When all the polenta is mixed in, cook, beating continuously over the heat for 3–4 minutes. Remove from the heat and mix in the chopped parsley and season to taste. Spread evenly in the bottom of a lightly oiled shallow dish, or on lightly oiled foil, leave to cool and set to about $\frac{3}{4}$ inch/2 cm thick. When cool, cut out twelve circles with a pastry cutter $1\frac{1}{2}$ inches/3.5 cm diameter or twelve $1\frac{1}{2}$ inch/3.5 cm squares. Brush each shape, both sides, with the remaining oil and season with salt and pepper. Set aside for cooking when other ingredients are ready.

FOR THE OLIVE PASTE

Purée or mash the olives with just enough olive oil to produce a thick green olive spread. Pre-heat the grill and grill the polenta shapes for 3–4 minutes each side until crisp and golden. Brush the aubergine slices on both sides with olive oil, season lightly with salt and pepper and fry, in batches if necessary, in a heavy based pan or on a well oiled griddle pan until browned on both sides and soft. Set aside on kitchen paper in a warm place. Fry the tomato slices quickly in a little olive oil over high heat for 30 seconds each side until just browned. Assemble the dish on four warm plates. Spread the polenta shapes with olive paste and place three on each plate. Rest two aubergine slices on top slightly overlapping, then two slices of tomato, also overlapping. Spoon roasted pepper strips on top and drizzle with juices. Spoon rich tomato sauce around the polenta base. Sprinkle with torn basil and serve with a refreshing green salad of mixed lettuce (e.g. round, frisee and lamb's) dressed with vinaigrette.

# Spicy Vegetable Peanut Satay Ⓥ

Peanuts, unlike other nuts, are designated a Carbohydrate for food combining so should only be mixed with other carbohydrates and Mix With Any foods. That's no problem for Kensington Dieters because it creates the option for a special satay made with vegetables instead of meat or poultry. Serve on plain boiled rice or if you prefer to reduce your Carbohydrate intake, a mixture of rice and Mix With Any vegetable 'rice'.

Food category – C
'1 in 5' – peanuts, rice (for serving, if used)
Serves – 4

INGREDIENTS

- 32 chunks of peeled carrot, ½ inch/ 1 cm
- 32 small shallots or small onions (approx ½ inch/1 cm diameter) or larger ones halved or quartered through the root
- 32 florettes of cauliflower, approx. 1 inch/2.5 cm
- 32 pieces of red pepper, 1 inch/2.5 cm dice
- 32 pieces of yellow pepper, 1 inch/ 2.5 cm dice

FOR THE MARINADE

- juice of three limes
- 1 tablespoon clear honey
- 1 tablespoon fresh finely grated root ginger

FOR THE SATAY

- 16 wooden or bamboo skewers, about 8 inches/20 cm long
- 4 tablespoons crunchy peanut butter
- 4 tablespoons Tamari (non-wheat) soy sauce
- 1 tablespoon lemon juice (or lime)
- ½ teaspoon chilli paste or chilli powder
- 1 clove garlic, finely crushed, optional
- 1 tablespoon groundnut or sunflower oil
- 2 tablespoons finely chopped salted peanuts
- ¼ pint water
- 2 tablespoons finely chopped fresh coriander, for garnish

FOR SERVING
- cooked basmati or long grain rice for four

or

- rice with Mix With Any Vegetable 'Rice' for four (see page 217)

You'll need a wire mesh on which to cook the vegetables over an oven tray or dish to catch any sauce which drips.

METHOD
Blanch the vegetables in simmering water until just soft enough to be

pushed on to a wooden skewer, about 8 minutes for the carrots and onions, 5 minutes for the cauliflower florettes and peppers. Test with a skewer and when ready drain and set aside to dry. Mix the marinade ingredients in a large bowl, add the dry, part-cooked vegetables. Mix to coat well, cover and leave for at least an hour, turning in the marinade occasionally. Soak the wooden skewers in cold water for at least an hour. Make the satay sauce. In a mixing bowl, blend together the peanut butter, soy sauce, lemon juice, chilli and garlic if used. Cover and set aside until ready to cook. When ready to cook, pre-heat the oven to 230 C/450 F/Gas Mark 7.

Drain the marinade ingredients from the vegetables through a sieve into a small bowl and wipe the large marinading bowl with kitchen paper. Allow the vegetables to dry a little in a warm place for a few minutes. In the large marinading bowl, mix together two tablespoons of satay sauce mixture and the oil, add the vegetable pieces and toss or mix until well coated, add the chopped salted peanuts and mix to coat well. Thread the vegetable pieces onto the wooden skewers. Roast the vegetable satay in the oven on a wire mesh over a tray, turning occasionally, for 8–10 minutes, until the coating is slightly crisp and coloured and the vegetables are cooked. Alternatively grill under a hot grill, turning often until the coating is well coloured and the vegetables are cooked.

Meanwhile, in a small non-stick saucepan, mix the retained marinade with the remaining satay sauce and enough water to make a thickish pouring sauce. Warm over a low heat until hot but not boiling, then pour into a serving bowl with a spoon. Serve the vegetable satays onto beds of rice on warm plates, garnish with chopped coriander and pass the warm peanut satay sauce around.

### PULSES

With the exception of soya, all dried beans, chickpeas and most lentils belong to the same group of foods, the pulses. In terms of your '1 in 5' food rotating they all need to be treated as the same food and any pulse or pulses should be eaten on the same day in any five, then none of them again for the next four days. I know this might come as a surprise to vegetarians who may be using pulses, albeit they are Carbohydrate rich, as a staple food and source of Protein. The health and particularly weight management benefits of reducing pulses to '1 in 5' far outweighs the reduction in Protein intake from this source, which can, in any case, be replaced with nuts and seeds.

Most dried beans are now available in tins and I personally prefer to use tinned varieties rather than go to all the trouble and time of soaking dried beans overnight in several changes of water before cooking them. It's just too fiddly for me so I treat tinned beans as a fast convenience food for quick meals. Use any variety of bean in salads and vegetable cassoulets or purée with garlic, olive oil and herbs to make a pâté.

Lentils are easier and quicker to cook and, I think, more versatile than beans. Use yellow or red lentils for Indian dhal and slate grey/green or brown, continental lentils or puy lentils for salads or – as the following recipes show – as a substitute for meat in several favourite dishes. Lentils don't need to be soaked for long periods, if at all, and they don't seem to have quite the same unhappy consequences for the digestive tracts unused to them in quantity. All the same, whether it's beans or lentils, my advice is to eat small amounts only with plenty of vegetables and some other Carbohydrate. Like all the Carbohydrates, pulses should only be combined with Mix With Any foods and other Carbohydrates.

# Basic Lentils Ⓥ

The same basic lentil recipe can be used to produce a number of dishes which would normally combine meat Proteins with Carbohydrates. Cook your lentils like this first then use them in any of the ways shown below for delicious and healthy meals which fit perfectly into your Kensington Diet. Lentils can be cooked in plenty of water and any excess drained off when they are ready. This is particularly true for this recipe where the lentils are left slightly undercooked to avoid them breaking down, which lentils often do. Final cooking takes place when cooking the dish in which the lentils are used.

Food category – C
'1 in 5' – lentils (garnish)
Serves – 4

INGREDIENTS

- 2 tablespoons olive oil
- 1 medium onion, finely chopped
- 1 large clove garlic, crushed and mashed
- 1 bay leaf
- freshly ground black pepper, to taste
- 6 oz/175 g green or brown lentils, washed under cold running water
- 1½ pints/900 ml Basic Vegetable Stock (see page 48), or water

METHOD 1

Heat the oil in a large heavy based saucepan, over a low heat and sauté the onions and garlic until the onion is soft and clear, about 5–10 minutes. Add the bay leaf and a good seasoning of black pepper and cook for a further 1–2 minutes. Allow the pan to cool. Add the lentils to the pan and cold stock, turn to a low heat, cover and bring to a simmer. Cook for 25–30 minutes until the lentils are firm and whole but not hard. Drain, remove the bay leaf and use as required in your chosen dish.

METHOD 2

Heat the oil in a large heavy based saucepan, over a low heat and sauté the onions and garlic until the onion is soft and clear, about 5–10 minutes. Add the bay leaf and a good seasoning of black pepper and cook for a further 1–2 minutes. Allow the pan to cool. Add the lentils and cold stock to the pan, cover and place in a cold oven. Set the oven to 180 C/350 F/Gas Mark 4 and cook from cold for 50–55 minutes until firm and whole but not hard. Drain, remove the bay leaf and use as required in your chosen dish.

VARIATION

- Puy lentils are the aristocrat of lentils. They're more expensive but they stay firm and whole when cooked so you could replace all or a portion of the lentils in the above recipe with puy lentils and expect a good nutty texture to the lentils in the finished dish.

NOTE

Simmer the Basic Lentils for 15–20 minutes more until fully cooked to make a delicious light meal in themselves, especially good when dressed with warm herb vinaigrette and chopped tomatoes.

# Spaghetti with Lentil Sauce ⓥ

Simplicity itself – here's how. It's essential the tomato sauce is reduced until it's thick and rich before using.

Food category – C
'1 in 5' – lentils (pulses), wheat or corn (pasta)
Serves – 4

INGREDIENTS

- 6 oz/175 g chestnut mushrooms, trimmed, wiped and medium sliced
- 1–2 tablespoons olive oil
- 1 large clove garlic, crushed
- 1 portion Basic Lentils (see page 195)
- 1½ portions Rich Tomato Sauce (see page 272)

- 1 teaspoon finely chopped fresh marjoram (or ½ teaspoon dried)
- 1 teaspoon finely chopped fresh thyme (or ½ teaspoon dried)
- sea salt and freshly ground black pepper, to taste

FOR SERVING

- spaghetti (wheat or corn) for four, (or other pasta shape)

METHOD

In a heavy based saucepan over a medium heat, sauté the mushrooms in the olive oil until soft and lightly browned, about 5 minutes. Add the garlic and cook for a further 1–2 minutes. Add the Basic Lentils and cook for 3–4 minutes, stirring often to warm through. Add the Rich Tomato Sauce, herbs and seasoning. Mix well and bring to a simmer. Cook for 10–15 minutes while you prepare the cooked spaghetti to your taste. I suggest you toss it with a tablespoon each of olive oil and finely chopped basil. Serve the spaghetti topped with plenty of lentil sauce in warm bowls, followed by a refreshing vinaigrette dressed green salad.

VARIATION

- Reduce your Carbohydrate intake and increase your intake of fresh vegetables by serving with Mix With Any Vegetable Pasta (see page 209).

# Lentil Lasagne ⓥ

Another simple dish once the Basic Lentils are ready.

Food category – C
'1 in 5' – lentils (pulses), wheat (lasagne)
Serves – 4

INGREDIENTS

- 2 tablespoons olive oil
- 1 small onion, finely sliced
- 1 clove garlic, crushed
- 1 carrot, finely chopped
- 2 sticks celery, finely sliced
- 1 serving Basic Lentils (see page 195)
- 2 servings, well reduced, Rich Tomato Sauce (see page 272)

- 1 teaspoon finely chopped fresh oregano (or ½ teaspoon dried)
- 1 teaspoon finely chopped fresh sage (or ½ teaspoon dried)
- sea salt and freshly ground black pepper, to taste
- 6 oz/175 g lasagne

FOR THE WHITE SAUCE

- 4 fl oz/125 ml single cream
- 8 fl oz/250 ml vegetable stock or water
- 1 oz/30 g unsalted butter
- ¼ teaspoon nutmeg

- pinch mustard powder
- 2 heaped tablespoons plain flour
- sea salt and white pepper powder, to taste

FOR SERVING

- mixed salad for four
- Basic Vinaigrette made with whole grain mustard (see page 73)

You'll require a shallow ovenproof dish large enough to take all the lentil sauce.

METHOD

Pre-heat the oven to 200 C/400 F/Gas Mark 6. Heat the oil in a large heavy based saucepan over a medium heat and sauté the onion, garlic, carrot and celery, stirring occasionally, until the onion is soft and clear and the vegetables are softened, about 5–10 minutes. Add the lentils, tomato sauce and herbs, stir, bring to a simmer, season to taste with salt and pepper then remove from the heat and set aside. Half fill a large saucepan with lightly salted water and bring to the boil. Add ½ tablespoon of olive oil. Immerse the lasagne sheets in the boiling water, placing them in separately so they don't stick together. Boil for 8 minutes or until just cooked. Drain and arrange the lasagne sheets around the edge of a colander or sieve – without touching – to drain completely.

Lightly oil the ovenproof dish and arrange a layer of lasagne on the bottom. Spread half the lentil sauce over, then arrange another layer of lasagne and spread the remaining sauce over that. Finally add a last layer of lasagne. Mix the cream with the vegetable stock. Melt the butter in a non-stick saucepan over a medium heat with the nutmeg and mustard. When it stops foaming add the flour and cook, stirring frequently, for 3 minutes to make a thick paste. Add the cream and stock mixture a quarter at a time, stirring vigorously all the time to produce a smooth white sauce. The sauce needs to be a thick coating consistency, if it is too thick adjust with some of the remaining stock. Season to taste with white pepper and sea salt. Cook for one minute, stirring continuously. Pour the white sauce over the lasagne, sprinkle with freshly grated black pepper and cook in the oven for 30 minutes. Brown under a hot grill to finish if more colour is required. Serve onto warm plates accompanied by dressed mixed salad.

# Lentil Moussaka ⓥ

When cooked like this, moussaka can remain a firm favourite in your KD repertoire. Serve with a salad of sliced tomatoes, black Kalamata olives and thinly sliced mild onions, all dressed in lemon juice and olive oil.

Food category – C
'1 in 5' – lentils (pulses), potatoes
Serves – 4

INGREDIENTS

- 3 large potatoes
- 2 medium aubergines, cut into $\frac{1}{4}$ inch/6 mm slices
- olive oil for brushing and frying
- 2–3 cloves garlic, crushed
- 1 serving Basic Lentils (see page 195)
- 1½ servings Basic Tomato Sauce, not puréed (see page 271)

- 14 oz/440 g tin Italian plum tomatoes, drained, cored and seeded, flesh roughly chopped (retain juice)
- 1 teaspoon dried marjoram
- sea salt and freshly ground black pepper, to taste

FOR THE WHITE SAUCE

- 4 fl oz/125 ml single cream
- 8 fl oz/250 ml vegetable stock or water
- 1 oz/30 g unsalted butter
- $\frac{1}{4}$ teaspoon nutmeg

- pinch mustard powder
- 2 heaped tablespoons plain flour
- sea salt and white pepper powder, to taste

FOR SERVING
• Tomato and Onion Salad with black        • lemon juice and olive oil dressing
  olives for four (see page 246)

METHOD

Pre-heat the oven to 190 C/375 F/Gas Mark 5. Bring the whole potatoes to the boil in lightly salted water and boil for 12 minutes. Drain, immerse in cold water until cool and set aside. Brush the aubergine slices with olive oil on both sides and fry, in batches, over high heat until lightly browned on both sides and soft. Set aside on kitchen paper. In a heavy based saucepan over a medium heat, sauté the garlic in a tablespoon of olive oil for 2 minutes, add the lentils, tomato sauce, chopped tomatoes and marjoram, mix well and bring to a simmer. Season to taste with salt and black pepper and remove from heat to cool. Peel the potatoes if preferred, and slice thinly.

Lightly oil the ovenproof dish. Place a layer of aubergine slices in the bottom leaving enough slices for another layer later. Arrange a layer of potato slices on the aubergines. Spoon the lentil sauce onto the potatoes, add another layer of potato slices and a final layer of aubergine slices on top of that. Make the topping. Mix the cream with the vegetable stock. Melt the butter in a non-stick saucepan over a medium heat with the nutmeg and mustard. When it stops foaming add the flour and cook, stirring frequently, for 3 minutes to make a thick paste. Add the cream and stock mixture a quarter at a time, stirring vigorously all the time to produce a smooth white sauce. The sauce needs to be a thick coating consistency, if it is too thick adjust with a little water. Season to taste with white pepper and sea salt. Cook for one minute stirring continuously.

Pour the white sauce over the lasagne, sprinkle with freshly grated black pepper and cook in the oven for 30 minutes. Brown under a hot grill to finish if more colour is required. Serve onto warm plates accompanied by the salad.

# Lentil Chilli ⓥ

Another quick and delicious use of lentils for those who like spicy chilli. Serve with plain boiled long grain rice or Mix With Any vegetable 'rice'.

Food category – C
'1 in 5' – pulses – lentils and beans, rice
Serves – 4

INGREDIENTS

- 2 tablespoons olive oil
- 1 onion, sliced
- 1 large clove garlic, finely sliced
- 1 green chilli pepper, seeded and finely sliced
- 1 teaspoon chilli powder
- 1 teaspoon cumin seeds (or ½ teaspoon cumin powder)
- 1 large green or red pepper, cored, seeded and cut into slices
- 1 serving Basic Lentils (see page 195)

- 1½ servings Basic Tomato Sauce, not puréed (see page 271)
- 14 oz/440 g tin Italian plum tomatoes, drained, seeded and cored flesh, roughly chopped (retain juice)
- 14 oz/440 g tin red kidney beans, drained and washed
- 1 tablespoon yeast extract (i.e. Marmite)
- sea salt and freshly ground black pepper, to taste

FOR SERVING

- plain boiled long grain rice for four (or Vegetable Rice – see page 217)

- 1 tablespoon finely chopped fresh coriander, for garnish

METHOD

Heat the oil in a large heavy based saucepan, over a medium heat and sauté the onion until it is soft, about 5 minutes. Add the garlic, sliced chilli pepper, chilli powder, cumin seeds and green pepper, stir and cook for a further 2 minutes. Add the lentils, tomato sauce, chopped tomatoes, kidney beans and yeast extract, stir and bring to a simmer, making sure the yeast extract dissolves completely. Simmer for 15 minutes. Cook the rice accompaniment. Adjust the consistency of the chilli with the retained tomato juice if necessary. I prefer a thick sauce without any of the thin separated juices from the tomatoes in evidence, so I would bring the chilli to a rapid boil to disperse these before serving. Season with salt and freshly ground black pepper to your taste. Serve in warm bowls on white rice and garnish with chopped coriander.

VARIATIONS

- Reduce the pulse contents of this dish by replacing half the amount of basic lentils with an equivalent quantity of pre-cooked bulgur (cracked) wheat. Your chilli will have a nice chewy texture to it, but don't forget to allow for the wheat in your food rotation.

- You can thicken your chilli rapidly and add the savoury flavour it requires if you replace the yeast extract with a tablespoon of vegetarian soya free gravy mix. Blend to a paste in a little water and stir into the chilli while it is simmering. The original Bisto gravy mix will do nicely, but check the contents as there may still be some packs with soya flour included.

# Lentil Curry ⓥ

Dhal or dahl or dal, whatever your preferred spelling, is the collective name, in India, for many different pulses. The distinctive taste of red or yellow lentils flavoured with spices and garlic is delicious and makes a perfect accompaniment to vegetable curries and, if your food rotation allows, Indian breads.

Food category – C
'1 in 5' – lentils (pulse)
Serves – 4

INGREDIENTS

- 8 oz/250 g red lentils
- 1 pint/600 ml water
- 1 teaspoon turmeric powder
- 1 teaspoon chilli powder
- 1 teaspoon ground coriander
- 2 tablespoons sunflower or groundnut oil
- 1 teaspoon cumin seeds
- 1 onion, finely chopped

- 1 heaped teaspoon finely grated fresh ginger root
- 1 green chilli, seeded and finely sliced
- 3 ripe tomatoes, skinned, seeded and chopped
- ½ teaspoon tomato purée
- sea salt for seasoning

FOR SERVING

- 3 cloves garlic, peeled and sliced across into thin chips
- 2 tablespoons sunflower or groundnut oil

- 2 tablespoons finely chopped fresh coriander
- Mixed Vegetable Curry for four (see page 248)

METHOD

In a saucepan over a medium heat, bring the lentils to the boil in three-quarters of the water. Stir in the turmeric, chilli and ground coriander. Cover and simmer for 15–20 minutes until just tender. You can test by removing a few lentils from the pan and biting into them or crushing them to make sure they are not hard. Heat the oil in another saucepan, over a medium to high heat, and fry the cumin seeds, onions, ginger and green chilli, stirring often, until the onion is golden but not browned. Stir in the chopped tomatoes and tomato purée then add the lentils and water. Bring back to the simmer, cover and cook for a further 20–25 minutes.

Meanwhile, prepare the garlic chip garnish. Fry the garlic slices in the oil until nutty brown on both sides. Take care because they burn quickly, so cook a few at a time and remove them to drain on kitchen paper as soon as they turn golden. Retain the oil. When the lentils are cooked, adjust the dhal to the consistency you like by mashing the lentils if you prefer a very mushy dhal, or adding extra water from that retained if desired. Season to taste with salt, pour the oil flavoured by frying the garlic onto the dhal and mix in. Pour into a warm serving dish and scatter the garlic slices over, then the chopped coriander if used. Serve with a variety of Mix With Any vegetable curries and, if your food rotation allows, naan bread, chapatties or boiled basmati rice.

VARIATIONS

- Yellow split lentils can be substituted for the red lentils. There may be a slight variation in the cooking time to produce the consistency of dhal you like.
- Also experiment by varying the amounts and types of spices used. Cooking dhal is not haute cuisine but home-style cooking, where you use what you have available to flavour the staple item. Try curry powder, mustard, tikka masala spice and so on.

# Casserole of Beans and Vegetables with Filled Dumplings (v)

A mixed Carbohydrate dish, perfect comfort food for a cold winter's night.

Food category – C
'1 in 5' – wheat (dumplings), beans (pulses)
Serves – 4

INGREDIENTS

- 1 large onion, sliced
- 1 oz/30 g unsalted butter
- 1 tablespoon olive oil
- 5 medium carrots, peeled and cut on the angle into ½ inch/1 cm slices
- 2 leeks, washed, trimmed and cut into ¾ inch/2 cm slices
- 2 sticks of celery, washed, trimmed and cut into ½ inch/1 cm slices
- ¼ butternut squash, flesh only, cut into 1 inch/2.5 cm dice (about 1 cup)
- 2 × 14 oz/440 g tins Italian plum tomatoes, drained, seeds and cores discarded and flesh roughly chopped (retain juice)
- 2 bay leaves, torn in half
- 1 teaspoon dried mixed provençal herbs
- ½ pint/300 ml white wine
- 1 pint/600 ml Basic Vegetable Stock (see page 48)
- 16 oz/500 g tin butter or cannelini beans, drained and washed
- sea salt and freshly ground black pepper, to taste

FILLING FOR THE DUMPLINGS

- 1 oz/30 g unsalted butter
- 1 small onion, very finely chopped
- 4 oz/125 g flat or chestnut mushrooms, very finely chopped
- sea salt and freshly ground black pepper, to taste

FOR THE DUMPLINGS

- 4 oz/125 g self-raising flour plus extra for working dough
- ¼ teaspoon fine sea salt
- 2 oz/60 g vegetarian suet
- 2 tablespoons finely chopped fresh parsley
- 4–6 tablespoons water
- freshly ground black pepper, to taste

FOR SERVING

- butter sautéed Savoy cabbage (see page 188)

METHOD

Pre-heat the oven to 190 C/375 F/Gas Mark 5. Heat the butter and olive oil in a large casserole dish on the hob, over a low heat, and sauté the onion until just soft and clear. Add the carrots, leeks, celery, squash and tomatoes, mix to combine well and cook for 2–3 minutes. Add the bay leaves and herbs, season well with salt and pepper and pour in the wine and enough vegetable stock to come halfway up the vegetables. Stir well, cover and place in the middle of the oven. Cook in the oven for 50–55 minutes, stirring two or three times, until the carrots are just cooked but reasonably firm. Meanwhile make the filling and the dumplings.

In a small saucepan, over a low heat, melt the butter and sauté the onion until just soft and clear. Add the mushrooms and a little salt and pepper seasoning, mix and continue to cook for about 30 minutes, stirring occasionally, until the mixture is soft and combined well with no excess water from the vegetables. Set aside to cool. Sift the flour and salt into a mixing bowl and use a fork to stir in the suet, parsley and some pepper seasoning. Add water a little at a time and work in with the fork to produce a soft dough. With floured hands, lift the dough onto a floured surface and – with the minimum of handling – roll into a sausage shape. You'll need a thin sausage for 13 small dumplings or a thick one for 9 larger dumplings. Divide the sausage of dough into 9 or 13 pieces, set one piece aside and roll the remaining 8 or 12 pieces into round balls. With your little finger make a hole into the centre of each dumpling, spoon some mushroom filling in, leaving enough room to plug the holes with small pieces broken from the retained piece of dough. You'll need to brush the holes with a little water before plugging them up, then reform the dumplings to make sure they are sealed.

When it is cooked, take the casserole from the oven, remove about a quarter of the vegetables (with plenty of carrots) and a little of the liquor and purée until smooth. Stir back into the casserole with the butter or cannelini beans and extra stock from that retained, if required. Arrange the dumplings on top of the vegetables and beans, and replace in the oven for 20–25 minutes until the dumplings are puffed up and cooked. Leave the dish uncovered if you want dumplings that are crisp on top, cover if you like your dumplings soft. Serve in warm bowls on a bed of sautéed Savoy cabbage, if desired.

TIP
☞ Even though this is a Carbohydrate dish and could be thickened with flour, potato starch or cornflour, I've suggested it be thickened by including extra vegetables (especially carrots), a portion of which can be puréed as I've described. For one thing it tastes good and for another it's the method of choice for thickening sauces with Proteins so it's a good habit to get into.

- The dumplings can be stuffed with a stiff purée of other Mix With Any Vegetables. Try filling half the dumplings with Buttered Purée of Spinach with Nutmeg (see page 225, lines 1–7) to add variety.

## STUFFING

Most home made stuffing mixtures usually combine breadcrumbs with eggs and commercial products mix bread with meat products or, at the very least, soya or nuts. None of these are much use to KD eaters, whether for stuffing poultry or meat joints or for vegetables. But a good stodgy bread and herb stuffing is so very tasty. So, when your food rotation allows, here's a good basic stuffing recipe to use with a Carbohydrate roast. Alternatively, mix it with grated vegetables and use for stuffing vegetables such as roast marrow or onions. See page 138 for more on stuffing vegetables.

# Herb Stuffing ⓥ

Food category – C
'1 in 5' – wheat (bread)
Serves – 4

INGREDIENTS

- 4 oz/125 g soft white bread, without crusts
- 1 small onion, diced
- 2 oz/60 g vegetarian suet, roughly chopped
- 1 cup finely chopped fresh parsley
- 1 tablespoon finely chopped fresh sage (or half a tablespoon dried)
- sea salt and freshly ground black pepper, to taste
- cold water

METHOD

Blend all the dry ingredients together in a food processor. Process, in brief pulses, adding a little cold water at a time, to produce a ball of soft dough. Lightly grease the inside of a shallow ovenproof dish and press the stuffing into it. Roughen up the top with a fork and leave to stand until ready to cook. Use as a stuffing as described or cook on its own by placing in a hot oven (200 C/400 F/ Gas Mark 6) for 25–30 minutes and finish under the grill to brown the top if required.

## OTHER CARBOHYDRATES

There are several Carbohydrates you can use to add variety and texture to your meals and to help you reduce your use of the more common starch foods.

**Millet** is a slightly chewy grain, like buckwheat when cooked, although rather more sticky in consistency. I find that cooked millet, frozen then thawed before use, becomes grainier. Use millet like rice or creamed polenta with Mix With Any foods such as Roasted Mediterranean Vegetables (page 233) and Tomato Sauce (page 271).

**Pearl barley** has traditionally been used to help fatten up the underweight. It has a pleasant chewy texture and is slightly glutinous when cooked so it can act as a thickener if added to vegetable stews and casseroles.

**Buckwheat** is often found as buckwheat pasta and pancakes in health food shops. Although not the same family of grain as regular wheat, it usually has regular wheat mixed with it in prepared products like pasta. That's a help if you are trying to reduce your wheat intake but not so good if you want to cut out regular wheat altogether, so check the labels. Use buckwheat pasta with any Mix With Any sauce or pasta dressings and the pancakes with fillings made from Mix With Any vegetables. Try canneloni made with buckwheat pancakes, filled with Shredded Vegetable Crudités (page 110), topped with White Sauce (pages 198–9), cooked in the oven and browned under the grill.

# MIX WITH ANY FOODS – MAINLY VEGETABLES

In this section you'll find recipes, ideas and advice about what to serve alongside your Protein or Carbohydrate foods, or even under and around them. As the name indicates, Mix With Any refers to those foods which can be combined satisfactorily with either of the two other main food categories. Here's a reminder of what fits into the Mix With Any category.

## 'MIX WITH ANY' FOODS

### Vegetables, Salads and Vegetable Juices

All vegetables and salads except the few which are listed as Carbohydrates elsewhere, are Mix With Any foods. All combine well with either Proteins or Carbohydrates.

### Oils and Fats

Butter, Cream, Dripping, Fish Oils, Fromage Frais, Nut Oils, Olive Oil, Suet, Vegetable Oils

If slimming is a concern, oils and fats should be used sparingly, especially when combining with carbohydrates. Oils and fats mix with *either* proteins *or* carbohydrates.

### Condiments and Flavourings

Condiments, Herbs, Spices, and Natural Flavourings

Including: chillies, garlic, pepper, salt, vinegars, pickles, soy sauce, mustard, natural essences and lemon juice. All condiments and flavourings can be combined with any other food if used sparingly. Fresh herbs can be used more generously.

In the alphabetical directory at the back of the book, Mix With Any foods are shown as M/A.

The Mix With Any vegetables are essential to Kensington Diet eating, and this part of the book deals mainly with how to use them successfully in your meals. Throughout this chapter, you'll find ideas for how to use them as accompaniments to Proteins or Carbohydrates in main course and light meal dishes, and as dishes in their own right.

A substantial fresh vegetable intake is essential to good health, and food combining The Kensington Diet way will make a high intake inevitable. Most Mix With Any vegetables are low calorie, low fat, high moisture and high soft fibre foods, so they're also helpful if you're concerned about weight management. But the Mix With Any vegetables can help you in many, less obvious, ways and their use in KD eating brings you further benefits you might not expect.

### VEGETABLE PREPARATION AND COOKING KD STYLE

A major key to succeeding with The Kensington Diet is to make your food more attractive, more enjoyable and easier to make, as well as better for you. In The Kensington Diet, Mix With Any vegetables are prepared and cooked for nutrition, flavour, colour and texture, and will also give you opportunities for fantastic presentation without major effort. Here's how.

For KD cooking, Mix With Any vegetables are often prepared in the shapes and style of different types of pasta. Not only do ribbons, batons or noodles sliced from colourful fresh vegetables look superb alongside either Proteins or Carbohydrates in a meal, but they are also quick to cook. In fact, the preparation methods that follow take longer to read than to do. For instance, if you have a mandolin vegetable slicer it will take less than 5 minutes to prepare Noodles for four; preparing rice simply takes one cut longer. Mix With Any vegetable ribbon and noodle 'pasta' are remarkably similar to regular pasta in that they soften during cooking and are best cooked *al dente*.

Another use for vegetable 'pasta' is as a way of reducing your calories. Bad food combining imposes two calorie penalties (as well as the health penalties it involves) by including two generally higher calorie foods, Carbohydrates *and* Proteins, in the same meals.The good combining of The Kensington Diet removes one calorie penalty by making sure Proteins and Carbohydrates are not eaten together. Replacing some of the traditional Carbohydrate pasta you would have in a meal with vegetable 'pasta', can reduce the calorie penalty even further. Simply replace a proportion of wheat or buckwheat spaghetti with Mix With Any vegetable 'noodles', or a proportion of wheat or corn tagliatelle with vegetable ribbon 'pasta', to give yourself attractive and healthy, lower calorie, higher fibre options.

Try Mix With Any vegetable 'pasta' with Proteins like Bolognese Sauce on Vegetable 'Spaghetti' (page 148) or Beef Stroganoff on ribbon 'pasta' (page 150). Vegetable Pasta with Basic Tomato Sauce (page 271) can be served with garlic bread or slices of grilled or fried polenta. The possibilities are almost endless . . . Another delightful thing about making vegetable 'pasta' is how a normal amount of vegetables becomes a huge pile of 'noodles' or 'pasta' ribbons when sliced up. You really do feel as if you're at a feast. Try to get the best and freshest vegetables for using in this way.

Your food processor and mandolin food slicer will obviously come into their own when preparing vegetable 'pasta', but please do be careful with the mandolin if you use one. Never take chances trying to get 'just one more' slice. Use plenty of vegetables to provide the amount of 'pasta' you need, be very conservative with each carrot or courgette or other vegetable, and stop slicing well before your fingers come anywhere near the blades. If you have a holder for the vegetables, use it wherever possible. Any pieces of vegetable that you can't slice on the mandolin can be kept for other dishes.

Mix With Any 'pasta' can be cooked in various ways and the recipes below suggest the best for each type. However, as a general point, when boiling or poaching vegetable 'pasta' I prefer to use vegetable stock and then retain it, fortified by the 'pasta' I've just cooked, for other dishes. However, if the 'pasta' is to be used in a Protein meal you could cook it in chicken or beef stock. Always add the vegetable 'pasta' to boiling stock or cooking water and stir occasionally for even cooking. Mix With Any 'pasta' can be cooked, or if necessary, rewarmed, in a microwave – check the instructions on your machine.

Carrot 'pasta' imparts colour to the stock or water it is poached or boiled in, so cook it in different water or stock to the other vegetables if you want to avoid colouring them, then mix together, if required, after cooking.

## RIBBON 'PASTA'

can be made from courgettes, from carrots and parsnips, from round root vegetables such as turnips, swedes, kohlrabi and celeriac and from leeks. Pick long courgettes for ribbon 'pasta'. For wide ribbons, trim and wash the courgettes and take shavings from the whole width of the vegetable with a swivel type potato peeler. After the first shaving, which will be all skin, take part white flesh and a little green skin with each shaving, working around the courgette, so as many ribbons as possible have both colours. Keep taking shavings until you reach the pulp, which can be discarded. For narrower ribbons, split the courgettes lengthways and scoop out the pulp from the centres with a small spoon. Make your ribbons by taking shavings from the edges of the scooped out halves of courgette.

Use long carrots and parsnips for ribbon 'pasta'. Just peel and trim as usual then, for wide ribbons, take long shavings from the length of the whole roots with a swivel type potato peeler. For thinner ribbons, cut the roots lengthways into slices the width of the ribbons you want and take shavings from the edges of the slices.

Round roots should be peeled and trimmed then cut, from top to bottom, into slices the thickness of the ribbons you want. Make your ribbons by taking shavings as long as you want, around the slices, with a swivel type potato peeler.

Make leeks into ribbon 'pasta' by trimming and washing as usual, then remove and retain for some other dish several of the tougher outer layers. Slice the remaining tender young parts of the leeks lengthways through the centre, into ribbons of the desired width.

Vegetable ribbon 'pasta' can be steamed, poached in a small amount of boiling stock or lightly salted water, microwaved in a little stock or water or sautéed in a little oil. Different ribbons cook at different rates, root vegetables taking the longest and courgettes being the quickest. None of them take longer than 6 minutes to cook regardless of the method of cooking. The results should be soft cooked ribbons of vegetables with a little crunch in them.

# Carrot, Courgette and Leek Ribbon 'Pasta' ⓥ

Food category – M/A

Serves – 4

INGREDIENTS

- 2 pints/1.2 litres Basic Vegetable Stock (see page 48)
- 4 medium courgettes, trimmed and shaved into ribbons
- 4 medium carrots, peeled, trimmed and shaved into ribbons
- 4 medium leeks, trimmed and sliced into ribbons

METHOD

Bring $\frac{1}{2}$ pint/300 ml of vegetable stock to the boil in a large saucepan or wok and add the carrot ribbons. Toss gently in the stock then cover and poach, stirring occasionally, for 4–5 minutes until just cooked but still with some crunch. Remove the carrot ribbons into a bowl, cover and keep warm without further cooking. Pour the cooking stock into a bowl and retain for future use. Bring $\frac{1}{2}$ pint/300 ml of fresh stock to the boil and add the leek ribbons, toss gently, cover and poach for 3–5 minutes until soft. Leeks can be quite fibrous so check they are sufficiently cooked. Remove the leek ribbons to the bowl with the carrots.

Make the stock in the wok up to $\frac{1}{2}$ pint/300 ml and bring to the boil as before. Add the courgette ribbons, toss gently, cover and poach for 2–3 minutes until just soft but still with some firmness. Remove the courgette ribbons to the warm serving bowl and when ready to serve, gently toss all the vegetable ribbons together, seasoning with freshly ground black pepper and any dressing or herbs you desire. Serve.

# Leek and Parsnip Ribbon 'Pasta' Sauté ⓥ

Leeks can be quite fibrous when cooked quickly so it's important you use the freshest and youngest leeks you can find. Even then, use the middle, more tender layers and retain the outer two or three layers for making stock.

Food category – M/A

Serves – 4

INGREDIENTS

- 3 tablespoons olive oil
- 6 medium parsnips, peeled, trimmed and shaved into ribbons
- 6 medium leeks, trimmed and sliced into ribbons

- sea salt and freshly ground black pepper, to taste

METHOD

Heat two tablespoons of oil in a wok or large frying pan, over a medium heat, and sauté the parsnip ribbons, mixing often, for 5–6 minutes, until soft and well coloured. Season with salt and pepper and set aside on kitchen paper to drain off excess oil. Add the remaining oil and, when hot, sauté the leek ribbons, mixing often, for 4–5 minutes, until soft and coloured. Replace the parsnips in the pan and cook for a further 1–2 minutes, adjust seasoning and serve.

VARIATION

- For a Protein meal, fry two tablespoons sesame seeds in the hot oil for 2–3 minutes before adding and cooking the parsnip ribbons.

### NOODLE 'PASTA'

can be prepared from a similar variety of vegetables to ribbon 'pasta'. Whichever vegetable is used, you're looking for long strips about the thickness of cooked spaghetti, or a large matchstick. Undoubtedly, a mandolin vegetable slicer makes things very much easier, but vegetable noodles can be prepared using a sharp knife. I've used a small, serrated Kitchen Devil knife quite successfully for this.

Trim and wash good sized courgettes and shred into long noodles using the smallest size of shredding blade on your mandolin, or slice the courgettes into thick matchstick thick slices with a sharp knife or mandolin, then, with a knife, cut each slice into long noodles. Take slices or noodles from all around the courgette and discard the pulp from the centre.

Pick long carrots and parsnips for noodles. Peel and trim as usual, then shred into long noodles on a mandolin with the smallest shredding blade or cut the carrots or parsnips into matchstick thick slices with the mandolin or a sharp knife. Cut the slices into long noodles with a knife. When using a mandolin for parsnips, take noodles or slices from around the core so any you have to discard will not be the best parts.

The best methods for cooking vegetable noodle 'pasta' are steaming or poaching in a small amount of boiling vegetable stock or lightly salted water, microwaving in a little stock or water, or sautéing in olive oil. Root vegetables take longer than courgettes to cook, but none of the noodles take longer than 8 minutes. The results should be soft, cooked noodles of vegetables with a little crunch in them. If poaching, cook carrot noodles in separate stock or water from other vegetables to avoid colouring them.

# Carrot and Courgette Noodle 'Pasta' ⓥ

Food category – M/A
Serves – 4

INGREDIENTS

- 2 pints/1.2 litres Basic Vegetable Stock (see page 48)
- 6 medium carrots, peeled, trimmed and shredded into noodles
- 6 medium courgettes, trimmed and shredded into noodles

METHOD

In a large saucepan or wok, bring to the boil 1 pint/600 ml of vegetable stock and add the carrot noodles, toss gently in the stock, then cover and poach, stirring occasionally, for 6–7 minutes until softened and just cooked but still with some crunch. Remove the carrot noodles into a bowl, cover and keep warm without further cooking. Pour the cooking stock into a small bowl and retain for future use.

Bring the remaining stock to the boil and add the courgette noodles, toss, gently cover them and poach for 3–4 minutes, until just soft but still with some firmness. Remove the courgette ribbons to the warm serving bowl with the carrots and, when ready to serve, gently toss the vegetable noodles together, seasoning with freshly ground black pepper and any dressing or herbs you desire. Serve.

VARIATION

- In a wok or large pan, sauté the carrot noodles for 2 minutes in two tablespoons of oil suitable to the finished dish, i.e. olive oil for western style vegetables or Protein main courses, groundnut oil for Oriental vegetables or Proteins, or sunflower oil for either. Add the courgette noodles and a further tablespoon of oil and cook, covered, for a further 4–5 minutes, stirring occasionally, until all the noodles are soft and just cooked but still a little firm.

## PENNE-STYLE 'PASTA'

is best made from round root vegetables such as turnip, celeriac, swede and kohlrabi, but large parsnips and carrots are also suitable. All you have to do is peel and trim the vegetables as usual, then shred them into long batons about $\frac{1}{4}$ inch/6 mm thick, with the appropriate sized shredding blade on your mandolin. With a knife cut the long batons on a slight diagonal, into equal sized lengths of about 1 inch/2.5 cms. Alternatively, with a sharp knife, cut the vegetables into $\frac{1}{4}$ inch/6 mm slices and the slices into equal sized short batons about 1 inch/2.5 cms long and $\frac{1}{4}$ inch/6 mm thick.

All penne 'pasta' made from root vegetables are best boiled in plenty of stock or lightly salted boiling water, or poached in a smaller amount of liquid. They will cook in about the same time, 8–10 minutes, so you can cook together a mixture of penne 'pasta' made from different roots, but because the flavour of some roots is very strong and can affect the others, I prefer to cook them separately and mix them for serving.

Serve your cooked penne-style 'pasta' tossed in butter or oil, seasoned with freshly ground black pepper, and sprinkled with chopped fresh herbs, or with other dressings, flavourings and accompaniments of your choice. Mixed penne 'pasta' makes an attractive vegetable dish to accompany many Protein or Carbohydrate main course dishes, or a light meal dish when served as suggested below.

# Mixed Root Penne-Style 'Pasta' with Herbs Ⓥ

Food category – M/A
Serves – 4

INGREDIENTS

- 1 heaped cup carrot penne 'pasta'
- 1 heaped cup celeriac penne 'pasta'
- 1 heaped cup kohlrabi penne 'pasta'
- 1 heaped cup swede penne 'pasta'
- 2 pints/1.2 litres Basic Vegetable Stock (see page 48)

- 1 oz/30 g unsalted butter
- 2 tablespoons finely chopped fresh thyme
- sea salt and freshly ground black pepper, to taste

METHOD

Poach the carrot penne 'pasta' in $\frac{1}{2}$ pint/300 ml of vegetable stock, brought to boiling in a large saucepan. Stir occasionally, for 8–10 minutes, until just cooked but still firm. Transfer to a warm dish and keep warm without further cooking. Remove the stock from the pan and retain it. Poach the celeriac in a fresh ½ pint/300 ml of stock for 8–10 minutes until similarly cooked and remove to the warm dish with the carrots. Add the stock to that from the carrots. Cook the kohlrabi and swede penne 'pasta' together in the remaining vegetable stock, for 8–10 minutes until cooked but still slightly firm.

Mix the cooked vegetable 'penne' together with the butter and herbs to coat evenly. Serve on a bed of Tomato Sauce (see page 271) sprinkled with golden toasted pine kernels for a Protein meal, or golden wheat or corn croutons for a Carbohydrate meal – if your food rotation allows.

# Aubergine 'Noodles' ⓥ

Aubergines are very oil-thirsty. Brushing them with oil for cooking enables you to control the amount you use.

Food category – M/A
Serves – 4

INGREDIENTS
- 2 large aubergines, washed and trimmed
- olive oil, for brushing
- 1 teaspoon cumin powder
- sea salt and freshly ground black pepper, to taste

METHOD
Pre-heat the oven to 200 C/400 F/Gas Mark 6 and lightly oil a shallow baking sheet. Remove ½ inch/1 cm slices from all round the aubergines, trim off the ends and discard the stalk. Retain the block of aubergine to make Aubergine Purée (see page 145). Brush the aubergine slices on both sides with oil and cut the slices into ½ inch/1 cm 'noodles'. Brush the newly cut edges of the 'noodles' with oil so that they are lightly coated on all sides.

In a large bowl, sprinkle the aubergine 'noodles' with the cumin powder and salt and pepper seasoning and toss lightly with your fingers to ensure even seasoning. Spread the aubergine 'noodles' on the baking sheet and cook in the top of the oven, turning several times, for 25–30 minutes until soft and well coloured. Serve as desired.

VARIATIONS
- Grill under a hot grill until well coloured and soft.
- Mix with two tablespoons Peanut Satay (C) (page 193) or

Cashew Satay (P) (page 168), whichever is appropriate to your meal, thread onto pre-soaked wooden or bamboo skewers, and grill or roast on a wire mesh, as above, for aubergine satay.

### MIX WITH ANY VEGETABLE 'RICE'

This is simplicity itself and is really a variation of the Mix With Any noodle 'pasta' method, above. All you have to do is take the long noodles cut with your mandolin or knife, and chop them into $\frac{1}{4}$ inch/6 mm 'grains' to make the 'rice'. I use a Chinese cooking cleaver for this. Taking care to keep the long noodles together in bundles when you 'noodle' the vegetables, will make it very easy to chop them into 'grains'.

The 'rice' can be mixed together as soon as it is chopped because any difference in cooking time between the different vegetables is negligible. Vegetable 'rice' is best made from long vegetables such as carrots, parsnips and courgettes. It can be steamed in 6–7 minutes, poached in a little stock in 5–6 minutes or stir fried in oil in 5–6 minutes. When ready the vegetable 'rice' should be cooked but reasonably firm and certainly not mushy.

Use vegetable 'rice' in similar ways to regular rice except you can also happily combine it with Proteins.

# Carrot and Courgette Boiled Vegetable 'Rice' (v)

This is particularly good with Chinese or Indian meat, fish or poultry dishes cooked in sauces. Or mix with regular rice to reduce your Carbohydrate intake as well as to enhance the presentation of a meal.

Food category – M/A
Serves – 4

INGREDIENTS

- 2 pints/1.2 litres Basic Vegetable Stock (see page 48) or lightly salted water
- 6 medium carrots, peeled, trimmed, noodled and chopped into vegetable 'rice'

- 6 medium courgettes, trimmed, noodled and chopped into vegetable 'rice'
- sea salt and freshly ground black pepper, to taste

METHOD

Bring the stock to a fast boil in a large saucepan, add the vegetable 'rice', bring back to the simmer for 5–6 minutes until the 'rice' is cooked but still firm. Drain, season and serve as desired.

# Carrot and Courgette Fried 'Rice' ⓥ

I include some variations suitable for light meals.

Food category – M/A
Serves – 4

INGREDIENTS

- 3 tablespoons groundnut or sunflower oil
- 1 clove garlic, finely sliced
- 1 tablespoon finely grated fresh ginger root
- 1 green pepper, cored, seeded and finely sliced
- 4 medium carrots, peeled, trimmed, noodled and chopped into vegetable 'rice'
- 4 medium courgettes, trimmed, noodled and chopped into vegetable 'rice'

- 2 cups fresh bean sprouts, blanched under boiling water and drained
- 12 oz/350 g frozen petit pois
- 2 tablespoons spring onion, cleaned, trimmed and finely sliced
- soy sauce, for seasoning
- sesame oil, for seasoning
- sea salt and freshly ground black pepper, to taste

METHOD

Heat the oil in a wok or large pan over a high heat. Add the garlic, ginger and green pepper and cook for 1–2 minutes, stirring continuously. Add the vegetable 'rice' and stir fry, stirring constantly for 2–3 minutes. Add the bean sprouts and peas and continue to stir fry for another 2–3 minutes, until all the vegetables are cooked. Season with soy sauce, salt and pepper and cook for 2 minutes. Add 10–12 drops of sesame oil, stir once to disperse and serve immediately in warm bowls.

PROTEIN VARIATIONS

The following *Proteins* can be pre-cooked prior to stir frying the 'rice', then added with the seasoning:

- Uncooked prawns, chopped small if necessary, then stir fried in sunflower or groundnut oil with prepared chilli sauce.
- Uncooked chicken can be diced small, then stir fried in sunflower or groundnut oil with sesame seeds and soy sauce.
- Pork fillet diced small, then stir fried in sunflower or groundnut oil with prepared hoi sin sauce.

- Bacon diced small into lardons (small dices), then stir fried in its own fat with thinly sliced green chilli.
- Eggs made into a thin, plain omelette, then shredded into thin slices.
- Raw cashews toasted under a hot grill until golden brown.

CARBOHYDRATE VARIATIONS

The following *Carbohydrates* can be pre-cooked prior to stir frying the 'rice', then added with the seasoning:

- Fresh or frozen sweetcorn kernels boiled in lightly salted water until cooked, then drained ready for use.
- Raw peanuts blanched in plenty of boiling water for 2 minutes. Drain, cool and rub off the skins. Stir fry for 2–3 minutes in sunflower or groundnut oil with finely chopped red chilli.

### JULIENNE MIX WITH ANY VEGETABLES

Mix With Any vegetables cut into thin matchstick strips – classically named julienne – provide attractive presentation options and are quick to cook. Add julienne vegetables to casseroles and salads or sprinkle them in a sauce at the last minute to add texture. Serve cooked julienne as a bed for fish, chicken or meat, or toss cooked julienne in butter and herbs as a side dish to make an attractive addition to any meal.

Julienne (yes, it's a verb too!) root vegetables and courgettes by shredding short, 1–1½ inches/2.5–3.5 cm, pieces of vegetable with the fine shredding attachment of a mandolin or food processor. Alternatively, with a sharp knife, take matchstick thick slices from vegetables prepared in the usual way and cut into pieces 1–1½ inches/2.5–3.5 cm long, then cut the slices into matchstick sized batons.

If poaching or boiling a variety of different vegetable julienne, cook the different varieties separately: add each to a small amount of boiling stock or lightly salted water, stir occasionally for 6–7 minutes, then mix together after cooking. If steaming, different vegetables can be mixed together before steaming for 8–9 minutes. Different julienne vegetables can be mixed and sautéed together in a little oil. When ready, the julienne vegetables should be cooked through but still with some firmness to the bite and certainly not mushy.

### GRATED MIX WITH ANY VEGETABLES

An alternative to Julienne is to grate the vegetables, which are then very quick to cook. Just prepare your vegetables in the usual way, if necessary cut them into pieces the length of the shavings you require, and grate the pieces on a regular hand grater or with the grating attachment on a food processor. Grated vegetables can be ready after poaching in simmering stock or lightly salted water for 2–3 minutes.

Use grated vegetables in similar ways to Julienne and also as the basis for stuffings. Mix a combination of grated and pre-cooked Mix With Any vegetables, with nuts or offal for stuffing Mix With Any vegetables, fish, meat or poultry – as in the roast chicken recipe on page 165 – and use eggs to bind the mixture if desired. For a stuffing to accompany Carbohydrates such as roast potatoes, mix the cooked grated vegetables with breadcrumbs or grated potato. Season with your preferred herbs or spices and roast in a dish or use for stuffing Mix With Any vegetables.

## Side Salad of Grated Mix With Any Vegetables (v)
Food category – M/A
Serves – 4

INGREDIENTS
- 1 onion, very finely chopped
- 4 carrots, trimmed, peeled and finely grated
- 1 large celeriac, trimmed, peeled and finely grated
- 4 courgettes, trimmed and finely grated
- 1 tablespoon finely chopped fresh chives
- 1 serving Mustard Mayonnaise (see page 278) or Basic Vinaigrette (page 73)

- 1 serving green salad (see page 247)
- 2 medium tomatoes, seeded and finely chopped
- juice of 1 lemon
- best olive oil for sprinkling
- sea salt and freshly ground black pepper, to taste

TASTE SENSATION
Tabasco sauce

You'll require a mould for the presentation of this salad. A 3 inches/8 cm diameter ring mould or round pastry cutter about 1inch/ 2.5 cm deep is best, but a cup or individual ramekin will work for a slightly different look.

METHOD

In a large bowl mix the onion with the grated vegetables, chives and just enough of the mayonnaise or vinaigrette to bind the mixture together and enable it to retain a shape. You don't want it too wet or it won't hold when moulded. Season to taste with salt and pepper. To one side of each of four large plates, place a ring mould, fill and press in enough dressed grated vegetables to fill completely when pressed firmly but gently into the moulds with the back of a small spoon. Remove the moulds to leave the salad. Alternatively, fill a small cup or ramekin and turn out onto the plates. Top the moulded vegetable salads with chopped tomatoes. Arrange green salad around the moulded vegetables. Sprinkle the green salad and tomatoes with lemon juice, olive oil and seasoning and sprinkle a few drops of Tabasco onto the top of the tomatoes. Serve.

VARIATIONS

- Try adding finely sliced celery and diced tomato to the moulded salad for extra flavour and texture.
- If your food rotation allows, try adding toasted sesame seeds or chopped nuts for a Protein salad.
- If your food rotation allows, try adding cooked sweetcorn kernels for a Carbohydrate salad.

## MASHED AND PURÉED MIX WITH ANY VEGETABLES

Mashed and puréed vegetables add interesting colours and flavours to meals with either Proteins or Carbohydrates, but they also add a pleasant selection of moist and soft textures. This is particularly useful in balancing meats and poultry and often reduces the need for special sauces. A delicious creamy purée is frequently all that's needed.

Mashes are coarser in texture than purées, being simply crushed so some of the vegetables are left in pieces. Make mashes with a hand held potato masher; force well mashed vegetables through a fine metal sieve with a wooden spoon to make a purée, although the easiest way to make purées is with a food processor. Sieving after processing will ensure a really fine, smooth purée. A good purée should be smooth and even, with a consistency that can be served in scoops like soft ice cream. Adjust the consistency of mashes and purées that are too wet by gently heating the vegetables over a low heat in their cooking pan, while mixing with a wooden spoon. You can always add water or stock to moisten if necessary.

Butter, cream and milk can also be added to the vegetables when they are mashed or puréed. They add flavour and help produce a good consistency, but don't forget milk is a Protein, and should only be used for vegetables which are intended for a Protein meal.

Root vegetables make good mashes and purées, and can be combined together to make many different flavours and colours, but other Mix With Any vegetables can also be used. Try peas or spinach, for example. When cooking vegetables for purées, make sure they are well cooked and soft, so they will break up quickly and easily when processed. You can always rewarm mashes and purées in a microwave before serving.

# Buttered Parsnip Mash ⓥ
Food category – M/A
Serves – 4

INGREDIENTS
• 4 large parsnips, peeled and          • unsalted butter
  chopped into large dice               • sea salt and ground white pepper

METHOD
Boil the parsnips in lightly salted water until soft and well cooked. Drain and crush to a coarse mash with a fork or potato masher. Mix in enough butter to produce a satisfactory texture and season to taste. Serve as required.

# Purée of Swede ⓥ
Food category – M/A
Serves – 4

INGREDIENTS
• 1 large swede, peeled and chopped     • unsalted butter for mixing
  into large dice                       • sea salt and ground white pepper

METHOD
Boil the swede in lightly salted water until soft and well cooked. Process to a smooth consistency and, if a very fine purée is desired, force through a fine sieve with a wooden spoon. Mix in enough butter to produce a firm purée then season to taste. Adjust the consistency, if too wet, by warming gently in the cooking pan over a low heat, beating constantly, until a firm purée is produced. Serve.

# Carrot Purée ⓥ

Food category – M/A
Serves – 4

INGREDIENTS

- 6 large carrots, peeled and
  chopped into large dice
- 1–2 tablespoons crème fraîche

- 2 tablespoons finely chopped fresh
  coriander or parsley
- sea salt and ground white pepper

METHOD

Boil the carrots in lightly salted water or vegetable stock until soft and
well cooked. Drain and process with enough crème fraîche to produce a
smooth purée. If a very fine purée is desired, force through a fine metal
sieve with a wooden spoon. Mix in seasoning to taste. If the consistency
is too wet, adjust to a firmer purée by warming in the cooking pan, over
a low heat, beating continuously to remove excess water. Serve
sprinkled with chopped herbs.

# Carrot and Parsnip Purée with Garlic ⓥ

Food category – M/A
Serves – 4

INGREDIENTS

- 4 large carrots, peeled and
  chopped into large dice
- 2 large parsnips, peeled and
  chopped into large dice

- 2 cloves garlic, peeled and halved
- 1–2 tablespoons crème fraîche
- sea salt and ground white pepper

METHOD

Boil the carrots in plenty of lightly salted water or vegetable stock for 5
minutes, add the parsnips and continue to cook until all the vegetables
are soft. Drain the boiling liquid from the vegetables onto the garlic
cloves and set aside to blanch for 5 minutes. Process the vegetables and
garlic with sufficient crème fraîche to make a smooth purée. If a very
fine purée is desired, force through a fine metal sieve with a wooden
spoon. Mix in seasoning to taste. If the consistency is too wet, adjust to a
firmer purée by warming in the cooking pan, over a low heat, beating
continuously to remove excess water. Serve as required.

# Purée of Brussels Sprouts ⓥ

Food category – M/A

Serves – 4

INGREDIENTS

- 1 small onion, very finely chopped
- 2–3 oz/60–90 g unsalted butter
- 1½ lbs/750 g Brussels sprouts, trimmed and peeled
- sea salt and ground white pepper

METHOD

In a medium sized saucepan, sauté the onions in a small amount of the butter until soft. Add to the sauté enough lightly salted water for cooking the sprouts. Boil the sprouts in the water until soft and well cooked. Drain and process, with sufficient butter to make a smooth purée. Season to taste. If the consistency is too wet, adjust to a firmer purée by warming in the cooking pan, over a low heat, stirring continuously and gently, to remove excess water. Serve as required.

### PRESENTATION IDEAS

The attractive, often vivid colours of puréed and finely chopped Mix With Any vegetables, lend themselves to spectacular presentations. With little effort you can enliven light meals or give a special touch to main course dishes. Be creative with contrasting and complementary colours so the vegetables look good together and the combination of colours enhances the main item of the meal, and don't forget how they will taste together, too. Purées need to be fairly firm for this style of presentation.

# Layered Spinach and Carrots ⓥ

Cooking spinach and carrots this way takes about 8–10 minutes, although they can be kept warm for a few minutes until you're ready to arrange them on the plate. This combination of vegetables goes well with the light meat of chicken breast stuffed with goat's cheese and sage.

Food category – M/A

Serves – 4

INGREDIENTS

- 1lb/500 g fresh whole leaf spinach, washed and coarse stalks removed (or frozen leaf spinach, thawed)
- ¼ teaspoon nutmeg, optional
- 1 oz/30 g unsalted butter

- ½ pint/300 ml Basic Vegetable Stock (or chicken stock for Protein meals) (see pages 48–50)
- 8 medium carrots, grated
- sea salt and freshly ground black pepper, to taste

TASTE SENSATION

1 medium onion, finely sliced, for garnish, optional

1 tablespoon olive oil, for shallow frying

For this recipe you'll need at least one 3–4 inch/8–10 cm ring mould or pastry cutter about 1½ inches/3.5 cms deep – four would make things easier.

METHOD

Place the spinach in a large saucepan over a low heat with the nutmeg, turning it over once or twice during cooking, until it softens and is just cooked through. Purée with the butter in a food processor or chop roughly with a sharp knife and mix with the butter. Leave over the warm saucepan in a fine sieve to allow excess liquid to drain. When ready to prepare the presentation, discard any drained juices and warm the spinach over a low heat in the pan for 1–2 minutes. Bring the stock to a simmer in a saucepan and add the grated carrot. Poach for 2–3 minutes until just soft, drain well, season with freshly ground black pepper and replace in the saucepan to keep warm until ready to use. Fry the onion rings in the oil over a high heat until golden brown and crisp. Layer the spinach and carrots in the mould on the plate. Gently press into place a layer of spinach in the bottom of the mould; don't press hard but it needs to be firm enough to take the shape. Add a layer of grated carrots and press down, then add another layer of spinach and press down again. Remove the mould to leave the vegetables shaped and in approximately ½ inch/1 cm layers. Garnish with crisp fried sliced onions and serve.

VARIATIONS

- Layer puréed carrots and parsnips with sautéed julienne of courgette.
- A creamy celeriac purée can be made the same way as the carrot purée on page 223. Layer with mixed, grated vegetables which have been sautéed in butter.

## STEAMING MIX WITH ANY VEGETABLES

over plain water or stock made with aromatic herbs is one of the healthiest ways to cook. There's no fat involved and less loss of nutrients than with most other cooking methods. The resulting flavour, too, is superb.

Fan type vegetable steamers are the most common in use and they're readily available from cookware and health food shops. They are quite cheap and adjust to fit in the bottom of various sizes of saucepan. Place yours over about 1 inch/2.5 cm of water or stock in the pan, so the simmering liquid will not come over the base of the steamer and touch the vegetables it contains. There are special steamers like saucepans made to stack on top of other pans. They hold more, but I find the vegetables in them take longer to cook. Stackable bamboo steamers from Chinese supermarkets and cookware shops are very effective over boiling water in a saucepan or wok.

You can steam several different vegetables together if you add them to the steamer in sequence so they finish cooking at the same time. For instance, soft or 'open' vegetables like courgette and cauliflower take less time to steam than firm vegetables like roots and beans. In general, though, the steaming time for each vegetable is just a little longer than for boiling.

It's a good idea to experiment with your steamer to get an idea of how long different vegetables take and what sizes they must be prepared to for the result you want, but it's worth the effort to find out. The recipe below will give you a good idea of what to do.

# Medley of Seasonal Steamed Vegetables ⓥ

The method is written for a fan steamer in a saucepan. You may need to alter the times for other steamers.

Food category – M/A
Serves – 4

INGREDIENTS

- 4 medium carrots, trimmed, peeled and cut into ½ inch/1 cm dice
- 6 oz/175 g fine green or Kenya beans, washed, trimmed in 2 inch lengths
- ½ cauliflower in 1 inch/2.5 cm florettes
- 2 medium leeks, cleaned, trimmed and cut into ¾ inch/2 cm slices
- 2 medium courgettes, cleaned, trimmed and cut into ¾ inch/2 cm slices

- 6 oz/175 g mange tout, whole, washed and trimmed
- 1 oz/30 g unsalted butter, optional
- sea salt and freshly ground black pepper, to taste
- 2 tablespoons finely chopped fresh parsley or chives, for garnish

METHOD

Prepare the steamer by bringing about 1 inch/2.5 cm of water in the saucepan to a good fast simmer, about 25 minutes before you'll need the vegetables ready to serve. Put the carrots and green beans in the steamer and lower it into the saucepan. Cover and cook for 10 minutes. Add the cauliflower florettes, cover and cook for 4 minutes. Add the leeks, cover and cook for 2 minutes. Add the courgettes and cook for 2 minutes. Add the mange tout and finish cooking for a further 4 minutes.

Lift the steamer from the pan – push a fork through the lifting loop. Retain the steaming liquor for stock. The steamed vegetables can be kept warm (not hot or they will continue to cook and go soft) in a covered dish for a few minutes until you are ready to serve, but they should not be kept too long. Serve topped with knobs of butter, if used, lightly season with salt and pepper, and add a good sprinkling of chopped fresh parsley or chives.

## STIR FRYING

is another quick and healthy way to cook Mix With Any vegetables as an accompaniment or the basis for a light meal. Stir fried vegetables should be hot and crunchy but definitely not raw.

Although a large heavy based frying pan will do, stir frying is best done in a fairly heavy wok which is correctly shaped to enable you to constantly stir and mix the vegetables over a very high heat. This ensures the vegetables cook quickly as they repeatedly touch the surfaces of the hot wok. I use quite heavy, plain metal woks from a Chinese supermarket, a smaller one with a long wooden handle for modest amounts of vegetables and a large one with two side handles for bigger meals. Both woks have flat bases which makes them more stable than the round based type and I mix the vegetables with two spoons, one in each hand. It's fun and the results are great.

Ideally, a mixed vegetable stir fry should take only 5–7 minutes to cook, and some vegetables are ready even sooner, so it is important to have all the ingredients prepared in advance. Clean and trim all the vegetables and cut them into a variety of shapes. To create texture in the stir fry try chunks, dices, matchsticks, flakes and ribbons, for example. Cut the ingredients small enough to cook rapidly and not to become soft and limp. For example cut root vegetables the same thickness as mange tout, slice celery, leeks and onions a little thicker but similar to each other, and in general prepare all vegetables so they will cook together at a given time. Florettes of cauliflower and broccoli should not be large and can be sliced in half if they are – be guided by the thickness of the stalk to give you an idea of how long they will take to cook.

Start by heating the wok or frying pan over a high heat so it becomes hot, then add the oil which will become hazy straight away, immediately add the hard vegetables, such as carrots and stir. Add the softer vegetables in stages and keep stirring.

# Stir Fry of a Variety of Mix With Any Vegetables (v)

Food category – M/A
Serves – 4

INGREDIENTS

- groundnut or sunflower oil for stir frying
- 1 teaspoon finely chopped fresh ginger root
- 4 medium carrots, sliced diagonally into narrow strips
- 6 oz/175 g mange tout, trimmed and large ones halved diagonally
- 4 medium sticks celery, trimmed and in ¼ inch/6 mm diagonal slice

- 2 medium leeks, cut into ½ inch/1 cm rounds
- 4 medium courgettes, split lengthways and cut into ¼ inch/6 mm crescents
- toasted sesame oil, optional
- 2 cups bean sprouts
- 1 small clove garlic, finely sliced, optional
- 2 finely chopped spring onions
- 1–2 tablespoons Tamari (non-wheat) soy sauce

- 1 teaspoon clear honey or good pinch sugar, optional
- sea salt and freshly ground black pepper, to taste

- 2 tablespoons Basic Vegetable Stock (see page 48), optional

METHOD

Heat a wok or large saucepan over very high heat; add 2 tablespoons of oil, immediately add the chopped ginger and stir fry for 1 minute. Add the carrots and mange tout, stir for 1 minute then add the celery, leeks, courgettes and 10–12 drops sesame oil, if used. Continue the stir fry for approximately 4 minutes. Pour a kettle of boiling water over the bean sprouts in a sieve and drain well.

Push the vegetables in the wok aside and add the garlic and spring onions to the bottom of the wok and cook for 1 minute. Add the bean sprouts, a good seasoning of soy sauce and the honey if used. Stir all the vegetables together still over a high heat, and cook for 1 minute then adjust to taste with salt and freshly ground black pepper. Serve immediately into warm bowls.

TIPS

☞ For vegetables that are served with some liquor, add 1–2 tablespoons vegetable stock near the end of cooking, cover and cook for 1 minute and you have a little broth to serve as well, although the vegetables may lose some colour.

☞ For a drier stir fry add a little extra oil at the start of cooking and add the soy sauce earlier in the cooking to reduce while stirring.

VARIATIONS

Food category – P
The following Proteins can be pre-cooked prior to stir frying the vegetables, then added with the seasoning to warm through before serving:

- Uncooked prawns, stir fried in sunflower or groundnut oil along with chopped red chillis (or simply add whole cooked and peeled prawns to the stir fry).
- Uncooked chicken, thinly sliced and tossed in Chinese five spice powder, then stir fried in sunflower or groundnut oil along with sesame seeds and soy sauce.
- Pork fillet thinly sliced then stir fried in sunflower or groundnut oil and served with prepared hoi sin sauce.

- Eggs made into a plain omelette then shredded into thin slices.
- Raw cashews stir fried in groundnut or sunflower oil until golden brown.

Food category – C

The following Carbohydrates can be pre-cooked prior to stir frying the vegetables, then added with the seasoning to warm through before serving:

- Fresh or frozen sweetcorn kernels boiled until cooked in lightly salted water, then drained.
- Raw peanuts, blanched in plenty of boiling water for 2 minutes. Drain, cool and rub off the skins. Stir fry for 2–3 minutes in sunflower or groundnut oil along with finely chopped red chilli.
- Rice (non-egg) vermicelli noodles, soaked in boiling water for 2 minutes then drained.

# Stir Fry of Mix With Any Vegetables Thai-Style ⓥ

Food category – M/A

Serves – 4

INGREDIENTS

- 2 tablespoons groundnut or sunflower oil
- 1 teaspoon finely chopped fresh ginger root
- 2 small cloves garlic, thinly sliced
- 1 small green chilli pepper, seeded and finely sliced
- 4 medium carrots, peeled, halved lengthways and cut diagonally into thin crescent slices
- 6 oz/175 g mange tout, trimmed and large ones halved diagonally
- 1 stick lemon grass, outer leaves removed, trimmed, cut in fine slices
- 4 medium sticks celery, trimmed and cut in ¼ inch/6 mm diagonal slices
- 1 green pepper, cored, seeded and finely sliced
- 1 red pepper, cored, seeded and sliced into ½ inch/1 cm dice
- toasted sesame oil, to taste
- 2 cups bean sprouts
- 4 oz/125 g shiitake mushrooms, trimmed, wiped clean, thinly sliced
- 1–2 tablespoons Tamari (non-wheat) soy sauce, to taste
- 1 tablespoon lime juice

- 1 good pinch soft brown sugar or 1 teaspoon clear honey, optional
- 2 tablespoons finely grated fresh coconut (or desiccated coconut)
- 2 tablespoons finely chopped fresh coriander
- zest of half a lime, for garnish
- sea salt and freshly ground black pepper, to taste
- 2 tablespoons coconut milk, optional
- 2 tablespoons Basic Vegetable Stock (see page 48), optional

METHOD

Heat a wok or large saucepan over very high heat; add 2 tablespoons of oil and immediately add the chopped ginger, garlic and green chilli. Stir fry for 1 minute, then add the carrots, mange tout and lemon grass. Stir for 1 minute then add the celery, the green and red peppers and 10–12 drops sesame oil. Continue the stir fry for approximately 4–5 minutes.

Pour a kettle of boiling water over the bean sprouts in a sieve and drain well. Add the bean sprouts and mushrooms to the wok and cook for 1 minute. Add 1–2 tablespoons soy sauce, the lime juice, sugar and coconut. Stir everything together over the high heat, and cook for 1 minute longer, then adjust to taste with salt and freshly ground black pepper. Remove from the heat, mix in the chopped coriander and lime zest and serve immediately into warm bowls.

TIPS

☞ For vegetables that are served with some liquor, add 1–2 tablespoons coconut milk or vegetable stock near the end of cooking, cover and cook for 1 minute and you have a little broth to serve as well, although the vegetables may lose some colour.

☞ For a drier stir fry add a little extra oil at the start of cooking and add the soy sauce and lime juice earlier in cooking to reduce the liquid while stirring.

VARIATIONS

Food category – P
The following Proteins can be pre-cooked prior to stir frying the vegetables, then added with the seasoning to warm through before serving:

- Uncooked prawns, stir fried in sunflower or groundnut oil along with chopped green chillis (or simply add whole cooked and peeled prawns to the stir fry).
- Uncooked chicken, thinly sliced and tossed in Chinese five spice

powder, then stir fried in sunflower or groundnut oil and served
with grated coconut.

- Pork fillet thinly sliced and stir fried in sunflower or groundnut oil
  and served with sesame oil and Tamari soy sauce.

Food category – C

The following Carbohydrates can be pre-cooked prior to stir frying the
vegetables then added with the seasoning to warm through before
serving:

- Raw peanuts, blanched in plenty of boiling water for 2 minutes.
  Drain, cool and rub off the skins. Stir fry for 2–3 minutes in
  sunflower or groundnut oil along with finely chopped green chilli.
- Rice (non-egg) vermicelli noodles, soaked in boiling water for 2
  minutes then drained.

# Stir Fried Spinach and Bean Sprouts ⓥ

You can stir fry just a few vegetables together, in a flash, to produce
wonderful light meals or accompaniments. This preparation of spinach,
cooked until it's just wilted, goes well with the Hot and Sour Fish on
page 162, or the Chinese spiced variation of Quick Roast Loin of Pork
in *The Kensington Diet* (pages 245–7).

Food category – M/A
Serves – 4

INGREDIENTS

- 2 tablespoons groundnut or
  sunflower oil
- 2 cloves garlic, finely sliced
- 3 cups bean sprouts, blanched in a
  sieve under a kettle full of boiling
  water

- Tamari (non-wheat) soy sauce
- 1½ lbs/750 g fresh young spinach
  leaves, washed and trimmed
- toasted sesame oil
- sea salt and black pepper, to taste

METHOD

Toss the bean sprouts into a sieve and blanch by pouring a kettle of
boiling water over. Drain while you heat a wok or large saucepan over
very high heat; add the oil. Add the sliced garlic immediately, give it 2
rapid stirs then quickly add the bean sprouts. Dress with 2 or 3 good
shakes of soy sauce and stir fry for 1 minute. Add the spinach and stir
fry for 30–45 seconds, until the spinach just softens but does not have

time to release its water into the wok. Remove from the heat, sprinkle with a few drops of sesame oil and season to taste with salt and pepper. Serve immediately.

# Roasted Mediterranean Vegetables ⓥ

I love roasted vegetables, they look, smell and taste so good. I have to confess to being occasionally disappointed by some of the results I've been subjected to, though. Vegetables can sweat and become soggy, rather than roasted soft with crispy edges. They ought to be so easy, yet if they are packed too tightly together in the wrong sort of roasting tin at the wrong temperature, the result is a mushy disappointment. So I've come up with this foolproof method (albeit under the influence of two cups of strong coffee after four days of abstinence from caffeine). These vegetables are so good, serve in any way you can think of.

Food category – M/A
Serves – 4

INGREDIENTS

- olive oil for roasting and frying
- 2 large red peppers, quartered lengthways, seeded and cored
- 1 large yellow pepper, quartered lengthways, seeded and cored
- 1 large courgette, trimmed, quartered lengthways and cut to 2 inch/5 cm lengths to make long wedges
- 1 medium aubergine, trimmed, halved crossways and the halves cut lengthways into 4–6 long wedges (2 inches/5 cm × 1 inch/ 2.5 cm)
- 2 medium mild onions (red or Spanish), peeled, trimmed and cut into 4 × ¾ inch/2.5 mm slices
- 1 small bunch fresh rosemary, broken into pieces
- 2 tablespoons fresh oregano leaves, stripped from stems (or two teaspoons dried)
- 8 medium stalks asparagus
- 2 firm heads little gem lettuce, split in half lengthways
- 2 firm heads chicory, split in half lengthways
- 8 firm, ripe plum tomatoes, halved lengthways and seeded
- 16 black olives
- 2 tablespoons finely chopped fresh marjoram (or two teaspoons dried)
- sea salt and freshly ground black pepper, to taste

TASTE SENSATION

balsamic vinegar for seasoning

You'll need a ridged griddle pan and two lightly oiled baking sheets or shallow baking trays for this recipe. To avoid washing up, I usually line the baking sheets with foil and lightly oil the foil.

METHOD

Pre-heat the oven to 225 C/440 F/Gas Mark 7. Heat the ridged griddle pan over a high heat and, when hot, coat with a little oil. In batches, fry the peppers, courgettes, aubergines and onions in the pan for about 30–60 seconds each side so they become lightly coated with oil and scorched with ridges. Transfer to the baking sheets when ready. You may have to oil the pan a couple of times during this process. Arrange the vegetables on the baking sheets so they are not too crowded and are skin sides up. Sprinkle with the rosemary and oregano and drizzle with a little more olive oil. Cook in the top half of the oven for 10 minutes only. Turn the vegetables skin sides down, swap the positions of the baking sheets over, and roast for a further 15 minutes by which time the vegetables will be soft and slightly charred at the edges. Remove to a warm dish and cover with foil to keep warm without further cooking. Meanwhile, pan griddle the asparagus, little gem halves and chicory halves as you did the other vegetables.

On one of the empty baking sheets, arrange, cut sides down, the tomatoes and the little gem and chicory halves, the asparagus and black olives. Sprinkle with marjoram and drizzle with a little olive oil. Roast in the top of the oven for 5 minutes, then turn cut sides down where applicable, and cook for a further 10 minutes until soft and slightly charred. Arrange all the vegetables for serving on warm plates, season with salt and freshly ground black pepper and drizzle lightly with balsamic vinegar.

SERVING SUGGESTIONS

Food category – P
- If your food rotation allows, sprinkle the vegetables with Parmesan shavings (taken from a piece with a swivel type potato peeler) or golden toasted pine nuts.

Food category – C
- If your food rotation allows, sprinkle the vegetables with garlic and herb croutons, either wheat bread or polenta (see page 68).

# Roasted Winter Vegetables ⓥ

You can cook winter vegetables in a way similar to that which I've described for the summer varieties.

Food category – M/A
Serves – 4

INGREDIENTS

- 4 large carrots, peeled and trimmed
- 4 small parsnips, peeled and trimmed
- 1 small swede, peeled and trimmed
- 1 small squash (i.e. kabocha, pumpkin or butternut squash), halved and seeded
- 2 small red onions, peeled and trimmed, leaving root end intact
- olive oil for roasting and frying
- 1 small bunch fresh rosemary, broken into pieces
- 2 tablespoons finely chopped fresh thyme (or two teaspoons dried)
- 12 large garlic cloves, unpeeled
- sea salt and freshly ground black pepper, to taste

TASTE SENSATION
Worcestershire sauce

As before, you'll need a ridged griddle pan and two lightly oiled baking sheets or shallow baking trays for this recipe.

METHOD
Pre-heat the oven to 225 C/440 F/Gas Mark 7. Cut all the root vegetables and the squash into long wedges or segments about 2 inches/ 5 cm × 1 inch/2.5 cm and about $\frac{1}{2}$ inch/1 cm at the thickest parts. Carrots and parsnips should be cut to length, thin parts split into halves and thick parts quartered lengthways. The swede can be sliced to the correct sized wedges as can the squash, which will need the rind removed after cutting. The onions can be quartered into wedges through the root. Blanch the root vegetables and squash, by plunging them into plenty of lightly salted boiling water for 4–5 minutes, drain and pat dry with kitchen paper.

Heat the ridged griddle pan over a high heat and when hot, coat with a little oil. In batches, fry the carrots, parsnips, swede, squash and onion wedges on the pan for about 30–60 seconds each side, so they become lightly coated with oil and scorched with ridges. Transfer to the baking sheets when ready. You may have to oil the pan a couple of times during this process. Arrange the vegetables on the baking sheets so they are not too crowded and are cut sides down, sprinkle with the rosemary and thyme, drizzle with a little more olive oil and season with salt and freshly ground black pepper. Cook in the top half of the oven for 15 minutes only. Turn the vegetables cut sides up, add the garlic cloves, swap the positions of the baking sheets over in the oven, and roast for a further 15–20 minutes, by which time the vegetables will be soft and slightly charred at the edges. Arrange all the vegetables for serving on warm plates, season with salt and freshly ground black pepper and drizzle lightly with Worcestershire sauce.

SERVING SUGGESTIONS

Food category – P
• If your food rotation allows, sprinkle the vegetables halfway through cooking – when the garlic is added – with chopped streaky bacon, shelled walnut halves or tinned chestnuts, washed, drained and halved.

Food category – C
• If your food rotation allows, cook thin wedges of potatoes or sweet potatoes, par boiled for 10 minutes, with the other vegetables from the beginning of cooking.

# Pressed Terrine of Vegetables ⓥ

This is a wonderful looking dish to serve as a starter with tomato sauce and salad leaves, or as an accompaniment. The Mediterranean vegetables go particularly well with the roast French rack of lamb, page 152. The vegetables need to be pre-cooked and left in the mould under weight for at least 2 hours, so it can be prepared early and warmed when needed for a light lunch or dinner party.

You'll need at least one mould such as a terrine dish, loaf tin or cake tin. If you have two moulds or dishes exactly the same, that's even better because one can be filled and the other used with weight inside it to press the vegetables into shape. I use two loaf tins about 10 inches/25 cm × 4 inches/10 cm × 3 inches/8 cm deep.

Food category – M/A
Serves – 4–6

INGREDIENTS

- Approximately 8 oz/250 g spinach (or Savoy cabbage) leaves, washed, tough stalks and ribs removed, enough to double line the mould you're using
- 1 oz/30g unsalted butter
- 6 oz/175 g shallots, peeled and finely sliced
- ½ red cabbage finely sliced
- 1 pint/600 ml Basic Vegetable Stock (see page 48)
- 6 oz/175 g whole fine green or Kenya beans, washed, tops removed

- ¼ teaspoon of cinnamon
- 6 carrots, grated
- 4–6 whole young leeks (enough to make a layer in the terrine mould)
- olive oil
- sea salt and freshly ground black pepper, to taste
- 1 tablespoon finely chopped fresh coriander

METHOD

Cook the vegetables as follows: in a large pan of slightly salted water, blanch the spinach or Savoy cabbage leaves a few at a time until they are just wilted – a few seconds – then remove to cold water to stop them cooking further and set to drain.

Melt a teaspoon of butter in a saucepan over a low heat and sauté the shallots until they are softened but not brown. Add the red cabbage, 1 tablespoon vegetable stock, a quarter teaspoon of cinnamon and salt and black pepper seasoning. Mix well, cover and cook until the cabbage is soft but still with a little crunch. About 15–20 minutes. Drain and set aside. Add the fine beans to one third of the boiling vegetable stock and simmer for 3–4 minutes until just cooked but still with some crunch. Remove to cold water to stop them cooking and set aside to drain. Retain the stock for future use.

Poach the grated carrots in one third of the boiling vegetable stock, tossing once or twice, until soft but still with a little crunch, about 4–6 minutes, drain and set aside, retaining the stock for future use. Poach or steam the leeks in one third of the boiling vegetable stock until they are soft, remove to cold water to stop them cooking and set aside to drain. Retain the stock for future use. When cool and well drained, split lengthways to make filling the mould easier. Line the mould you are to use with cooking foil, leaving enough overlapping the top edge to fold over and cover the top when the mould is full, brush inside with olive oil.

Line the mould with two layers of wilted spinach or cabbage leaves.

Cover the bottom with one layer first overlapping up the sides, then line the sides, allowing plenty for folding over onto the top of the vegetables when the mould is filled, then repeat with another layer in the same way. Add the vegetables in turn to give layers about $\frac{3}{4}$ inch/2 cm deep, season between the layers with salt and pepper. Start with the shallots and red cabbage, then add a good layer of whole green beans laid lengthways. Mix the carrots with the coriander and put them in the mould. Finally add the split leeks lengthways and overlapping along the mould. Don't worry if the vegetables are just above the top. Fold the spinach or cabbage over the top of the leeks, using extra pieces to make sure the top is well covered with a couple of layers.

Cut a piece of foil to lay on the top then fold the extra foil of the lining over to completely encase the vegetables. Weight the top of the mould. Either put a second identical mould containing weights on top, or place a piece of card cut to the inside dimensions of the mould. Weight with a brick or tins of food. Place in the refrigerator, with a dish under to catch any drips from the mould, for at least 2 hours. When required for the meal, lift from the mould with the foil, unwrap and cut through while cold, into approximately 1 inch/2.5 cm slices which can be microwaved when on the plate to the required serving temperature. Alternatively place the mould in the oven for 20–25 minutes at 180 C/ 350 F/Gas Mark 5 to warm through. Remove from the mould as before and slice while warm.

# Oven Cooked Ratatouille ⓥ

This may not be the traditional ratatouille but cooked this way it uses much less oil and it's equally delicious. Ratatouille is best served warm rather than hot and really benefits from being allowed to rest after cooking, to allow the flavours to blend. So you can make your ratatouille well before you need it (even the previous day) and warm it through, if necessary, when required.

Food category – M/A
Serves – 4

INGREDIENTS
- 4 tablespoons olive oil
- 1 large red pepper, deseeded and chopped into $\frac{3}{4}$ inch/2 cm dice

- 1 large yellow pepper, deseeded and chopped into $\frac{3}{4}$ inch/2 cm dice

- 4 medium courgettes, quartered lengthwise and chopped into ¾ inch/2 cm dice
- 2 medium or 1 large aubergine, sliced lengthwise, pulp discarded and chopped into ¾ inch/2 cm dice
- 1 large clove garlic, crushed, optional
- 2–3 tablespoons tomato purée or paste

- 4 bay leaves, each torn into 3–4 pieces, optional
- 4 oz/125 g black olives
- 2 × 16 oz/500 g tins of plum tomatoes, drained, juice retained, deseeded and chopped
- sea salt and freshly ground black pepper, to taste

You'll need a lidded ovenproof dish for the ratatouille. A heavy based casserole dish or saucepan with a lid and ovenproof handle will do nicely.

METHOD

Pre-heat the oven to 200 C/400 F/Gas Mark 6. Heat two tablespoons of the oil in a heavy based frying pan over a fairly high heat and fry half the peppers and courgettes rapidly, tossing or mixing occasionally to stop burning. Add half the aubergine to the pan and continue cooking. This preliminary cooking is to add flavour and mix the ingredients so don't worry that the vegetables are only just softened. Add half of the crushed garlic, about a tablespoon of tomato purée, half the bay leaves and olives and plenty of seasoning. Mix and pour the contents of the pan into the ovenproof dish, add half the chopped plum tomatoes and mix again.

Wash and dry the pan and repeat with the remaining half of all the ingredients. Add half the retained tomato juice, mix well, cover the dish and transfer the ratatouille to the oven. Cook for 45–55 minutes, gently turning and mixing about every 15 minutes or so. Add some of the retained tomato juice if the ratatouille appears to be drying out. When ready the vegetables should not be broken up but still holding their shape. The liquor should be a good thick tomato sauce. Remove from the heat and set aside to cool.

# Quick Sauté Ratatouille ⓥ

This is a more traditional way of cooking ratatouille but the vegetables are diced quite small to make it quicker to cook.

Food category – M/A

Serves – 4

INGREDIENTS

- 1 small red onion, cut into ½ inch/1 cm dice
- 6–8 tablespoons olive oil
- 1 large clove garlic
- 2 large red peppers, cored, seeded and cut into ½ inch/1 cm dice
- 4 medium courgettes, trimmed, quartered lengthways, pulp discarded, flesh cut into ½ inch/1 cm dice
- 1 small bunch rosemary

- 1 tablespoon finely chopped fresh oregano (or 1 teaspoon dried)
- 2 medium aubergines, washed and trimmed
- 4 ripe plum tomatoes, skinned, seeded and chopped (or a 14 oz/440 g tin of tomatoes, drained, seeded, and chopped)
- sea salt and freshly ground black pepper, to taste

METHOD

In a large heavy based frying pan, over a low heat, sauté the onion in a tablespoon of olive oil, without browning, until just soft. Add the garlic and cook for another 2 minutes. Transfer to a large saucepan. Sauté the red pepper dice, over a slightly higher heat, until just softened and transfer to the pan with the onions. Sauté the courgette dice in a further tablespoon of olive oil until just softened, transfer to the saucepan. Mix the vegetables in the pan together and add the herbs. Remove 4 × ½ inch/1 cm slices from the sides of the aubergines and trim off the ends, discard the stalk. Cut the aubergine slices and ends into ½ inch/1 cm dice. Retain the flesh for Aubergine Purée if desired (see page 146). Sauté the aubergine dice in another two tablespoons of olive oil, over a moderate heat, until soft. Add to the vegetables in the saucepan. Add the chopped tomatoes, bring to a simmer and cook gently, uncovered, for 10–15 minutes, to blend the flavours and reduce the tomatoes. Allow to cool to almost room temperature, season with salt and freshly ground black pepper and serve.

MEAL SUGGESTIONS

Food category – P

- Beat skinless chicken breasts between sheets of Clingfilm until about ½ inch/1 cm thick. Season with salt, freshly ground black pepper and a sprinkling of mixed dried herbs. Fry on a hot, well oiled, ridged griddle pan or grill under a hot grill for 3–4 minutes on each side until cooked through and lightly coloured. Serve with warm ratatouille sprinkled with finely chopped fresh coriander.

Food category – C
* Serve warm ratatouille with triangles of shallow fried polenta and onions (see page 70) and a dressed green salad (see page 247).

# Mix With Any Vegetable Casserole ⓥ

Another favourite of mine, wholesome is the word that comes to mind for this warming tasty casserole. It really is simplicity itself, taking just 15 minutes in the kitchen, after which it can be virtually left to cook itself.

Food category – M/A
Serves – 4

INGREDIENTS

* 2 tablespoons olive oil
* 1 large onion, peeled and cut into eight chunks
* 2 large cloves garlic, finely sliced
* 8 oz/250 g button mushrooms, trimmed, wiped and quartered (left whole if small)
* 6 large carrots, split lengthways and cut diagonally into ¼ inch/6 mm slices
* 2 large leeks, washed, trimmed and cut into ½ inch/1 cm slices
* 2 × 14 oz/440 g tins Italian plum tomatoes, drained, seeds and cores discarded and flesh roughly chopped (retain juice)

* 2 bay leaves, torn in half
* 2 teaspoons dried mixed provençal herbs
* 1 teaspoon Dijon mustard
* ½ pint/300 ml white wine or cider
* 1 pint/600 ml Basic Vegetable Stock (see page 48)
* 12 oz/375 g frozen petit pois
* sea salt and freshly ground black pepper, to taste

TASTE SENSATION
Worcestershire sauce

METHOD

Pre-heat the oven to 190 C/375 F/Gas Mark 5. In a large casserole dish on the hob, over a low heat, heat the olive oil and sauté the onion until it begins to soften, about 3–4 minutes. Add the garlic, mushrooms, carrots, leeks and tomatoes and cook for 2–3 minutes, mixing occasionally to combine well and coat in oil. Add the bay leaves, herbs and Dijon mustard, season well with salt and pepper and pour in the wine and enough vegetable stock to come halfway up the vegetables. You are unlikely to use all the stock. Mix to combine well, cover and place in the middle of the oven. Cook in the oven for 55–60 minutes, stirring two or three times, until the carrots are cooked but reasonably firm when tested with the sharp point of a knife.

Take the casserole from the oven, remove about a quarter of the vegetables (with plenty of the carrots) and a little of the liquor and purée until smooth. A food processor or blender does this best but you can mash then force the vegetables through a fine metal sieve with a wooden spoon. Stir the purée back into the casserole along with the petit pois. If necessary add a little extra stock from that retained to adjust the consistency of the casserole as you like it. Stir in plenty of Worcestershire sauce and salt and pepper seasoning to your taste. Replace in the oven for 5 minutes. Serve, when ready, in warm bowls as a light lunch or supper, or as part of a larger meal.

VARIATIONS

Food category – P
- Take four chicken quarters or pork chops on the bone, trimmed of fat. Season both sides and brown for 3 minutes on each side, in the two tablespoons of oil, in the casserole over a medium heat, before starting to cook the vegetables. Remove to a dish and cover while sautéing the onions and vegetables as described. Replace in the casserole dish with the herbs and any meat juices. Continue as before until all the ingredients are cooked. Thicken by puréeing a proportion of the vegetables, as above and serve with a garnish of chopped fresh chives.

Food category – C
- This recipe is a variation of the Bean and Dumpling Casserole on page 203, the dumplings from which would be perfect here. Just make the dumplings as described and place on top of the casserole after it has been cooking in the oven for 40 minutes, cover and cook for 20–25 minutes, when the dumplings will have become puffed up and soft. Remove the dumplings to keep warm while you thicken the casserole by puréeing a proportion of the vegetables as described, add and cook the petit pois and adjust the seasoning. Serve the casserole into warm bowls topped with dumplings.

or

- Add ½ cup of pearl barley to the sautéed onions with the garlic and vegetables and continue as before. With this variation the pearl barley will thicken the casserole and you may choose not to purée any vegetables to increase the consistency further, although I still prefer to do so. Serve in warm bowls garnished with fresh finely chopped thyme.

# Griddled Chicory Hearts Ⓥ

This method of cooking is lighter on oil than shallow frying and quickly produces a hot crunchy and delicately flavoured vegetable, perfect with almost anything. I particularly enjoy it with Chicken Breast Stuffed with Goat's Cheese and Sage, page 164.

Food category – M/A
Serves – 4

INGREDIENTS

- 4 medium chicory hearts, trimmed of old leaves, washed and dried
- olive oil
- sea salt and freshly ground black pepper, to taste

- 1 teaspoon finely chopped fresh sage, optional

METHOD

The chicory will take about 4–6 minutes to cook. Heat a well oiled ridged griddle pan on the hob. Split the chicory in half lengthways. Brush with olive oil and season well with salt and black pepper on both sides. Place cut side down on the griddle pan and cook for 2–3 minutes until softening on the outside and attractively marked with colour. Turn and repeat on the other side. When cooked the chicory may be kept warm for a few minutes until ready for serving.

ALTERNATIVE COOKING

Cook on an oiled wire grill mesh, for 2–3 minutes each side, under a hot grill.

STARTER SERVING SUGGESTIONS

Food category – P

- Sprinkle with balsamic vinegar and shavings taken from a block of Parmesan with a swivel type potato peeler.

Food category – C
- Serve on thin slices of seasoned potato cooked on the ridged griddle pan for 2–3 minutes each side and drizzled with vinaigrette.

# Griddled Courgettes ⓥ

Courgettes can be rather bland and unexciting, but cooked on the ridged griddle pan they are transformed in both appearance and flavour. Serve with a few halves of cherry tomatoes warmed in smooth tomato sauce then sprinkled with hot sautéed parsley in butter and you have an excellent light starter to put before a more substantial main course at a special lunch or dinner. Or serve as an attractive vegetable accompaniment as part of a main course.

Food category – M/A
Serves – 4

INGREDIENTS

- 4 medium courgettes, washed and trimmed and cut on the diagonal into 6 × ¼ inch/6 mm slices per person
- olive oil

- sea salt and freshly ground black pepper, to taste

FOR SERVING

- 1 serving Basic Tomato Sauce, puréed smooth (see page 271)
- 8–10 ripe cherry tomatoes, preferably both the red and yellow ones, washed and cut across into halves

- 4 tablespoons finely chopped fresh parsley
- 1 oz/30 g unsalted butter
- lamb's lettuce, washed and dried, for garnish

METHOD

Brush the courgette slices with olive oil and season well with salt and black pepper on both sides. Adjust the consistency of the tomato sauce so it will pour and warm to not quite simmering. Heat a lightly oiled ridged griddle pan on the hob until very hot and beginning to smoke. Cook the courgette slices on the griddle pan, in batches, for 2–3 minutes each side until just softened and attractively marked with colour. Place the courgette slices firmly on the pan and do not be tempted to move them around for at least 2 minutes, or you will not get the attractive charred ridges across the slices but will have a jumble of faint lines instead. Keep the pan oiled and hot for each batch of courgette slices. Keep cooked slices warm but not so hot that they continue to cook, while you cook the remaining slices and until ready to serve. While cooking the last batch of courgette slices add the cherry tomato halves to the warm tomato sauce and remove from the heat.

When all the courgette slices are ready, sauté the parsley in the butter over a high heat for 1–2 minutes with a little salt and pepper. Arrange courgette slices on warm plates with warm cherry tomato halves and tomato sauce spooned over and drizzle with sautéed parsley in hot butter. Garnish with small bunches of lamb's lettuce. Serve immediately.

# Griddled Asparagus and Leeks ⓥ

I like the dramatic black marks made by the hot ridges of the griddle pan on vegetables. Here's another variation which can be striking as a starter in its own right or when served over a slice of grilled fish, or on a base of socca or wholewheat pastry base. It's best to blanch the leeks and asparagus before cooking on the griddle pan.

Food category – M/A
Serves – 4

INGREDIENTS

- 16 fresh asparagus spears, washed, peeled if necessary, and tough stalk removed
- 8 medium leeks, washed and trimmed to asparagus length; remove several layers of outer leaf and retain for another use

- 8 medium spring onions, washed and trimmed
- sea salt and freshly ground black pepper, to taste

FOR SERVING

- Warm Herb Vinaigrette for four (see page 277)
- small bunch of rocket leaves, washed and dried, for garnish

METHOD

Have a large pan of boiling water and a bowl of iced water ready for blanching. Blanch the asparagus in the boiling water for 3 minutes, remove and plunge into the iced water. Blanch the leeks in the boiling water for 4–5 minutes, remove and plunge into the iced water. Drain the asparagus and leeks and pat dry with a clean cloth. Brush the leeks, asparagus and spring onions with olive oil and season well with salt and black pepper. Heat a lightly oiled, ridged griddle pan on the hob until very hot and beginning to haze. Prepare a dish to keep batches of cooked vegetables warm without extra cooking.

Cook the leeks on the griddle pan, for 2–3 minutes each side, until just softened and attractively marked with colour. Remove and keep warm. Cook the asparagus on the griddle pan for 2–3 minutes each side until just softened and wilting and attractively marked with colour. Remove to keep warm. Cook the spring onions on the griddle pan for 1–2 minutes each side until hot and attractively marked. To cook the vegetables place them firmly on the pan and do not be tempted to move them around too soon or you will not get the attractive charred ridges across them but will have a jumble of faint lines instead. Keep the ridged pan oiled and hot for each batch of vegetables. Warm the Herb Vinaigrette in a small saucepan. Arrange asparagus, leeks and spring onions in a random pile on warm plates and drizzle with warm parsley vinaigrette, garnish with a few rocket leaves. Serve immediately.

# Tomato and Onion Side Salad Ⓥ

Food category – M/A
Serves – 4

INGREDIENTS

- 4 medium slicing (beef) tomatoes, thinly sliced
- 2 small, sweet onions (red or Spanish), peeled and very thinly sliced
- 1 serving Basic Vinaigrette made with Garlic and Tabasco (see page 73)

- 2 tablespoons capers, drained
- sea salt and freshly ground black pepper, to taste

METHOD

On four side plates arrange slices of tomato mixed with slices of onion. Spoon a tablespoon or so of vinaigrette over each salad and scatter on a few capers. Season with a little salt and plenty of freshly ground black pepper.

# Green Side Salad ⓥ

Food category – M/A
Serves – 4

INGREDIENTS

- 6 oz/175 g mange tout, washed
  and trimmed
- mixed salad leaves for four,
  washed and patted or spun dry
- 2 celery sticks, thinly sliced
- 2 servings Basic Vinaigrette made
  with grain mustard (page 73)

- lemon juice
- 2 spring onions, finely chopped
- sea salt and freshly ground black
  pepper, to taste

TASTE SENSATION

toasted sesame oil

METHOD

Plunge the mange tout into boiling water for 2–3 minutes until just cooked but firm to the bite then transfer to cold water to cool and stop them cooking. Mix together in a bowl enough coarsely torn salad leaves for four portions. When ready to serve, drain, and pat the mange tout dry and add to the bowl with the sliced celery. Dress the salad with Grain Mustard Vinaigrette, salt and pepper seasoning and lemon juice to your taste, mix with your fingers until all the leaves and mange tout are lightly coated. Arrange piles of the green salad onto four plates. Sprinkle with chopped spring onions, season with a little black pepper and drip a few drops of sesame oil on each salad. Serve immediately.

# Herby Green Side Salad ⓥ

As I've already mentioned, this salad is perfect for serving with chicken. Use different herbs to accompany meats, fish and Carbohydrate dishes such as pasta or boulangère potatoes.

Food category – M/A
Serves – 4

INGREDIENTS

- mixed salad leaves for four,
  washed and patted or spun dry

- 1 cup finely chopped fresh
  coriander leaves

- 1 tablespoon finely chopped fresh parsley
- 2 servings Basic Vinaigrette made with garlic and Tabasco (see page 73)

- 2 tablespoons finely chopped fresh chives
- sea salt and freshly ground black pepper, to taste

TASTE SENSATION
hazelnut or walnut oil

METHOD
In a large bowl, mix enough coarsely torn salad leaves for four portions. Add the coriander leaves and chopped parsley. When ready to serve, dress the salad with Basic Vinaigrette and salt and pepper seasoning to your taste. Mix with your fingers until all the leaves are lightly coated. Arrange a serving of the herby leaves on each of four plates and sprinkle each with chopped chives and a few drops of nut oil. Serve immediately.

# Mixed Vegetable Curry ⓥ

This curry is thickened by puréeing a proportion of the vegetables to make a rich vegetable curry in little over half an hour. You choose from creamy and mild or hot and spicy. Both versions go very well with plain boiled basmati rice, but the mild version is better with white meats like tandoori spiced chicken and the hotter version is best with lamb.

Food category – M/A
Serves – 4

INGREDIENTS
- 2 oz/60 g unsalted butter
- 1 medium onion, finely chopped
- 2 large cloves garlic
- 2 teaspoons chilli powder
- 1 teaspoon turmeric
- 1 teaspoon ground cumin
- 3 carrots, peeled, trimmed, large roots split lengthways and cut diagonally into $\frac{1}{4}$ inch/6 mm slices

- 1 swede or turnip, peeled, trimmed, in $\frac{1}{2}$ inch/1 cm dice
- 6 oz/175 g Kenya green beans, washed, trimmed, 2 inch/5 cm lengths
- sea salt for seasoning
- 1 pint/600 ml Basic Vegetable Stock (see page 48)
- 2 small leeks, washed, trimmed and cut into $\frac{1}{2}$ inch/1 cm slices

- 6 oz/175 g cauliflower florettes, about ¾ inch/2.5 cm pieces
- 6 oz/175 g frozen petit pois

- 5 fl oz/150 ml natural yogurt
- 2 tablespoons finely chopped fresh coriander, for garnish

METHOD

Melt the butter in a large saucepan over a medium heat and fry the onion and garlic, stirring occasionally, until golden brown. Add the chilli, turmeric and ground cumin, stir well and cook for 1 minute. Add the carrots and swede and if the beans are quite thick add them as well. Mix the vegetables with the spices, onion and garlic over the heat, until well coated. Season with a little salt, add ½ of the vegetable stock, mix and bring to a good simmer, cover and cook, stirring once more, for 5 minutes. After the 5 minutes add the beans if thin, the leeks and the cauliflower florettes, add more stock if necessary – you need just enough to come halfway up the vegetables. Stir well to combine and coat with the spicy stock, cover and simmer, with occasional stirring, for 15 minutes.

With the sharp point of a knife, test that all the vegetables are just cooked, take the curry from the heat. Remove and purée about a quarter of the root vegetables and leeks in a food processor or blender. Use a few tablespoons of the curry stock, or a little of the remaining vegetable stock, to help the vegetables blend down to a smooth purée. Add the peas and the puréed vegetables to the curry, adjust the consistency with extra stock, if you like your curry more moist then return to the heat, uncovered to simmer for a further 5 minutes. You are unlikely to need all the stock. Remove from the heat and allow to cool a little before seasoning to your taste with salt and your choice of mild or spicy curry ingredients.

FOR A MILD CREAMY CURRY

Add and stir in natural yogurt to your taste. The yogurt is treated as a Mix With Any food and will not compromise your Kensington Diet eating, but you can replace it with soured cream, which is also M/A, if you prefer. Garnish with chopped fresh coriander.

FOR A HOT SPICY VEGETABLE CURRY

INGREDIENTS

- 1–2 tablespoons prepared curry cooking sauce (I use Sharwoods Madras sauce)

- 14 oz/440 g tin plum tomatoes, drained, seeded, and chopped

METHOD

In place of the yogurt above, add and mix in curry sauce to your taste, fold in the tomatoes without breaking them up further, return the saucepan to the heat and bring the curry back to just simmering for 1 minute.

SERVING SUGGESTION
- Serve your vegetable curry garnished with chopped coriander.

Food category – C
- Serve the curry with boiled basmati rice and Lentil Dhal (page 202).

Food category – P
- Serve with your choice of diced chicken or lamb, marinated in yogurt and tandoori spices and grilled, barbecued or roasted.

VARIATIONS
- The same method can be used for a variety of different vegetable combinations – try carrot with cauliflower, turnip with beans and peas, swede and carrot with whole baby onions.

# Aubergine Curry ⓥ

This dish uses another method for Mix With Any vegetable curries and can be applied to small whole trimmed okra instead of aubergines if you prefer. The dish is best as an accompaniment for Mixed Vegetable Curry (page 248) and dhal or rice for a Carbohydrate meal, or Mixed Vegetable Curry and meat or poultry for a Protein meal.

Food category – M/A
Serves – 4 (as an accompaniment)

INGREDIENTS
- 1 oz/30 g unsalted butter
- 2 tablespoons sunflower or groundnut oil
- 1 teaspoon cumin seeds, optional
- 1 large onion, peeled and cut into eight, segments separated
- 2 cloves garlic, finely sliced
- 1 teaspoon finely grated fresh root ginger
- 1 teaspoon chilli powder
- ½ teaspoon cumin powder
- ½ teaspoon turmeric

- 2 medium aubergines, washed, trimmed and cut into 1 inch/2.5 cm dice (or 1½ lbs, 750 g whole okra, washed, trimmed of excess stalk)
- 14 oz/440 g jar or tin of passata or crushed tomatoes

- 1–2 tablespoons prepared curry cooking sauce such as Sharwoods Madras, optional, for a hotter curry
- sea salt for seasoning
- 1 tablespoon fresh coriander, finely chopped

METHOD

Pre-heat the oven to 200 C/400 F/Gas Mark 6. In a large frying pan with an ovenproof handle, or a similar sized oven tin, heat the butter and oil on the hob over a medium heat. Add the cumin seeds and fry until they crackle. Add the onions, garlic and ginger and fry until the onions are golden brown. Add the chilli, ground cumin and turmeric and cook for a further 1 minute. Add the aubergines or okra and stir to coat with the oil and spices. Place in the oven and cook for 25–30 minutes, stirring occasionally until the aubergine pieces are tender when tested with the sharp point of a knife.

Pour the passata or chopped tomatoes into a fine sieve over a bowl and leave, without disturbing, for excess water and juice to drain off. Retain this juice. When the aubergines are cooked, return the pan to the hob and over a medium heat add and stir in the tomatoes and simmer for 2–3 minutes until the tomatoes reduce to a thick sauce. Remove from the heat, cool a little and adjust the consistency, to your preference, with the retained tomato juice and then flavour, to your taste, with salt and curry sauce if used. Stir in chopped coriander and serve.

# DESSERTS AND DRINKS

## EVERYTHING YOU NEED TO KNOW
## ABOUT DESSERTS

Let's face it, desserts serve no useful purpose. Nutritionally, there is nothing in desserts that can't be provided by the courses served before. Invariably desserts are high in fats, refined starches or sugars, sometimes in all three. In Kensington Diet terms desserts all too often involve bad combinations of Proteins, such as eggs, with Carbohydrates such as sugar and flour. Lots of desserts are variations of the same ingredients, which means they make food rotation a problem. It's official – if you want to eat healthily or are trying to control your weight, desserts are decidedly unhelpful. You should definitely be very cautious about eating regular or large quantities of high sugar and high fat desserts. That's the bad news, but you already knew that.

Desserts taste good, they bring a counterpoint of flavours and textures to a meal, they enable you to conclude a series of savoury courses with something sweet or offer refreshment after richness. Desserts can provide an interlude for companionable conversation after a meal. Desserts are comfort food. The good news is, with KD there's no reason to forego these pleasures.

Since your desserts are almost certainly going to compromise the rules of healthy eating to some extent, the key is to make the compromise as acceptable as possible. An occasional moderate sized dessert will cost you in terms of your health and weight management but this is readily offset by the benefits of Kensington Diet eating. All the tastes, textures and pleasures of desserts can be yours with no great health or weight penalty as long as you remember these guidelines.

Choose your dessert to combine with the rest of your meal to keep to your '1 in 5' food rotation. Don't over-indulge in your desserts by eating large portions or the same kind of dessert too often. If you particularly want to indulge in a dessert, the best way is to eat sparingly of light food in the courses before it – then enjoy yourself.

## SWEET DESSERTS

A major ingredient in many desserts is sugar. The sugars are any form of granulated sugars, honeys and maple syrup. You can add high sugar content jams and preserves and dried fruits to the list as well because their predominant ingredient is sugar. Sugar is designated as a Carbohydrate so, strictly speaking, desserts which contain both sugar and Proteins such as eggs, nuts or cheese, aren't suitable. Nor would it be correct to eat sugary desserts after a Protein meal containing meat, fish or poultry in any course. But sugar, in some form, to some degree, is found in virtually all foods. If you've eaten vegetables or even meat or poultry you've consumed some sugar. Sugars are, of course, Carbo- hydrates, but they do not need to be treated with the same caution as the other group of Carbohydrates, the starches.

So in a Protein meal containing eggs, fish, meat, poultry, milk, soya or nuts, if you keep the portions small and don't eat them too often, you'll suffer no great health penalty from eating a relatively small amount of sugar. That means you'll be OK with small, infrequent amounts of ice cream (try chocolate, coffee, vanilla, coconut, toffee but not fruit varieties), sorbets (made without egg white or fruit – try mint, coffee, chocolate) and egg-based sweet desserts (try crème brûlée and crème caramel). Desserts containing starch Carbohydrates are still to be avoided, of course, when following a Protein meal.

Sugar-rich desserts with Carbohydrate meals containing rice, po- tatoes, grains and so forth, create no problems except for your calorie intake. So with Carbohydrate meals you might try profiteroles filled with cream and smothered in chocolate sauce – but only once in a while!

## LITTLE BITES

If the notion of eating even small and infrequent amounts of calorie rich desserts containing eggs, cream, chocolate and sugar, fills you with horror, there is another way to have your cake and eat it. Well, not your cake exactly, but certainly some delectable endings to your meals without the penalties of too much fat or sugar.

My favourite way of ending a special meal, is with a glass of sweet dessert wine and two or three hand made chocolates. The damage, if any, to my body is minimal and it's more than balanced by the contentment I feel.

Just a bite or two of some special sweet or savoury morsel can be all it takes to satisfy the desire that nags your taste buds after a meal. The following are some more suggestions for the kinds of little morsels which will fit with your Kensington Diet: with Protein meals, try any nuts (except peanuts) whether whole, shelled, raw, roasted or wrapped in chocolate, just be careful of the amount of salt on some roasted nuts. Carbohydrate possibilities are shortbread, brandy snaps, peanuts and peanut Florentines, or those lovely party treats which are clusters of cereals such as corn flakes or crisped rice in chocolate and dried fruits – especially figs and dates. These small titbits go well with a special dessert wine or sweet liqueur, or if your prefer, with good, ground decaffeinated or whole coffee, preferably served black.

But why not try a Middle Eastern favourite – coffee flavoured with cardamom. Cardamom seems to balance the effects of caffeine and makes it less potent, which means you're more likely to have a decent night's sleep after whole coffee flavoured with cardamom than after coffee without. Ground coffee with cardamom already included is available in any Middle Eastern food shop and some shops selling Cypriot, Greek and Turkish foods. The following distributor is happy to provide a list of local suppliers. Just give them a ring:

**Idriss Natural Foods, 9–10 Brember Road, South Harrow, Middlesex 0181 869 9827/28**

Since compromise is inevitable, some of the sweet, semi-sweet and savoury dessert recipes which follow, do bend the rules, but without breaking them too badly. For your combining and '1 in 5' food rotation purposes, sugar is treated as a Mix With Any food, and the category of the dish is identified by the other main ingredients used.

The portion sizes in the recipes are deliberately small and most of the recipes advise making the desserts in individual servings using ramekins or other small dishes or plates. This enables you to keep control of your portion sizes and the amount of high fat or sugar rich dessert which you will eat. So a selection of suitable small serving dishes would be an asset to your Kensington Diet.

# Nut Macaroons ⓥ

This recipe is for almond macaroons but you can substitute desiccated coconut or ground hazelnuts.

Food category – P
'1 in 5' – eggs, nuts (your choice)
Serves – 4

INGREDIENTS

- 3 oz/90 g ground almonds
- 2 oz/60 g caster sugar
- pinch ground cinnamon
- 5–6 drops natural vanilla extract (or a teaspoon freshly grated lemon zest)

- 1 egg white

METHOD

Pre-heat the oven to 180 C/350 F/Gas Mark 4. Mix the ground almonds, caster sugar and cinnamon. In a mixing bowl stir the vanilla extract into the egg whites and mix in the ground almond mixture until well combined. The mixture needs to be firm enough to mould into shapes. With damp hands, scoop out enough of the mixture and form into a simple shape – a round ball about half as big as a golf ball is easiest – the mixture will make 12. Place on a flat non-stick baking sheet or rice paper on a baking sheet, and bake for 15–20 minutes until firm and golden. Set aside to cool to room temperature before serving.

TIP

☞ Coconut macaroons will require two egg whites for the same amount of mixture.

# Cups of Chocolate ⓥ

A rich chocolate dessert topped with coffee cream and sprinkled with cinnamon, these cups of chocolate look like cappuccinos when served on a saucer with a teaspoon.

Food category – P
'1 in 5' – eggs
Serves – 4

INGREDIENTS

- 6 oz/175 g best dark bitter chocolate, broken into pieces
- 3 oz/90 g unsalted butter, at room temperature
- 3 rounded tablespoons caster sugar
- 4 whole eggs

- 2 egg whites
- 2 fl oz/60 ml double cream
- 2 tablespoons triple strength coffee (percolated or filtered), cold
- ground cinnamon or cocoa powder, for garnish

METHOD

Pre-heat the oven to 160 C/325 F/Gas Mark 3. You will need a mixing bowl which fits safely in the top of a saucepan over an inch or two of gently simmering water, but without touching the water. Also, a deep oven dish for a 'water bath' (*bain-marie*) and four tea cups and saucers or individual ramekins. Put the chocolate in the bowl over the simmering water and stir occasionally until melted.

In another bowl, off the heat, beat the butter and 2 tablespoons of the sugar until the mixture is light and fluffy. Beat the 4 whole eggs into this mixture, one at a time. In another clean bowl whisk the egg whites to the soft peak stage.

When the chocolate is a smooth liquid, remove the pan from the heat and mix the butter mixture into the chocolate. When completely mixed in, remove the bowl from the saucepan and mix a tablespoon of the whisked egg white into the chocolate mixture with a metal spoon, then gently fold in the remainder. Pour the mixture into the teacups until each is about three-quarters full. Place the cups or ramekins in the oven dish 'water bath' (*bain-marie*) and pour cold water into the dish until it is two-thirds of the way up the outside of the cups or ramekins. Cook in the oven for 35–40 minutes, until the top of the mixture is firm and springy to the touch. Cool to room temperature for serving. When ready, beat the cream with the remaining sugar until it thickens then beat in the coffee until you have a thick coffee cream. Top the cups with the coffee cream, sprinkle with cinnamon and serve on saucers with teaspoons.

# Lemon Pot ⓥ

This is a really refreshing dessert which you can prepare and keep for 24 hours before serving.

Food category – P
'1 in 5' – eggs
Serves – 4

INGREDIENTS

FOR THE FILLING
- 4 lemons, preferably unwaxed
- 3 whole eggs

- 4 tablespoons caster sugar

FOR THE MERINGUE TOPPING
- 2 egg whites
- 2 tablespoons caster sugar

- ½ tablespoon lemon juice

FOR THE GARNISH
- peel of half a lemon from above
- 2 tablespoons water

- 1 tablespoon caster sugar

You'll need a deep oven dish for use as a 'water bath' (*bain-marie*) and four individual ramekins.

METHOD

Pre-heat the oven to 180 C/350 F/Gas Mark 4. Make the filling: Squeeze and strain the juice from the lemons and finely grate the peel from all but one half of one of them. Retain the ungrated peel from the remaining half lemon for use as garnish. In a mixing bowl lightly whisk together the eggs with the sugar, the strained lemon juice and the grated zest. Fill the ramekins to three-quarters full with the mixture and fit a small square of foil as a cap over the top of each ramekin.

Place the ramekins in the 'water bath' and pour water into the dish until it is two-thirds of the way up the outsides of the ramekins. Cook in the oven for 25–30 minutes until set. Once cooked this far, the lemon pots can be kept in the refrigerator until you're ready to finish cooking the topping just prior to serving. This will take 10 minutes. Bring to room temperature beforehand. When ready, reduce the oven temperature to 150 C/300 F/Gas Mark 2.

Make the meringue topping: In a clean mixing bowl, whisk the egg whites together until they make stiff peaks. Whisk in the sugar a little at a time and continue whisking until the mixture forms stiff white peaks. Add the lemon juice and whisk again to the stiff peak stage until the mixture holds its form when scooped up. Put spoonfuls of this mixture onto the top of the lemon mixture in the ramekins until they are slightly overfilled. Cook in the oven for 10 minutes until lightly coloured and just set.

Trim the pith from the retained lemon peel and slice the peel into fine julienne. Place in a small saucepan with 2 tablespoons of water and a tablespoon of caster sugar and bring to a rapid simmer. Simmer until the liquor reduces to a thin syrup taking care not to let it burn, about 4–5 minutes. Remove from the heat and set aside to cool. To serve, garnish the meringue topping with sugar glazed julienne strips of lemon zest.

# BL's Potted Cheesecake Ⓥ

Thumbscrews and the bastinado applied to a special client extracted permission to give you this recipe.

Food category – P
'1 in 5' – eggs, cow's milk cheese
Serves – 4

INGREDIENTS

- 6 oz/175 g cream cheese (Light Philadelphia works well)
- 3 tablespoons caster sugar
- 2–3 tablespoons lemon juice

- 4 eggs
- pinch salt
- 4–5 drops natural vanilla extract

FOR THE TOPPING

- 5 fl oz/150 ml soured cream
- 1 rounded dessertspoon caster sugar

- 2 drops natural vanilla extract
- freshly grated nutmeg, for garnish

You'll need a deep oven dish for a 'water bath' and four individual ramekins.

METHOD

Preheat the oven to 325 C/160 F/Gas Mark 3. Beat the cheese until really smooth and creamy then gradually beat in the sugar and lemon juice, then beat the eggs in one at a time. Add the salt and vanilla extract, beat again and pour the mixture into the ramekins until they are two-thirds full. Place the ramekins in the 'water bath' and pour water into the dish until it is two-thirds of the way up the outside of the ramekins. Cook in the oven for 30–35 minutes. The mixture will still be very soft and liquid after this time.

Make the topping. Mix the soured cream with the sugar and vanilla extract. Spoon the topping carefully onto the potted cheesecake, starting from the outsides until the tops are entirely covered. Return to the oven for 10 minutes then cool and chill in the refrigerator until ready to serve When ready, garnish with a sprinkling of ground nutmeg and serve.

# Bakewell Pot ⓥ

This is how to make an old favourite which is a poor combination of foods, into a new favourite which, just about, fits into your KD eating.

Food category – P
'1 in 5' – eggs, ground almonds
Serves – 4

INGREDIENTS

- 4 dessertspoons jam (e.g. strawberry, raspberry or blackberry)
- 3 oz/90 g unsalted butter at room temperature

- 3 oz/90 g caster sugar
- 1 large egg (or 2 small)
- 4 oz/125 g ground almonds

FOR SERVING
- whipped cream, optional

You'll need four shallow, individual, earthenware dishes about 4 inches/ 10 cm diameter and 1 inch/2.5 cm deep.

METHOD

Pre-heat the oven to 180 C/350 F/Gas Mark 4. Lightly grease the dishes and spread a teaspoon of your chosen jam in the bottom of each. Mix together the butter, sugar, egg and ground almonds until you have a smooth mixture and divide it between the dishes on top of the jam. Bake for 30–35 minutes until the mixture is golden and firm on top. Allow to cool to room temperature, garnish each dish with a spoonful of whipped cream if desired, and serve.

# Floating Meringues on Custard with Hot Chocolate ⓥ

Here is a simple, stylish and utterly delicious version of a classic recipe. Soft, fluffy meringues floating on real custard with rich chocolate sauce.

Food category – P
'1 in 5' – eggs, milk
Serves – 4

## INGREDIENTS

### FOR THE CHOCOLATE SAUCE
- 1 fl oz/30 ml single cream
- ½ tablespoon caster sugar
- 2 oz/60 g best dark bitter chocolate, broken into pieces
- 1 teaspoon unsalted butter at room temperature

### FOR THE MERINGUES
- 3 egg whites
- 3 rounded tablespoons caster sugar
- 1 tablespoon lemon juice

### FOR THE CUSTARD
- ½ pint/300 ml whole milk (or half and half, whole milk and single cream for a really creamy sauce)
- ¼ teaspoon natural vanilla extract (or small vanilla pod)
- 4 egg yolks
- 2 rounded tablespoons caster sugar

## METHOD
Pre-heat the oven to 300 C/150 F/Gas Mark 2.

### FOR THE CHOCOLATE SAUCE
You'll need a small mixing bowl over a pan of gently simmering water for melting the chocolate but don't let the simmering water touch the bowl. In a small saucepan, stir the cream and sugar together and bring to the boil. Remove from heat immediately and set aside to cool a little. In the mixing bowl over the simmering water, melt the chocolate and butter, mixing together until smooth. Pour the warm cream mixture onto the chocolate and stir until completely mixed and smooth. Remove from the heat and set aside until ready to use. This is a useful chocolate sauce that can be made in advance and used warm or cold. If rewarmed do not overheat.

### SAUCE VARIATION
- Add 1 tablespoon of very strong coffee once removed from heat.

### FOR THE MERINGUES
You'll need a flat baking sheet covered with a sheet of lightly buttered greaseproof paper. In a clean mixing bowl, whisk the egg whites together until they make stiff peaks. Whisk in the sugar a little at a time and continue whisking until the mixture forms stiff white peaks. Add the lemon juice and whisk again to the stiff peak stage until the mixture

holds its form when scooped up. Put spoonfuls of the mixture onto the greaseproof paper on the baking sheet. You can build the meringues a little at a time to get a good shape, but leave about 2 inches/5 cm between them to allow for swelling during cooking. Cook in the oven for 10–15 minutes until springy and lightly coloured. Lift the greaseproof paper and meringues onto a cold tray and leave to cool. Be careful when handling as they will be quite sticky. For crisp meringues you need to cook the meringues for 1–1¼ hours so they dry out, but be careful they do not overcook and brown too much. You may need to lower the temperature of your oven to achieve the best result.

FOR THE CUSTARD

You'll need a large mixing bowl which will sit safely in the top of a large saucepan of gently simmering water without the water touching the bowl. Bring the milk to the boil in a saucepan with the vanilla extract or the seeds from the vanilla pod, if used. In the mixing bowl, off the heat, beat the egg yolks and sugar together until well blended. Place the bowl on the saucepan over the simmering water and stir continuously with a wooden spoon while adding the boiling milk a little at a time and keep stirring until the sauce thickens enough to coat the back of a spoon. Remove from the heat, pour into a Pyrex jug or similar and set aside, stirring occasionally to avoid a skin forming, until ready to use. You can make this sauce in advance and serve warm or cold.

TO SERVE

Rewarm the chocolate sauce over simmering water. Do not overheat or the chocolate will go grainy. (If this happens add a tablespoon or two of cold single cream and whisk in to return the sauce to its proper glossy smooth texture.) Divide the custard into four shallow bowls, drizzle with warm chocolate sauce, carefully lift the meringues with a metal slice or flat bladed knife and arrange on top of the sauces. Serve.

# Lemon Rice Pudding ⓥ

A superb, rich dessert for after a Carbohydrate meal.

Food category – C
'1 in 5' – rice
Serves – 4

INGREDIENTS

- rind of 1 lemon
- ½ pint/300 ml water
- ¼ pint/150 ml single cream
- 2 rounded tablespoons granulated sugar
- ¼ teaspoon vanilla extract
- 3 oz/90 g round grain pudding rice
- 1 tablespoon sultanas
- 2 tablespoons water
- 2 tablespoons double cream

You'll require four individual ramekins or small ovenproof dishes for this recipe.

METHOD

Finely grate half the peel of the lemon, trim the white pith from the remaining half of the peel and slice into very fine julienne strips about 2 inches long. In a heavy based, non-stick saucepan mix the water, single cream, one tablespoon of granulated sugar, the grated lemon zest, vanilla extract and rice. Bring to the boil over a medium heat, lower the heat for a gentle simmer, cover and cook, stirring often, for 25 minutes. Add the sultanas and cook for a further 10–15 minutes until the water and cream have been absorbed and the rice pudding is thick, rich and creamy. You actually want the rice a little over cooked. Add a small amount of water if necessary to avoid sticking or drying out. When cooked, set the rice aside to keep warm, until ready to serve.

Place the fine julienne of lemon peel in a small saucepan with the 2 tablespoons of water and the remaining tablespoon of sugar and bring to a rapid simmer. Simmer until the liquor reduces to a thin syrup, taking care not to let it burn, about 4–5 minutes. Remove from the heat and set aside. When ready to serve you will find the rice has thickened. Add the double cream and the lemon peel julienne with its lemon syrup, and stir well until the rice pudding is smooth and creamy again. Spoon the pudding into four ramekins and serve.

# Tiramisu KD Ⓥ

This is as wicked a dessert as you can get without being illegal – save it as an indulgence for very special occasions, about once a decade should be OK. Seriously, this really is a once in a while treat if you want to keep your figure, but it's a KD winner.

Food category – P
'1 in 5' – eggs, nuts (almonds), cheese (Quark, curd cheese)
Serves – 4

## INGREDIENTS

### FOR THE CAKE

- 2 oz/60 g unsalted butter at room temperature
- 2 rounded tablespoons sugar
- 2 heaped tablespoons cocoa powder
- 2 eggs, separated
- 2 rounded tablespooons ground almonds

### FOR THE CREAM

- 12 oz/375 g Greek yogurt
- 7 oz/200 g Quark, curd cheese
- 2 tablespoons sugar
- ½ teaspoon natural vanilla extract

### FOR SOAKING THE CAKE

- 1 tablespoon sugar
- 8–10 fl oz/250–300 ml triple strength black coffee, cold
- 3–4 tablespoons brandy or rum

### FOR SERVING

- 2 oz/60 g best plain chocolate, grated
- 2 teaspoons cocoa powder
- ½ teaspoon ground cinnamon

You'll require an 8 inch/20 cm shallow cake tin for cooking the sponge – I actually use a Le Creuset non-stick frying pan with an ovenproof handle as the shape isn't crucial. You'll also need four small clear glass dishes to show this dessert at its best. I use individual glass ramekins.

## METHOD

### FOR THE CAKE

Pre-heat the oven to 180 C/350 F/Gas Mark 4. Cream the butter and sugar together until soft, then beat in the cocoa powder. Beat in the egg yolks and ground almonds to a smooth mixture. Whisk the egg whites until they are stiff then fold them gently into the butter and almond mixture with a metal spoon. Pour the final mixture into the well greased cake tin. Bake for 30–40 minutes until firm on top and cooked through. Test with the sharp point of a knife which will be clean when withdrawn if the cake is cooked. Remove to a wire tray and set aside to cool.

### FOR THE CREAM

Gently whip the yogurt with the Quark cheese, sugar and vanilla extract to produce a smooth, light yogurt cream. In a mixing bowl, dissolve the sugar in the coffee and stir in the brandy. Cut the chocolate cake into 1 inch/2.5 cm slices. Arrange in the bottom of a shallow dish and pour the brandy and coffee mixture over. Set aside to allow the cake to become saturated. When everything is ready, arrange a layer of cake in the bottom of the four dishes. Add a layer of yogurt cream mixture and sprinkle with grated chocolate. Repeat with another layer of sponge soaked in coffee and brandy, more yogurt cream and finish with a sprinkling of cocoa powder and cinnamon. Chill before serving.

# Treacle Tartlets ⓥ

Rich, sticky and wonderful with a crème fraîche and tangy marmalade accompaniment.

Food category – C
'1 in 5' – wheat (breadcrumbs and pastry)
Serves – 4

INGREDIENTS

FOR THE PASTRY
- 6 oz/175 g plain flour
- 1 oz/30 g icing sugar
- 4 oz/125 g unsalted butter, chilled and diced

- 2–4 tablespoons cold water

(alternatively, use ready made shortcrust pastry without eggs)

FOR THE FILLING
- 10 tablespoons golden syrup (about ¾ of a 454 g tin of Tate and Lyles)
- 2 oz/60 g unsalted butter
- juice and finely grated zest of 1 lemon

- 1 teaspoon fresh ginger root, finely grated, optional
- 6 oz/175 g day old white bread

FOR SERVING
- 2 tablespoons orange or lemon marmalade

- 5 fl oz/150 ml crème fraîche

You'll require four lightly greased, individual size quiche dishes or similar sized tartlet tins.

METHOD
Pre-heat the oven to 180 C/350 F/Gas Mark 4.

FOR THE PASTRY

Sieve the flour and sugar together then mix them in a food processor with the butter and a teaspoon of water. If necessary add more water, a little at a time, until the pastry forms into a ball. Don't process too much or the pastry will become heavy. Alternatively, rub the butter into the sieved flour and sugar by hand to form crumbs, then mix in water, a little at a time, to form a ball of pastry. Cut the pastry into four equal pieces and flatten and roll each piece between sheets of Clingfilm to about $\frac{1}{4}$ inch/6 mm thick. Gently press the pastry into the greased quiche dishes so they are completely lined with pastry. Don't try to roll out the pastry and line and trim the dishes in the usual way. The pastry is wonderfully short and not very robust, so don't handle it directly, use the Clingfilm when working it. Trim the excess with a knife and use the trimmings to repair any tears or holes by patting patches into place. It's very forgiving and won't suffer from being repaired like this. Cook in the oven on a baking tray for 15–20 minutes until just cooked. If using tartlet tins, deduct 5 minutes from cooking time. The pastry is very crumbly when cooked.

FOR THE FILLING

In a saucepan over a low heat, melt and stir together the syrup, butter, lemon juice, zest and grated ginger if used. Slice and trim the crusts from the bread and whizz quickly in a food processor or use your hands to crumble the bread into crumbs. When the pastry cases are just about ready, mix the breadcrumbs into the warm mixture, beat together until well combined and immediately divide between the tartlets pastry cases, taking care not to break the pastry. Bake in the top of the oven for 30–35 minutes until the filling is golden brown. Set aside to cool before serving. The tartlets can be served warm or cold according to your preference. When ready to serve, warm the marmalade in the microwave or over a low heat but do not boil. It needs to be thin and runny. Serve in the quiche dishes or carefully turn out onto small plates. Arrange a quenelle of crème, drizzled with warm marmalade, on each of the treacle tarts. Serve.

# Papaya Fool ⓥ

Papaya or paw paw fruit, has an amazing enzyme capable of breaking down many times its own weight of proteins. This makes papaya a perfect exception to the 'no fruits with Proteins' rule. Here, papaya is made into a cooling fruit fool which can be served after any meal.

Food category – M/A
Serves – 4

INGREDIENTS

- juice and peel of half a lemon
- 12 fl oz/350 ml medium/sweet white wine (e.g. Liebfraumilch)
- 5 tablespoons sugar
- 1 ripe papaya, deseeded, skinned and chopped
- 2 tablespoons water
- agar gelling agent for 1 pint/600 ml fluid
- 6 fl oz/190 ml whipping cream

You'll require four individual dishes or sundae glasses into which the papaya fool can be poured for setting and serving.

METHOD

In a saucepan bring the lemon juice, wine and two tablespoons of the sugar to the boil, remove from the heat and set aside to cool a little. Process the papaya, with half the wine mixture, in a food processor or blender then set aside. Leave the remaining half of the wine mixture in the saucepan. With a sharp knife, trim the white pith from the lemon peel and slice the peel into very fine julienne strips. In a small saucepan bring the two tablespoons of water, one tablespoon of sugar and the julienned lemon peel to a fast simmer. Boil until the liquor reduces by about half then pour into a small basin. Spoon off most of the lemon syrup into the wine mixture in the saucepan, leaving the glazed zest in the basin to be used later for garnish. Sprinkle the agar over the cooled wine mixture in the saucepan. Place the saucepan over a medium heat and bring to a simmer, stirring continuously. Remove from the heat and allow to cool, stirring occasionally, until moderately warm.

Whisk the cream with the remaining two tablespoons of sugar until it thickens. Add the papaya and the whipped cream to the warm wine and agar mixture and stir to combine well. Pour the papaya fool mixture into four individual serving dishes or bowls and chill in the refrigerator until set. Serve garnished with sugar glazed julienne of lemon peel and a drizzle of the remaining lemon syrup.

VARIATION

- For a lighter dessert, omit the cream and two tablespoons of the sugar, and increase the wine content to 18 fl oz/550 ml. Otherwise proceed as described.

# Yoghurt with Chopped Nuts ⓥ

A Greek favourite that's simplicity itself, be sure to use natural vanilla extract, not artificial vanilla flavouring.

Food category – P
'1 in 5' – nuts (your choice)
Serves – 4

INGREDIENTS

- Greek style cow's milk yogurt for 4 people
- natural vanilla extract, to taste
- ground cinnamon

- 5 oz/150g chopped almonds (or nuts of your choice, not peanuts)
- maple syrup or clear honey

METHOD

Beat the yogurt with vanilla extract to your taste until smooth then serve into four cooled dessert bowls or glasses. Sprinkle with ground cinnamon and chopped almonds. Drizzle a small amount of maple syrup or clear honey over each bowl and serve.

VARIATIONS

- Replace cow's milk yogurt with goat's or sheep's milk yogurt for a different '1 in 5' option.
- Stir 2 tablespoons of strong black coffee into the yogurt to make coffee yogurt.
- Vary the chopped nuts and try hazelnuts, macadamia or Brazil nuts which are all separate '1 in 5' items.

# Dessert Salads ⓥ

This recipe makes a refreshing and slightly sweet dessert from a simple green salad, to give a light ending to your meal.

Food category – M/A
Serves – 4

INGREDIENTS

FOR THE DESSERT VINAIGRETTE

- 1 tablespoon white wine vinegar or fruit vinegar (e.g. raspberry)

- 4 tablespoons olive oil

- 1 level teaspoon smooth Dijon mustard
- ½ teaspoon fine sea salt

- 1 tablespoon clear honey or soft brown sugar

FOR THE SALAD
- mixed green salad leaves for four, washed, spun or patted dry (e.g. round lettuce, lamb's lettuce and little gem)

- sea salt and freshly ground black pepper, to taste
- zest of a lemon, finely grated, for garnish

TASTE SENSATION
maple syrup, optional

METHOD
Measure the vinaigrette ingredients into a large screw top jar. Screw down the top of the jar and shake vigorously until the ingredients blend and thicken into a smooth dressing. Alternatively, mix all the ingredients except the oil in a large bowl, then whisk in the oil a little at a time to produce the same result. Prepare the salad leaves by tearing to suitable size and cutting lettuce hearts into wedges. Mix together, in a large bowl, until well distributed. Toss the salad leaves in the dessert vinaigrette until evenly coated. Season to taste with salt, pepper. Divide and arrange the salad into four soup bowls, sprinkle with lemon zest and drizzle with a few drops of maple syrup if desired. Serve.

VARIATIONS
*The Salad*

Food category – M/A
- Vary the salad leaves to introduce other flavours such as the peppery taste of rocket or watercress as a contrast to the sweet vinaigrette.
- Add tender stalks of fresh celery, sweet onions, pickled sliced ginger or young fresh mange tout (blanched and refreshed in cold water) for their sweet taste in the salad.

Food category – C
- Add and mix in any dried fruit after dressing the salad – try chopped dates, sultanas, chopped dried figs, candied lemon peel, for instance.

TIPS
☞ For an orange dressing, replace the vinegar with the same

amount of store-bought orange juice and a few drops of natural orange essence. Then add 1 tablespoon of honey, a pinch of salt and freshly ground black pepper and whisk to blend into an orange dressing with olive oil or sunflower oil. Set aside in the refrigerator so the oil thickens a little and makes the dressing smoother. The dressing may not bind into a smooth vinaigrette as it would with vinegar and may require whisking before dressing the salad.

# Goat's Cheeses and Crudités with Walnuts ⓥ

Arranging the cheeses onto individual plates enables you to make an attractive presentation and control the portion sizes of what could otherwise be a fattening dish.

Food category – P
'1 in 5' – goat's and sheep's milk cheeses, walnuts
Serves – 4

INGREDIENTS

- 4 oz/125 g creamy goat's milk cheese (e.g. Chavroux)
- 1 tablespoon of very finely chopped mixed fresh herbs (or 1 teaspoon dried)
- prepared crudités, your choice for four, (see page 72)

- additional selection of goat's and sheep's milk cheeses (e.g. fetta, chèvre, Roquefort)
- raw walnuts for four, shelled or whole

METHOD

In a mixing bowl beat the cream cheese until soft, add the mixed herbs and combine well but gently and set aside in a refrigerator to cool. Slice one or two pieces of crudités into fine julienne, for garnish, and prepare the remainder as usual. Arrange 4 plates with a serving of each of the three selected cheeses, a scoop of the cream cheese and herb mixture with a little black pepper milled over, and a selection of crudités. Mix the remaining crudités together in a large serving bowl for passing around. Garnish each plate, and the serving bowl of crudités, with a little of the finely sliced crudités. Serve with a bowl of walnuts to pass around, not forgetting a nut cracker if needed.

# Cow's Milk Cheeses with Crudités and Salsa ⓥ

Food category – P
'1 in 5' – cow's milk cheeses
Serves – 4

INGREDIENTS

- prepared crudités, your choice for four (see page 72) (e.g. cherry tomatoes on the vine, carrots, celery, cauliflower florettes)
- your selection of 3 or 4 cow's milk cheeses (e.g. cheddar, double Gloucester, Edam, red Leicester)
- green salsa (or your choice of sweet pickle)

METHOD

Select one or two pieces of crudités and slice them into fine julienne strips for garnish. Arrange each of four plates with servings of your chosen cheeses and garnish with a few of the fine slices of julienne crudités. (Serving the cheeses separately means you can control the portions for those who are concerned about their weight). Arrange a selection of crudités into each of four side bowls and put the salsa pickles in serving bowls to pass around. Serve.

# EMBELLISHMENTS

Here is a selection of irresistible and attractive sauces, dressings and salsas to enhance almost any meal or dish they meet. I've included garnishes – yes, you should eat them – to create stunning presentations as well as my personal collection of taste sensations: small additions that will tantalise and surprise your tastebuds. All in all this section will help you create memorable meals that incite a 'must have that again' reaction.

## Basic Tomato Sauce (v)

A quick and simple tomato sauce. You want all the water from the tomatoes evaporated away until you reduce the ingredients to a really thick sauce, so it's best to use a deep saucepan to avoid splattering. Use this sauce as it is or add ingredients to create a variety of sauces. Alter the consistency with stock or olive oil, or even add a little sauce to vinaigrette and drizzle over vegetables, salads, meats, poultry or fish. Of course, you could always serve this sauce over pasta!

Food category – M/A
Serves – 4

INGREDIENTS
- 2 tablespoons olive oil
- 1 large onion, finely sliced
- 1–2 cloves garlic, finely chopped

- 16 oz/500 g tin or jar of
  passata (crushed and drained
  tomatoes), or equivalent of
  chopped plum tomatoes, skinned
  and deseeded.
- 1 tablespoon tomato purée
- good pinch of sugar to taste
- sea salt and freshly ground black
  pepper, to taste

METHOD

Heat the oil in a deep, heavy based saucepan, over a medium heat, sauté the onions and garlic, without browning, until the onions are soft and clear, 5–10 minutes. Add the passata and tomato purée, and a little salt and pepper seasoning, bring to a simmer and cook uncovered, stirring occasionally, until reduced to a thick tomato sauce, about 25–30 minutes. Season to taste with sugar, salt and pepper. For a smoother sauce, purée in a food processor or blender and force through a fine metal sieve with a spoon.

VARIATIONS

- For a herb tomato sauce, add 2 teaspoons of dried herbs with the tomatoes or 2 tablespoons of finely chopped fresh herbs at the end of cooking with the seasoning (try marjoram, oregano, provençal herbs, parsley).
- For a spicy tomato sauce, finely chop one half of a red chilli pepper, taking care to wash your hands well after preparation, add along with the onions and garlic, then add Tabasco sauce to taste with the other seasonings.

# Rich Tomato Sauce ⓥ

This is a spectacular tomato sauce for special meals which uses puréed vegetables for thickening. Use on pasta, as a bed for fish or meat courses, or spoon it around roast vegetables and slices of fried polenta. Again it's best to use a deep saucepan to avoid splashing as you reduce the ingredients to a thick sauce.

Food category – M/A
Serves – 4

INGREDIENTS

- 2 tablespoons olive oil
- 1 large onion, finely sliced
- 2 sticks celery, finely chopped
- ½ fennel bulb, finely chopped

- 4–6 carrots, peeled, trimmed and chopped small
- 16 oz/500 g tin or jar of passata (crushed and drained tomatoes), or equivalent of chopped plum tomatoes, skinned and deseeded.
- 1 clove garlic, finely chopped
- 1 tablespoon orange zest, finely grated

- ¼ teaspoon saffron powder
- 1 tablespoon tomato purée
- 1 cup white wine – optional
- 1 cup tomato juice
- 1 teaspoon sugar
- sea salt and freshly ground black pepper, to taste

METHOD

Heat the oil in a deep, heavy based saucepan, over a low to medium heat, cook the onions, celery, fennel and carrots together, without browning, until the onions are soft and clear, about 10 minutes. Stir occasionally during this time otherwise keep covered. Add tomatoes, garlic, orange zest, saffron, tomato purée and wine if used, and lightly season with salt and freshly ground black pepper. Bring to a gentle simmer and cook, uncovered, stirring occasionally, until all the vegetables are soft and the tomatoes are reduced to a thick sauce.

Purée in a food processor or blender and force through a fine metal sieve to make the sauce as smooth as possible. Adjust the consistency with a little tomato juice or water if the sauce is too thick for your taste or the dish for which it's required. Adjust the seasoning to your taste with sugar and more salt and pepper.

# Sage and Onion Sauce ⓥ

This is more a thin purée than a sauce since the thickening comes from processing the onions in the stock. It's a delicious way of thickening sauces without using a starch. Use as a bed for chicken or pork, or pour over roasted or steamed winter vegetables and roast potatoes.

Food category – M/A
Serves – 4

INGREDIENTS

- 1 tablespoon olive oil
- 2 large onions, sliced
- 1½ pints/900 ml Basic Vegetable Stock (see page 48)

- 1 cup finely chopped fresh sage leaves
- sea salt and freshly ground black pepper for seasoning

METHOD

Heat the oil in a heavy based saucepan, over a medium heat and sauté the onions until soft but not brown, about 5 minutes. Add two-thirds of the stock and simmer for 5–10 minutes until the onions are very soft. Remove from the heat, add the sage leaves and, with a hand blender or in a processor, purée to a smooth runny sauce. Use more stock if required to produce the consistency you like. Force the sauce through a fine metal sieve back into the saucepan and simmer for two more minutes, check and adjust the seasoning with salt and pepper. The sauce is now ready to serve.

VARIATION

• For a Protein sauce to be used with poultry or pork, substitute well flavoured chicken stock for the vegetable stock.

## Creamy Mushroom Sauce ⓥ

Really an adaptation of a thick and creamy mushroom soup. Pour over poultry, meat or fish, or use as a sauce for puréed, roast or steamed vegetables.

Food category – M/A
Serves – 4

INGREDIENTS

• 1 small onion, finely chopped
• 2 tablespoons olive oil
• 8 oz/250 g chestnut mushrooms, wiped clean and chopped (retain 2 small mushrooms whole for garnish)
• 4 oz/125 g oyster mushrooms, wiped clean and chopped
• pinch ground nutmeg
• 3 tablespoons dry sherry (or white wine)

• 8 fl oz/250 ml Basic Vegetable Stock, (see page 48)
• 1 small clove of garlic, finely chopped
• small bunch fresh thyme
• 5 fl oz/150 ml double cream
• sea salt and freshly ground black pepper, to taste

METHOD

In a heavy based saucepan, over a low heat, sauté the chopped onion in the olive oil, stirring occasionally, until soft but not browned, about 5–10 minutes. Add the chopped mushrooms, nutmeg, sherry or wine, two-thirds of the vegetable stock, garlic and thyme. Season lightly with black pepper and salt, (avoid adding salt if using stock cubes). Bring to simmer, and cook very gently, uncovered for 25–30 minutes, stirring occasionally. Slice the 2 small whole mushrooms very thinly. When the mushrooms in the sauce are soft and well cooked strain through a fine sieve into a bowl, pressing the mushrooms gently to extract all the juices. You should have about half the original quantity of stock, now flavoured with the concentrated flavours of mushrooms and herbs.

Return the mushroom liquor to the saucepan, bring to a gentle simmer, add the thin slices of mushrooms, then add and stir in the double cream and stir and simmer for 2–3 minutes more. Adjust the consistency to your preference if necessary, by adding extra stock. Adjust the flavouring with a further seasoning of salt and freshly ground black pepper if required. The sauce is now ready to use.

VARIATIONS
*   Try other herbs to suit the meals in which the sauce is to be used. Parsley is excellent for white fish, sage with pork and poultry.
*   For use with beef or lamb steak add and stir in a tablespoon of green peppercorns with the thinly sliced mushrooms and cream.

# Onion Gravy Ⓥ

A savoury Carbohydrate gravy thickened with flour and best made in the juices from roasted onions (see page 185).

Food category – C
'1 in 5' – wheat
Serves – 4

INGREDIENTS
*   2 teaspoons yeast extract (e.g. Marmite)
*   1 pint/600 ml hot Basic Vegetable Stock (see page 48)
*   quarter of an onion, thinly sliced

*   1 tablespoon sunflower or groundnut oil
*   1 tablespoon self raising flour
*   sea salt and freshly ground black pepper, to taste

METHOD
Dissolve the yeast extract in the hot vegetable stock. On the hob, in a roasting tin with juices from roasting onions or in a saucepan, rapidly fry the sliced onions in the oil, with frequent stirring, until soft and lightly

browned. Add the flour and cook for about a minute, stirring continuously as it foams. Add the vegetable stock and yeast extract and bring to a simmer, stirring continuously, until the mixture thickens into a rich gravy. Remove from heat and serve.

# Sweet Pepper Coulis ⓥ

Simply a smooth purée of roasted red or yellow peppers to add flavour and colour to many dishes. Use red peppers for a red sauce and yellow for a yellow sauce, as accompaniments to grilled or poached fish or light meat dishes, or with grilled vegetables.

Food category – M/A
Serves – 4

INGREDIENTS

- 2 large red peppers (or yellow peppers for a yellow sauce)
- 2 small shallots or ½ small onion, peeled and finely chopped
- 1 small clove garlic, peeled and finely chopped
- 2 tablespoons Basic Vegetable Stock (see page 48)

- 1 tablespoon white wine vinegar (or cider vinegar)
- 2 tablespoons extra virgin olive oil
- sugar to taste
- sea salt and freshly ground black pepper, to taste

METHOD

Grill the peppers under a very hot grill until well charred on all sides. Place in a bowl and cover with Clingfilm to cool. In a small, covered saucepan, over a low heat, simmer the shallots and garlic in the vegetable stock and wine vinegar, stirring occasionally, until the shallots are soft and clear. Core, deseed and skin the peppers taking care to remove all the black skin or it will colour the coulis. Retain the juices. Purée the peppers and juices with the shallot and garlic mixture in a food processor or blender then continue processing while adding the olive oil in a steady stream. Adjust the flavour to your taste with a pinch of sugar if required and sea salt and freshly ground black pepper.

VARIATIONS

- For use with more robust grilled or fried fish or roasted poultry, use herbs and flavoured oils to give a different taste to the coulis.
- For fish, try a sprig of tarragon, simmered with the shallots. Remove before processing and add tarragon flavoured olive oil.

- For poultry, try a sprig of rosemary, removed before processing and add rosemary flavoured oil.

# Warm Herb Vinaigrette Ⓥ

This recipe is for warm parsley vinaigrette which is delicious as a sauce on fish, poultry or just on steamed vegetables, but you could just as well use other herbs such as basil, tarragon or chives. Warm vinaigrette is attractive and so simple to make.

Food category – M/A
Serves – 4

INGREDIENTS

- 1 large bunch fresh, flat leaf parsley, trimmed of coarse stalks
- 2 servings Basic Vinaigrette made as you like it (see page 73)

METHOD

Blanch and refresh the parsley by pouring a kettle full of boiling water over it in a sieve or colander then immediately plunging it into cold water. Drain and dry the parsley in a salad spinner or on kitchen paper, then chop finely. When ready to dress your dish, warm the Basic Vinaigrette in a small saucepan but do not allow it to boil – you want it warm, not hot. Stir in the chopped parsley, remove from the heat and use immediately or the dressing will discolour the herbs and alter the flavour.

VARIATION

- Add a tablespoon of very finely chopped fresh, skinned and seeded tomato or shallot to the warm vinaigrette with the parsley or other herbs.

# Fennel Vinaigrette Ⓥ

An unusual vinaigrette variation, especially good with salads to accompany fish.

Food category – M/A
Serves – 4

INGREDIENTS

- one bulb fennel
- 10 tablespoons Basic Vinaigrette (see page 73)

METHOD

Chop the fennel roughly, retaining the fronds for garnishing the salad. Poach the chopped fennel in $\frac{1}{2}$ pint/300 ml of water or vegetable stock, until it is quite soft. Remove to cold water to cool rapidly. Drain and pat dry and, in a food processor, blend the fennel with the vinaigrette to create Fennel Vinaigrette.

# Mustard Mayonnaise ⓥ

A Mix With Any mayonnaise without eggs will make your Kensington Diet more enjoyable. Use as an accompaniment to cold poached salmon or trout or with cold chicken, spoon onto boiled new potatoes or spread in a sandwich with salad.

Food category – M/A
Serves – 4

INGREDIENTS

- 6 tablespoons boiling water
- 4 tablespoons Dijon mustard
- extra virgin olive oil, for blending

- lemon juice, to taste
- sea salt and freshly ground black pepper, to taste

METHOD

In a food processor or blender add the boiling water to the mustard while the machine is mixing, then add olive oil in a stream until the mixture binds to a good mayonnaise consistency. Season to taste with a little lemon juice, sea salt and freshly ground black pepper. The basic mayonnaise is now ready to serve, mix in the chopped herbs of your choice if desired.

VARIATIONS

- For even more flavour add 2–3 whole garlic cloves, blanched in boiling water for 2 minutes then skinned, before adding the olive oil.
- Add 1 cup of very finely chopped dill, tarragon, parsley, basil or chives to the finished mayonnaise.

# Simple Mayonnaise ⓥ

Here is another Mix With Any mayonnaise which is so easy you may not ever bother with anything else after this. This mayonnaise is for cold dishes and makes a wonderful cold potato salad when mixed with cooked new potatoes and chives.

Food category – M/A
Serves – 4

INGREDIENTS

- ½ pint/300 ml crème fraîche (or soured cream)
- 1 tablespoon Basic Vinaigrette (see page 73)
- Dijon mustard to taste
- sea salt and freshly ground black pepper, to taste

METHOD

In a bowl mix the crème fraîche with Dijon mustard and seasoning to your taste. Chill until ready to use.

VARIATIONS

- See the recipe for Mustard Mayonnaise, above, for herb and garlic variations which also apply to this version.

# Tartare Sauce ⓥ

Food category – M/A
Serves – 4

INGREDIENTS

- 1 tablespoon chopped capers, patted dry
- 1 tablespoon chopped cocktail gherkins
- 1 tablespoon finely chopped shallot
- 1 tablespoon finely chopped fresh parsley
- 1 serving of Simple Mayonnaise (see above) or Basic Mustard Mayonnaise (page 278)
- sea salt and freshly ground black pepper, to taste

METHOD

Mix all the ingredients in a mixing bowl, test the seasoning and adjust with salt and pepper if required and adjust the consistency with a little pickling liquor from the capers if necessary.

# Green Salsa ⓥ

Like a crispy, crunchy, tangy, tasty relish this salsa goes well spooned alongside or onto grilled or barbecued meats, poultry or fish as well as with cheeses, boiled new potatoes or slices of fried polenta.

Food category – M/A
Serves – 4

### INGREDIENTS

- 1 medium green pepper, cored and seeded
- 1 small cucumber, peeled and seeds scraped out and discarded
- 2 spring onions, trimmed and washed
- 4 oz/125 g green olives, pitted
- 4 oz/125 g (about ½ cup pickled gherkins or dill pickles)
- 1 tablespoon small capers, drained

- 1 clove garlic, finely crushed
- 2 tablespoons fresh parsley, finely chopped
- small squeeze lemon juice
- 2–3 tablespoons Basic Vinaigrette as you like it (see page 73)
- pinch sugar to taste
- sea salt and freshly ground black pepper, to taste

### METHOD

Chop the pepper, cucumber, spring onions, olives and gherkins into small dice. The size of the dice will give the character to the finished salsa. ¼ inch/6 mm dice is quite chunky, while ⅛ inch/3 mm is finer and easier to spread. Don't be tempted to use a food processor or you'll end up with a watery mush. Mix the chopped ingredients in a bowl with the capers, garlic, parsley and the lemon juice. Add vinaigrette a little at a time and combine until the dressing just coats all the ingredients, don't use so much that you get chopped salad in vinaigrette sauce. Season to taste with a little sugar and salt and pepper if desired although the pickled ingredients will have added salt already. Your salsa is now ready to use. Spoon onto arranged plates in individual servings or pass around in a bowl.

### VARIATIONS

Add spice and bite to your green salsa with any or all of the following:
- 1 tablespoon of finely chopped pickled green chilli peppers
- 1 teaspoon whole green peppercorns
- 1 teaspoon green jalapeno Tabasco sauce

# Summer Tomato Salsa ⓥ

Fresh and refreshing, this tomato based salsa is perfect with all kinds of grilled, fried or barbecued meats, fish and poultry but it's equally good spooned over baked jacket potatoes, as a filling for avocado halves or used as a dip for corn chips or potato skins.

Food category – M/A
Serves – 4

INGREDIENTS

- 1 lb/500 g fresh, ripe plum or salad tomatoes, seeds removed and stalk ends trimmed away
- 1 medium mild onion (red or Spanish)
- 1 small cucumber, peeled and seeds scraped out and discarded
- 2 bunches radishes, washed and trimmed

- 1 cup finely chopped fresh basil leaves (or mint)
- small squeeze lemon juice
- 2–3 tablespoons Basic Vinaigrette (see page 73)
- 1 teaspoon tomato purée, optional
- sea salt and freshly ground black pepper, to taste

METHOD

Chop the tomatoes into small dice and set aside in a fine sieve for 15–20 minutes, to drain off excess water. Remember the size of the dice will give the character to the finished salsa. $\frac{1}{4}$ inch/6 mm dice is quite chunky, while $\frac{1}{8}$ inch/3 mm is finer and easier to spread. Don't be tempted to use a food processor or you'll end up with a watery mush. Chop the onion, cucumber and radishes into small dice about the same size as the tomatoes. Mix all the chopped ingredients in a bowl with the basil and the lemon juice and combine well. Add vinaigrette a little at a time and combine until the dressing just coats and binds all the ingredients, don't use so much that you get chopped salad in vinaigrette sauce. Add and mix in the tomato purée, if used, to strengthen the tomato flavour and bind the salsa together more. Season to taste with a little salt and pepper. Your salsa is now ready to use. Spoon onto prepared plates in individual servings or pass around in a bowl.

VARIATION

For a spicy Mexican flavour, replace the cucumber with a medium red or yellow pepper, diced to the same size as the other ingredients. Add 1 teaspoon of finely chopped red chilli pepper, taking care to wash your hands well after preparation. Replace the chopped basil or mint with finely chopped fresh coriander. Replace the lemon juice with lime if desired. Add red Tabasco sauce to taste with other seasoning.

# GARNISHES AND TASTE SENSATIONS

This is a selection of some of my favourite ways to add taste notes and attractive garnishes to meals.

## Basic Pesto ⓥ

Here's a recipe for a traditional style Protein pesto and some variations to use with meat, fish and poultry dishes, as a flavouring for soups and stews, to mix with cream cheese, and of course for use with all Mix With Any vegetables.

Food category – P
'1 in 5' – pine nuts, Parmesan cheese
Serves – 4

INGREDIENTS
- 1 cup fresh basil leaves
- 5 oz/150 g pine nuts, toasted golden brown
- 1–2 cloves garlic, finely crushed
- 6–8 tablespoons best virgin olive oil
- 2 rounded tablespoons freshly grated Parmesan
- sea salt and freshly grated black pepper, to taste

METHOD
In a food processor or blender, purée the basil, pine nuts, garlic and half the olive oil together to an even mixture. Pour into a mixing bowl and blend in the Parmesan and enough of the remaining olive oil, a little at a time, to produce a thick smooth paste. Season to taste with salt and pepper. Your pesto is now ready for use.

VARIATIONS

Make any of the following variations to the processed ingredients and bring to the required consistency by adjusting the amount of oil used at the end:

- Add 1–2 tablespoons of lemon juice.

or

- Replace the pine nuts with walnuts, roasted in the top of a hot oven for 10–15 minutes, cooled and skinned by rubbing in a clean cloth.

or

- Replace the basil with parsley or coriander and add lemon juice and zest to taste.

# Alternative Pesto ⓥ

Now here's a recipe for pesto you can use for all those Carbohydrate meals such as pasta, pesto-flavoured mashed potatoes, pesto butter on baked jacket potatoes and to spread on bruschettas or polenta slices topped with roasted peppers and aubergines.

Food category – C
'1 in 5' – wheat (bread), peanuts
Serves – 4

INGREDIENTS

- 1 small day old loaf of bread
- 3 oz/90 g unsalted, roasted peanuts
- 1 cup fresh basil leaves
- 1–2 cloves garlic, finely crushed

- best virgin olive oil
- sea salt and freshly grated black pepper, to taste

METHOD

Cut the crusts from the loaf and process the bread into fine breadcrumbs. Set aside. Blanch the peanuts in boiling water for two minutes, remove, drain and when cool enough to handle rub off the skins with a clean cloth. In a food processor or blender, purée the peanuts, basil, garlic and four tablespoons of olive oil to an even mixture. Add one cup of the breadcrumbs and four more tablespoons of olive oil and blend again to combine the ingredients. Add more olive oil if necessary, a little at a time, to produce a thick smooth paste. Season to taste with salt and pepper. Your alternative pesto is now ready for use.

# Purée of Roasted Garlic Ⓥ

Delicious for drizzling over puréed vegetables with red meats, but equally good with pasta, polenta and baked jacket potatoes. If using with meat, cook the garlic at the same time as the joint and make the purée while it is resting before slicing.

Food category – M/A
Serves – 4

INGREDIENTS
- 2 whole bulbs garlic (about 1 cup of whole cloves), skin on
- 1–2 tablespoons olive oil
- approximately 5 fl oz/300 ml Basic Vegetable Stock (see page 48)
- sea salt and freshly ground black pepper, to taste

METHOD
Pre-heat the oven to 200 C/400 F/Gas Mark 6. In a small ovenproof dish or pan toss the garlic cloves in the olive oil until well coated and roast in the oven until just soft, about 10–15 minutes. Test by putting a clove on a sheet of foil, split the non-root end with a knife and press with a spoon, if the garlic flesh squeezes out like a paste then it's cooked. Squeeze out the flesh of all the cloves as described above. Put into a blender or mash through a fine sieve with enough vegetable stock to make a fairly thick running purée, suitable to drizzle on your dish. Season to taste with salt and black pepper.

# Mint Purée Ⓥ

Another powerfully flavoured purée which is particularly good with lamb, but try it on dishes of all kinds.

Food category – M/A
Serves – 4

INGREDIENTS
- 2 cups of fresh mint leaves, washed
- juice and finely grated zest of half a lemon
- pinch of sugar
- ½ pt/300 ml Basic Vegetable Stock (see page 48)
- sea salt and freshly ground black pepper, to taste

METHOD

Blanch the mint leaves in boiling water for 5–10 seconds. Drain and remove to a food processor or blender. Add the juice and zest of the lemon and the sugar, and purée, adding enough of the stock, a little at a time until you have a smooth, fairly thick running purée suitable for drizzling. Season to taste with salt and pepper.

VARIATIONS
- Try other herbs such as basil, thyme, oregano and parsley in place of the mint.

# Garlic Chips Ⓥ

These pungent chips of garlic add another dimension of flavour which you can scatter over just about anything. Particularly good on soups and Lentil Curry (see page 202).

Food category – M/A
Serves – 4

INGREDIENTS
- 4–6 large cloves garlic
- 1–2 tablespoons olive oil

METHOD

Peel the garlic cloves, cut them into matchstick thin slices and fry in a little olive oil until nutty brown on both sides. Cook a few at a time to avoid burning the garlic chips which 'turn' very quickly and need careful attention. Set aside on kitchen paper to drain off excess oil.

# CONVERSION TABLES

These conversions are approximate only. The difference between the exact and approximate conversions of liquid and dry measures amounts to only a teaspoon or two, and will not make any noticeable difference to your cooking results.

## DRY MEASURES

| METRIC | IMPERIAL |
|---|---|
| 15g | ½oz |
| 30g | 1oz |
| 60g | 2oz |
| 90g | 3oz |
| 125g | 4oz (¼lb) |
| 155g | 5oz |
| 185g | 6oz |
| 220g | 7oz |
| 250g | 8oz (½ lb) |
| 280g | 9oz |
| 315g | 10oz |
| 345g | 11oz |
| 375g | 12oz (¾lb) |
| 410g | 13oz |
| 440g | 14oz |
| 470g | 15oz |
| 500g | 16oz (1lb) |
| 750g | 24oz (1½lb) |
| 1kg | 32oz (2lb) |

## LIQUID MEASURES

| METRIC | IMPERIAL |
|---|---|
| 30ml | 1 fluid oz |
| 60ml | 2 fluid oz |
| 100ml | 3 fluid oz |
| 125ml | 4 fluid oz |
| 150ml | 5 fluid oz |
|  | (¼ pint) |
| 190ml | 6 fluid oz |
| 250ml | 8 fluid oz |
| 300ml | 10 fluid oz |
|  | (½ pint) |
| 500ml | 16 fluid oz |
| 600ml | 20 fluid oz |
|  | (1 pint) |
| 1000ml | 1¾ pints |
| (1 litre) |  |

## USEFUL MEASURES

| METRIC | IMPERIAL |
|---|---|
| 1cm | ½in |
| 2cm | ¾in |
| 2.5cm | 1in |
| 5cm | 2in |
| 6cm | 2½in |
| 8cm | 3in |
| 10cm | 4in |
| 13cm | 5in |
| 15cm | 6in |
| 18cm | 7in |
| 20cm | 8in |
| 23cm | 9in |
| 25cm | 10in |
| 28cm | 11in |
| 30cm | 12in (1ft) |

## OVEN TEMPERATURES

These oven temperatures are only a guide – always check the manufacturer's manual.

| | C (CELSIUS) | F (FAHRENHEIT) | GAS MARK |
|---|---|---|---|
| Very slow | 120 | 250 | 1 |
| Slow | 150 | 300 | 2 |
| Moderately slow | 160 | 325 | 3 |
| Moderate | 180 | 350 | 4 |
| Moderately hot | 190 | 375 | 5 |
| Hot | 200 | 400 | 6 |
| Very hot | 230 | 450 | 7 |

# THE KD FOOD DIRECTORY

| Key To The Directory | |
|---|---|
| Protein | P |
| Carbohydrate | C |
| Mix with Any | M/A |
| Fruit | F |
| Acidifying | Ac |
| Alkalising | Al |
| Neither Ac nor Al | N |
| '1 in 5' food | * |
| Use sparingly | ! |

| FOOD | CATEGORY | TYPE | NOTES |
|---|---|---|---|
| Abalone | P | Ac | * |
| Agar | M/A | Al | |
| Allspice | M/A | Ac | |
| Almonds | P | Al | * |
| Anchovies | P | Ac | * |
| Angelica | M/A | Al | |
| Arrowroot | C | Al | * |
| Artichoke | M/A | Al | |
| Asparagus | M/A | Ac | |
| Aubergine | M/A | Al | |
| Avocado | M/A | Al | |
| Bacon | P | Ac | * |
| Bamboo shoots | M/A | Al | |
| Barley | C | Ac | * |
| Basil | M/A | Al | |
| Barramundi | P | Ac | * |

| | | | |
|---|---|---|---|
| Bass | P | Ac | * |
| Bay leaves | M/A | Al | |
| Beans dried (all) | C | Ac | * |
| Beans green (all) | M/A | Al | |
| Bean sprouts | M/A | Al | |
| Beef | P | Ac | * |
| Beetroot | M/A | Al | |
| Biscuits (all) | C | Ac | * |
| Borage | M/A | Al | |
| Brazil Nuts | P | Al | * |
| Bread (all) | C | Ac | * |
| Bream | P | Ac | * |
| Broccoli | M/A | Al | |
| Brussels sprouts | M/A | Al | |
| Buckwheat | C | Ac | * |
| Bulgar wheat | C | Ac | * |
| Butter (fat) | M/A | N | ! |
| Buttermilk | P | Al | * |
| Cabbage | M/A | Al | |
| Calabrese | M/A | Al | |
| Capers | M/A | Ac | ! |
| Capsicum | M/A | Al | |
| Caraway seeds | P | Al | * |
| Cardamom | M/A | Ac | ! |
| Carob | P | Ac | * |
| Carrots | M/A | Al | |
| Cashew nuts | P | Ac | * |
| Cauliflower | M/A | Al | |
| Cayenne (chilli) | M/A | Al | ! |
| Celeriac | M/A | Al | |
| Celery | M/A | Al | |
| Celery salt | M/A | Al | ! |
| Celery seeds | P | Al | * |
| Chard | M/A | Al | |
| Cheese (all) | P | Ac | * |
| Chervil | M/A | Al | |
| Chicken | P | Ac | * |
| Chickpeas | C | Ac | * |
| Chicory | M/A | Al | |
| Chives | M/A | Al | |
| Chocolate | M/A | Ac | ! |
| Cinnamon | M/A | Ac | ! |
| Clams | P | Ac | * |
| Cloves | M/A | Ac | |
| Cockles | P | Ac | * |
| Coconut | P | Ac | * |
| Cod | P | Ac | * |
| Coffee (caffeinated) | M/A | Ac | ! |
| Collard greens | M/A | Al | |

| | | | |
|---|---|---|---|
| Comfrey | M/A | Al | |
| Condiments (all) | M/A | | ! |
| Coriander | M/A | Al | |
| Corn (maize) | C | Al | * |
| Cornflour | C | Ac | * |
| Courgette (zucchini) | M/A | Al | |
| Cous cous (wheat) | C | Ac | * |
| Crab | P | Ac | * |
| Crayfish | P | Ac | * |
| Cream | M/A | N | ! |
| Cress | M/A | Al | |
| Cucumber | M/A | Al | |
| Cumin | M/A | Ac | ! |
| Dandelion greens | M/A | Al | |
| Dill | M/A | Al | |
| Dill seeds | M/A | Al | |
| Duck | P | Ac | * |
| Eel | P | Ac | * |
| Eggplant (aubergine) | M/A | Al | |
| Eggs (all kinds) | P | Ac | * |
| Endive (chicory) | M/A | Al | |
| Fennel | M/A | Al | |
| Fennel seeds | M/A | Al | |
| Fenugreek sprouts | M/A | Al | |
| Fenugreek seeds | M/A | Al | |
| Filberts (hazelnuts) | P | Ac | * |
| Fish (all) | P | Ac | * |
| Flounder | P | Ac | * |
| Fromage frais | P | Al | * |
| Fruit (all) | F | Al | |
| Game (all) | P | Ac | * |
| Garbanzos | C | Ac | * |
| Garlic | M/A | Al | ! |
| Gelatine | P | Ac | ! |
| Ginger | M/A | Ac | ! |
| Goat (meat and milk) | P | Ac | * |
| Goose | P | Ac | * |
| Gourds (all) | M/A | Al | |
| Gramflour (chickpeas) | C | Ac | * |
| Guinea fowl | P | Ac | * |
| Haddock | P | Ac | * |
| Hake | P | Ac | * |
| Halibut | P | Ac | * |
| Hazelnuts | P | Ac | * |
| Herring | P | Ac | * |
| Honey | C | Ac | ! |
| Horseradish | M/A | Ac | ! |
| Ice cream (dairy) | P | Ac | * |
| Kale (collard greens) | M/A | Al | |

| | | | |
|---|---|---|---|
| Kelp | M/A | Al | |
| Kohlrabi | M/A | Al | |
| Lamb | P | Ac | * |
| Lard (animal fat) | M/A | Ac | ! |
| Leeks | M/A | Al | |
| Lemon grass | M/A | Al | |
| Lemon verbena | M/A | Al | |
| Lentils | C | Ac | * |
| Lettuce (all kinds) | M/A | Al | |
| Linseeds | P | Al | * |
| Liquorice | M/A | Ac | ! |
| Lobster | P | Ac | * |
| Love | M/A | Al | |
| Macadamia nuts | P | Ac | * |
| Macaroni (non-egg) | C | Ac | * |
| Mackerel | P | Ac | * |
| Maize corn | C | Al | * |
| Mange tout | M/A | Al | |
| Maple syrup | C | Ac | ! |
| Margarine | M/A | N | ! |
| Marjoram | M/A | Al | |
| Marrow | M/A | Al | |
| Meat (all) | P | Ac | * |
| Melons (all) | F | Al | ! |
| Milk (pasteurised) | P | Ac | ! |
| Milk (unpasteurised) | P | Al | ! |
| Millet | C | Al | * |
| Mint | M/A | Al | |
| Molasses | C | Ac | ! |
| Mullet | P | Ac | * |
| Mushrooms | M/A | Al | ! |
| Mussels | P | Ac | * |
| Mustard | M/A | Ac | ! |
| Mustard and cress | M/A | Al | |
| Nutmeg | M/A | Ac | ! |
| Oats | C | Ac | * |
| Octopus | P | Ac | * |
| Offal | P | Ac | * |
| Oil (all) | M/A | N | ! |
| Okra | M/A | Al | |
| Olives (marinated) | M/A | Ac | ! |
| Onion | M/A | Al | ! |
| Oregano | M/A | Al | |
| Oysters | P | Ac | * |
| Paprika | M/A | Ac | ! |
| Parsley | M/A | Al | |
| Parsnips | M/A | Al | |
| Partridge | P | Ac | * |
| Pasta (non-egg) | C | Ac | * |

| | | | |
|---|---|---|---|
| Pastry | C | Ac | * |
| Peanuts | C | Ac | * * |
| Pearl barley | C | Ac | * |
| Peas (fresh) | M/A | Al | |
| Pecans | P | Ac | * |
| Pepper (capsicum) | M/A | Al | |
| Pepper (spice) | M/A | Ac | ! |
| Pheasant | P | Ac | * |
| Pilchards | P | Ac | * |
| Pine nuts | P | Ac | * |
| Pistachios | P | Ac | * * |
| Plaice | P | Ac | * |
| Poppy seeds | M/A | Al | |
| Pork | P | Ac | * |
| Potato | C | Al | * |
| Poultry (all) | P | Ac | * |
| Prawns | P | Ac | * |
| Pulses (legumes all) | C | Ac | * |
| Pumpkin | M/A | Al | |
| Pumpkin seeds | M/A | Al | * |
| Quail | P | Ac | * |
| Quince | F | Al | |
| Rabbit | P | Ac | * |
| Radicchio | M/A | Al | |
| Radishes | M/A | Al | |
| Ray fish | P | Ac | * |
| Rice | C | Ac | * |
| Rosemary | M/A | Al | |
| Rutabaga (swede) | M/A | Al | |
| Rye | C | Ac | * |
| Saffron | M/A | Ac | |
| Sage | M/A | Al | |
| Sago | C | Ac | * |
| Salad greens | M/A | Al | |
| Salmon | P | Ac | * |
| Sardines | P | Ac | * |
| Savory | M/A | Al | |
| Scallops | P | Ac | * |
| Sesame seeds | P | Al | * |
| Shad | P | Ac | * |
| Shark | P | Ac | * |
| Shellfish (all) | P | Ac | * |
| Shrimps | P | Ac | * |
| Snails | P | Ac | * |
| Sole | P | Ac | * |
| Soya (all) | P | Ac | * |
| Spices (all) | M/A | see each | ! |
| Spinach | M/A | Al | |
| Split peas | C | Ac | * |

| | | | |
|---|---|---|---|
| Sprouted seeds | M/A | Al | |
| Squash | M/A | Al | |
| Squid | P | Ac | * |
| Sugars (all) | C | Ac | ! |
| Sugar snap peas | M/A | Al | |
| Sunflower seeds | P | Al | * |
| Swede (rutabaga) | M/A | Al | |
| Sweetcorn (maize) | C | Al | * |
| Sweet potato | C | Al | * |
| Swiss chard | M/A | Al | |
| Swordfish | P | Ac | * |
| Tapioca | C | Ac | * |
| Tarragon | M/A | Al | |
| Thyme | M/A | Al | |
| Tomato (cooked) | M/A | Ac | ! |
| Tomato (raw) | M/A | Al | |
| Trout | P | Ac | * |
| Truffle | M/A | Al | |
| Turbot | P | Ac | * |
| Tuna | P | Ac | * |
| Turkey | P | Ac | * |
| Turmeric | M/A | Ac | ! |
| Turnip | M/A | Al | |
| Turnip greens | M/A | Al | |
| Vanilla | M/A | Al | |
| Veal | P | Ac | * |
| Venison | P | Ac | * |
| Vinegars | M/A | Ac | ! |
| Walnuts | P | Ac | * |
| Waterchestnuts | M/A | Al | |
| Watercress | M/A | Al | |
| Wheat (all products) | C | Ac | * |
| Whiting | P | Ac | * |
| Winkles | P | Ac | * |
| Yams | C | Al | * |
| Yam flour | C | Ac | * |
| Yellow tail | P | Ac | * |
| Yoghurt | P | Al | |
| Zucchini (courgette) | M/A | Al | |

# INDEX

Additives, 19, 30
Allergies, 22, 23
Alternative pesto, 284
Anchovies: Warm walnut and anchovy dip, 107–8
Apples, 21
Apricots, 21
  Stewed apricot smoothie with whole blueberries, 39–40
Asparagus: Griddled asparagus and leeks, 245–6
Aubergines
  Aubergine curry, 250–51
  Aubergine 'noodles', 216–7
  Aubergine purée, 146
Autumn medley of stuffed vegetables, 140–44
Avocado
  Avocado soup, 54–5
  Prawn and avocado salsa salad, 82–4

Bacon
  Bacon, onion and tomato quiche, 125–6
  Scrambled eggs with mushrooms, tomatoes and bacon, 41–2
  Turkey, bacon and walnut salad, 80–81
Bakewell pot, 259
Bamboo shoots: Chinese chicken and bamboo shoot soup, 66–7
Bananas, 21, 32
  Banana and strawberry smoothie, 39
Barley, 21, 46, 176, 207
Basic lentils, 195–6
Basic pesto, 283–4

Basic quiche filling, 124–5
Basic tomato sauce, 271–2
Basic vegetable stock, 48–9
Basic vinaigrette, 73–4
Batters, 176
Bean curd: Chinese mushroom and bean curd soup, 65–6
Bean sprouts: Stir fried spinach and bean sprouts, 232–3
Beans, 21, 174
  baked, 33
  Bean pâté 114–5
  Bean salad, 100–102
  Bean soup, 60
  Black bean sauce, 111
  Casserole of beans and vegetables with filled dumplings, 203–6
  dried, 194, 195
Beef
  Beef stroganoff, 150–52
  Spaghetti bolognese KD style, 148–50
Berries, 21
  Summer berries and yogurt with blackcurrant coulis, 36
Black bean sauce, 111
Black olive purée, 61
Blackberries: Summer berries and yogurt with blackcurrant coulis, 36
Blackcurrants, 21
  Summer berries and yogurt with blackcurrant coulis, 36
BL's potted cheesecake, 258
Blue cheese sauce, 109

Blueberries
  Stewed apricot smoothie with whole
    blueberries, 39–40
  Summer berries and yogurt with
    blackcurrant coulis, 36
Bread, 23, 32, 33, 46, 176, 206
  Wheat bread crostini, 134
Broccoli, 228
Brussels sprouts: Purée of Brussels sprouts,
  224
Bubble and squeak, 43–4
Buckwheat, 21, 176, 207
Butter, 21, 175, 184
Butter sauces, 25
Buttered parsnip mash, 222
Buttered purée of spinach with nutmeg,
  206, 225

Cabbage: Quick braised red cabbage, 155,
  237
Caesar-style salad, 87–8
Caffeine products, 23
Cakes, 33
Calories, 20, 72
Calves' liver: Liver with oregano, 170–71
Capers: Smoked salmon, dill and caper
  salad, 81–2
Carbohydrates, 254
  beans/pulses, 21, 174
  breakfast, 33
  carbohydrate main courses, 174–207
  and desserts, 253, 254
  and fruits, 32
  garnishes, 46
  gluten cereals, 21, 174, 176
  and milk, 46
  and Mix With Any vegetables, 208, 209,
    210
  non-gluten grains, 21, 174
  as '1 in 5' foods, 23, 24, 30
  and proteins, 20, 26, 147, 174, 175, 210,
    252
  special cases, 21, 174
  sugars, 174
  and vegetables, 21, 174
  and weight management, 175–6
Cardamom, 254
Carrots, 210, 211, 213, 217, 228
  Carrot and courgette boiled vegetable
    'rice', 217–8
  Carrot and courgette fried 'rice', 218–9
  Carrot, courgette and leek ribbon 'pasta',
    212

Carrot and courgette noodle 'pasta', 214
Carrot and parsnip purée with garlic, 223
Carrot purée, 223
Layered spinach and carrots, 224–5
Cashew nut salad, 90–92
Cauliflower, 228
Celeriac, 211
Celery, 228
  Creamy celery soup, 52–3
Cereals, 23, 32, 33, 174
Champagne, 24
Cheesecake: BL's potted cheesecake, 258
Cheeses, 21, 23, 147, 148, 253
  Blue cheese sauce, 109
  Cheese and herb soufflé omelette, 115–7
  Chicken breast stuffed with goat's cheese
    and sage, 164–5
  Cow's milk cheeses with crudités and
    salsa, 270
  Goat's cheese and Roquefort quiche in a
    pot, 126–7
  Goat's cheeses and crudités with walnuts,
    269
Cherries, 21
Chicken, 23, 46, 148
  Chicken breast stuffed with goat's cheese
    and sage, 164–5
  Chicken liver pâté, 113–4
  Chicken liver salad, 78
  Chicken stock, 50–51
  Chinese chicken and bamboo shoot soup,
    66–7
  Roast chicken with rich chicken and
    vegetable sauce, 165–7
  Spicy quick roast chicken salad with salsa
    dressing, 79–80
Chickpeas, 21, 194
Chicory hearts, 120
  Griddled chicory hearts, 243–4
Chilli, 21
  Lentil chilli, 200–202
Chilli peppers, preparing, 55
Chinese chicken and bamboo shoot soup,
  66–7
Chinese mushroom and bean curd soup,
  65–6
Chinese salmon and vegetables soup, 67–8
Chives
  Quenelles of sour cream and chives, 132
  Tatin–style tart of peppers and onions
    with sour cream and chives, 130–32
Chocolate, 23, 253, 254

*Chocolate continued*
   Cups of chocolate, 255–6
   Floating meringues on custard with hot
     chocolate, 259–61
Citrus fruits, 21
   Citrus fruit salad, 34
Coconut, 21, 147
Coffee, 23, 24, 254
Cola, 23
Colour, food and, 27
Colourings, 47
Condiments, 21, 208–9
Conversion tables, 287–8
Corn, 21, 33, 190–94
Corn chips, 190
Corn pasta, 190
Corn starch, 46
Coulis, 25
   Summer berries and yogurt with
     blackcurrant coulis, 36
   Sweet pepper coulis, 276–7
Courgettes, 138, 211, 213, 217, 219
   Carrot and courgette boiled vegetable
     'rice', 217–8
   Carrot and courgette fried 'rice', 218–9
   Carrot, courgette and leek ribbon 'pasta',
     212
   Carrot and courgette noodle 'pasta', 218
   Griddled courgettes, 244–5
Cous cous, 176
   Summer vegetable cous cous, 179–81
Cow's milk cheeses with crudités and salsa,
   270
Cracked (bulgur) wheat, 176
Cream, 30, 33, 45–6, 175, 184, 253
   Creamy celery soup, 52–3
   Creamy mushroom sauce, 274–5
   Tatin-style tart of peppers and onions
     with sour cream and chives, 130–32
Crispbreads, 32, 33
Crostini
   Polenta crostini, 133–4
   Wheat bread crostini, 134
Croutons, 46, 176
   Polenta croutons, 69–70
   Wheat croutons, 68–9
Crudités, 72, 105–6
   Cow's milk cheeses with crudités and
     salsa, 270
   Goat's cheeses and crudités with walnuts,
     269
   Oriental-style shredded vegetable crudités,
     110–12

   Shredded vegetable crudités with classic
     sauces, 108–10
Cups of chocolate, 255–6
Currants, 21
Curries
   Aubergine curry, 250–51
   Curry and rice salad, 96–8
   Lentil curry, 202–3
   Mixed vegetable curry, 248–50
   Vegetable rice curry, 183–4

Dairy products, 23
Damsons, 21
Desserts, 71, 252–70
   Bakewell pot, 259
   BL's potted cheesecake, 258
   Cow's milk cheeses with crudités and
     salsa, 270
   Cups of chocolate, 255–6
   Dessert salads, 267–9
   Floating meringues on custard with hot
     chocolate, 259–61
   Goat's cheeses and crudités with walnuts,
     269
   Lemon pot, 256–8
   Lemon rice pudding, 261–2
   Nut macaroons, 255
   Papaya fool, 265–6
   Tiramisu KD, 262–4
   Treacle tartlets, 264–5
   Yogurt with chopped nuts, 267
Dill: Smoked salmon, dill and caper salad,
   81–2
Dips, 106
   Warm walnut and anchovy dip, 107–8
Dressings, 73
   Herb, 92–3
   Salsa, 79–80
   Sun dried tomato, 93–4
Dried fruits, 21, 32
Dripping, 21
Duck: Twice-cooked duck salad, 75–7
Dumplings: Casserole of beans and
    vegetables with filled dumplings, 203–6

Eggs, 21, 23, 147, 148, 206, 252, 253
   Grilled gammon rashers with eggs,
    mushrooms and bacon, 42–3
   Scrambled eggs with mushrooms,
    tomatoes and bacon, 41–2
   Scrambled eggs with ratatouille, 117–8

*Eggs continued*
  Scrambled eggs with smoked salmon,
    40–41
Elderberries, 21
Embellishments, 271–82
Emotional disorders, 22
Equipment, 28–9
Essences, 21
Exotic fruit salad, 34–5

Fats, 20, 21, 24, 30, 208, 253
Fennel, 120
  Fennel vinaigrette, 277–8
Fibre, 20, 72
Fish, 21, 23, 46, 84, 147, 148, 253
  Fish soup, 63–4
  Hot and sour fish, 162–3
  *see also* individual fish
Fish oils, 21
Fish stock, 47
Five Day Menu Arranger, 31
Flavourings, 21, 47, 208–9
Floating meringues on custard with hot
    chocolate, 259–61
Flour, 21, 252
Food combining, 17–20, 22, 24, 25, 26
  quick reference guide, 21
Food dependencies, 22
Food rotation, 20, 22–3, 24, 26, 31
  *see also* '1 day in 5' food rotation
Food sensitivities, 22
Four seasons rarebit, 121–2
French-style onion soup, 56
Frittata-style omelette, 172–3
Fromage frais, 21
Fruit, 21, 22, 24, 32, 33, 147
  acid/sub acid, 21
  Banana and strawberry smoothie, 39
  Citrus fruit salad, 34
  dried, 21, 32
  Exotic fruit salad, 34–5
  Grilled spiced fruits, 36–7
  Mixed fruit salad, 33
  Stewed fruit compote, 35
  *see also* individual fruits
Fruit juices, 21
Fruit smoothies, 38–40

Game, 21, 147
Gammon: Grilled gammon rashers with
    eggs, mushrooms and bacon, 42–3
Garlic, 21, 185
  Carrot and parsnip purée with garlic, 223

Garlic chips, 286
  Pork steaks with onion and garlic sauce,
    157–8
  Purée of roasted garlic, 285
Garnishes, 27, 46, 283–6
Gazpacho, 53–4
Ginger: Tomato and ginger sauce, 110–11
Gluten grains, 21, 174, 176
Goat's cheese and Roquefort quiche in a
    pot, 126–7
Goat's cheeses and crudités with walnuts,
    269
Grains, 253
  gluten, 21, 174, 176
  non gluten, 21, 174, 176
Grapefruit: Grilled grapefruit, 38
Grapes, 21
Gravy: Onion gravy, 275–6
Green salsa, 280
Green side salad, 247
Greengages, 21
Griddle fried tuna, 161–2
Griddled asparagus and leeks, 245–6
Griddled chicory hearts, 243–4
Griddled courgettes, 244–5
Grilled gammon rashers with eggs,
    mushrooms and tomatoes, 42–3
Grilled grapefruit, 38
Grilled haddock, 159–60
Grilled spiced fruits, 36–7
Guava, 21

Haddock: Grilled haddock, 159–60
Herbs, 21, 72, 176, 185
  Cheese and herb soufflé omelette, 115–7
  Herb and onion vinaigrette, 109
  Herb stuffing, 206
  Herby green side salad, 247–8
  Mixed root penne-style 'pasta' with herbs,
    215–6
  Pasta salad with herb dressing, 92–3
  Spaghetti with herbs and olives, 177–8
  Warm herb vinaigrette, 277
Horseradish mayonnaise, 111
Hot and sour fish, 162–3
Hyperactivity, 22

Ice cream, 253
Idriss Natural Foods, 254
Ingredients, 29–30

Jams, 32

Kallo, 47
KD cooking, 25–6
KD Food Directory, 289–94
KD overview of rules and advice, 23–4
KD strategies, 24
KD Waldorf salad, 88–90
Kebabs: Lamb kebabs, 153–5
Kiwi fruit, 21
Kohlrabi, 140, 211

Lamb
   Lamb kebabs, 153–5
   Liver with oregano, 170–71
   Liver in tomato sauce, 169–70
   Roast French rack of lamb, 152–3
Lasagne: Lentil lasagne, 197–9
Layered spinach and carrots, 224–5
Leeks, 211, 228
   Carrot, courgette and leek ribbon 'pasta',
      212
   Griddled asparagus and leeks, 245–6
   Leek and parsnip ribbon 'pasta' sauté,
      212–3
   Stuffed leek rarebit, 123–4
Lemons
   Lemon pot, 256–8
   Lemon rice pudding, 261–2
Lentils, 21, 194, 195
   Basic lentils, 195–6
   Lentil chilli, 200–202
   Lentil curry, 202–3
   Lentil lasagne, 197–9
   Lentil moussaka, 199–200
   Lentil salad, 99–100
   Lentil soup, 61–2
   Spaghetti with lentil sauce, 196–7
Liver with oregano, 170–71
Liver in tomato sauce, 169–70
Lychees, 21

Macaroons: Nut macaroons, 255
Maize see corn
Mangoes, 21
Marmalades, 32
Marrow, 138–9
Mayonnaise
   Horseradish mayonnaise, 111
   Mustard mayonnaise, 278
   Simple mayonnaise, 279
Meat products, 206
Meat protein sensitivity, 23
Meats, 21, 46, 147, 253

Medley of seasonal steamed vegetables,
      226–7
Melons, 21, 22, 24, 32
Meringues: Floating meringues on custard
      with hot chocolate, 259–61
Milk, 21, 23, 32, 33, 46, 147, 148, 253
Millet, 21, 207
Mint
   Mint purée, 285–6
   Yogurt and mint sauce, 108
Mix with Any (M/A) foods, 21, 22, 30, 31,
      208–51
   condiments and flavourings, 21, 208–9
   crudités, 106
   oils and fats, 21, 208
   salads, 71, 72, 73
   sauces, 176
   soups, 45, 46, 47
   sugar, 254
   vegetables, salads and vegetable juices,
      21, 208
Mix With Any vegetable casserole, 241–3
Mixed fruit salad, 33
Mixed root penne-style 'pasta' with herbs,
      215–6
Mixed vegetable curry, 248–50
Monosodium glutamate, 30, 47
Moussaka: Lentil moussaka, 199–200
Mushrooms
   Chinese mushroom and bean curd soup,
      65–6
   Creamy mushroom sauce, 274–5
   Grilled gammon rashers with eggs,
      mushrooms and bacon, 42–3
   Mushroom tartlets, 128–30
   in rarebits, 120
   Scrambled eggs with mushrooms,
      tomatoes and bacon, 41–2
   stuffed, 139
   Warm salad of mixed mushrooms, 104–5
Mustard, 21, 175
   Mustard mayonnaise, 278

Niçoise-style potato salad, 86–7
Niçoise-style tuna salad, 85–6
Noodle 'pasta', 209, 210, 213–14, 216–17
Nut oils, 21
Nuts, 21, 23, 26, 147, 194, 206, 253, 254
   Nut macaroons, 255
   Yogurt with chopped nuts, 267

Oats, 21, 33, 176

Offal, 21, 147
Oils, 21, 175, 208
Olive oil, 21, 30, 184
Olives
    Black olive purée, 61
    Spaghetti with herbs and olives, 177–8
Omelettes
    Cheese and herb soufflé omelette, 115–7
    Frittata-style omelette, 172–3
    Spanish-style omelette, 118–9
'1 day in 5' food rotation, 22–3, 30, 31, 45,
    127
    carbohydrates, 23, 175
    desserts, 252–3
    and food combining, 20, 22
    gluten grains, 176
    potatoes, 195
    proteins, 23, 24, 26, 147–8, 175
    pulses, 194
    sugar, 254
    wheat, 46, 176
Onions, 228
    Bacon, onion and tomato quiche, 125–6
    French-style onion soup, 56
    Herb and onion vinaigrette, 109
    Onion gravy, 275–6
    Pork steaks with onion and garlic sauce,
        157–8
    in rarebits, 120
    Roast of crispy potatoes and onions,
        185–6
    Sage and onion sauce, 273–4
    stuffed, 139, 141–2
    Tatin-style tart of peppers and onions
        with sour cream and chives, 130–32
    Tomato and onion side salad, 246
Oregano: Liver with oregano, 170–71
Oriental-style crudités, 111–12
Oriental-style shredded vegetable crudités,
    110–12
Oven cooked ratatouille, 238–9
Oven temperatures, 288

Paella, 182–3
Papaya, 21
    Papaya fool, 265–6
Parsnips, 211, 213, 217
    Buttered parsnip mash, 222
    Carrot and parsnip purée with garlic, 223
    Leek and parsnip ribbon 'pasta' sauté,
        212–134
    Parsnip ribbons, 59

Passionfruit, 21
Pasta, 23, 46, 176
    Pasta salad with herb dressing, 92–3
    Pasta salad with sun dried tomato
        dressing, 93–4
    Pasta stroganoff, 178–9
Pastry, 127, 176
    Shortcrust pastry, 128
Pâtés
    Bean pâté, 114–5
    Chicken liver pâté, 113–4
Peaches, 21
Peanuts, 21, 254
    Spicy vegetable peanut satay, 192–4
Pearl barley, 46, 207
Pears, 21
Penne-style 'pasta', 214–6
Peppers, 21
    Socca with mixed peppers, 134–6
    stuffed, 139
    Sweet pepper coulis, 276–7
    Tatin-style tart of peppers and onions
        with sour cream and chives, 130–32
Persimmons, 21
Pestos
    Alternative pesto, 284
    Basic pesto, 283–4
Pickles, 21
Pineapple, 21
Pizza KD style, 132–3
Ploughman's rarebit, 121
Polenta, 190
    Polenta crostini, 133–4
    Polenta croutons, 69–70
    Polenta stacked with ratatouille
        vegetables, 190–92
Pork, 23, 148
    Pork steaks with onion and garlic sauce,
        157–8
    Stuffed pork fillets, 155–7
Porridge, 33
Potatoes, 21, 23, 26, 33, 46, 84, 184–90,
    253
    Niçoise-style potato salad, 86–7
    Potatoes and root vegetables boulangère
        style, 188–90
    Roast of crispy potatoes and onions,
        185–6
    Spicy potatoes in tomato sauce, 186–8
Poultry, 21, 23, 147, 253
Prawns: Prawn and avocado salsa salad,
    82–4

Presentation, 27–8
Pressed terrine of vegetables, 236–8
Processed foods, 29–30, 176
Protein main courses, 147–73
Protein stocks, 47
Proteins, 22, 175
    animal products, 21, 26, 147
    and carbohydrates, 20, 26, 147, 174, 175,
        210, 252
    and desserts, 253, 254
    garnishes, 46
    milk, 33
    and Mix With Any vegetables, 208, 209,
        210
    non-animal products, 21, 26, 147
    as '1 in 5' foods, 23, 24, 26, 30
    pulses, 194
    and sauces, 25
    special cases, 21, 147
    and vegetable 'rice', 217
    yogurt, 32
Prunes, 21
Pulses, 21, 26, 174, 194–206
Pumpkin soup, 62–3
Purées, 25, 221–4
    Aubergine purée, 146
    Buttered purée of spinach with nutmeg,
        206, 225
    Carrot and parsnip purée with garlic, 223
    Carrot purée, 223
    Mint purée, 285–6
    Purée of Brussels sprouts, 224
    Purée of roasted garlic, 285
    Purée of swede, 222

Quenelles of sour cream and chives, 132
Quiches, 26, 124–7
Quick braised red cabbage, 155, 237
Quick sauté ratatouille, 239–41
Quick vegetable stock, 49

Rarebits, 119–24
Raspberries: Summer berries and yogurt
    with blackcurrant coulis, 36
Ratatouille
    Oven cooked ratatouille, 238–9
    Polenta stacked with ratatouille
        vegetables, 190–92
    Quick sauté ratatouille, 239–41
    Scrambled eggs with ratatouille, 117–8
Redcurrants, 21
Ribbon 'pasta', 209, 210, 211–13

Rice, 21, 23, 26, 33, 46, 181–2, 253
    Curry and rice salad, 96–8
    Lemon rice pudding, 261–2
    Paella, 182–3
    vegetable 'rice', 217–9
    Vegetable rice curry, 183–4
    Rice Dream, 33
    Rice noodles, 181
Rich tomato sauce, 272–3
Roast chicken with rich chicken and
        vegetable sauce, 165–7
Roast of crispy potatoes and onions, 185–6
Roast French rack of lamb, 152–3
Roasted Mediterranean vegetables, 233–4
Roasted winter vegetables, 235–6
Root soup, 58–9
Rösti and seasonal vegetables, 136–8
Rye, 21, 33, 176

Sage
    Chicken breast stuffed with goat's cheese
        and sage, 164–5
    Sage and onion sauce, 273–4
Salad leaves, 72
Salads, 21, 24, 25, 26, 71–112, 176, 195,
        208
    basic salad ingredients, 72–3
    Basic vinaigrette, 73–5
    Bean salad, 100–102
    Caesar-style salad, 87–8
    Cashew nut salad, 90–91
    Chicken liver salad, 78
    Crudités, 105–6
    Curry and rice salad, 96–8
    Dessert salads, 267–9
    Green side salad, 247
    KD Waldorf salad, 88–90
    Lentil salad, 99–100
    Niçoise salads, 84–7
    Niçoise-style potato salad, 86–7
    Niçoise-style tuna salad, 85–6
    Oriental-style shredded vegetable crudités
        110–12
    Pasta salad with herb dressing, 92–3
    Pasta salad with sun dried tomato
        dressing, 93–4
    pasta salads, 91–3
    Prawn and avocado salsa salad, 82–4
    Shredded vegetable crudités with classic
        sauces, 108–10
    Side salad of grated Mix With Any
        vegetables, 220–21

*Salads continued*
Smoked salmon, dill and caper salad,
    81–2
Spicy quick roast chicken salad with salsa
    dressing, 79–80
Tabbouleh, 95–6
Tomato and onion side salad, 246
Turkey, bacon and walnut salad, 80–81
Twice–cooked duck salad, 75–7
Warm salad of mixed mushrooms, 104–5
Warm vegetable salads, 102–4
Warm walnut and anchovy dip, 107–8
Salmon
Chinese salmon and vegetables soup,
    67–8
Salmon fillet with a charred oriental spice
    crust, 158–9
Scrambled eggs with smoked salmon,
    40–41
Smoked salmon, dill and caper salad,
    81–2
Salsas
Cow's milk cheeses with crudités and
    salsa, 270
Green salsa, 280
Prawn and avocado salsa salad, 82–4
Spicy quick roast chicken salad with salsa
    dressing, 79–80
Summer tomato salsa, 281–2
Salt, 20, 30, 47
Satays
Spicy vegetable peanut satay, 192–4
Turkey satay, 167–9
Sauces, 25, 30, 47, 106, 176
Basic tomato sauce, 271–2
Black bean sauce, 111
Blue cheese sauce, 109
Creamy mushroom sauce, 274–5
Liver in tomato sauce, 169–70
Pork steaks with onion and garlic sauce,
    157–8
Rich tomato sauce, 272–3
Roast chicken with rich chicken and
    vegetable sauce, 165–7
Sage and onion sauce, 273–4
Spaghetti with lentil sauce, 196–7
Spicy potatoes in tomato sauce, 186–8
Tartare sauce, 279
Tomato and ginger sauce, 110–11
White sauce, 198–9
Yogurt and mint sauce, 108
Scrambled eggs with mushrooms, tomatoes
    and bacon, 41–2

Scrambled eggs with ratatouille, 117–8
Scrambled eggs with smoked salmon, 40–41
Seeds, 21, 26, 147, 194
Sharonfruit, 21
Shellfish, 21, 147
Shortcrust pastry, 128
Shredded vegetable crudités, 110
Side salad of grated Mix With Any
    vegetables, 220–21
Simple mayonnaise, 279
Smoked salmon, dill and caper salad, 81–2
Smoothies
Banana and strawberry smoothie, 39
Stewed apricot smoothie with whole
    blueberries, 39–40
Socca with mixed peppers, 134–6
Sorbets, 253
Soups, 30, 45–70
accompaniments, 68–70
Avocado soup, 54–5
Basic vegetable stock, 48–9
Bean soup, 60
Black olive purée, 61
blending, 47–8
Chicken stock, 50–51
Chinese chicken and bamboo shoot soup,
    66–7
Chinese mushroom and bean curd soup,
    65–6
Chinese salmon and vegetables soup,
    67–8
Chinese-style 'five morsels' soups, 64–8
cream in, 45–6
Creamy celery soup, 52–3
Fish soup, 63–4
French-style onion soup, 56
Gazpacho, 53–4
Lentil soup, 61–2
Pumpkin soup, 62–3
Quick vegetable stock, 49
Root soup, 58–9
seasoning, 48
Thick vegetable soup, 57–8
Watercress soup, 51–2
Sour cream
Quenelles of sour cream and chives, 132
Tatin-style tart of peppers and onions
    with sour cream and chives, 130–32
Soy sauce, 21
Soya, 21, 26, 30, 147, 148, 194, 206, 253
Soya milk, 33
Soya products, 21, 23, 147

Spaghetti
  Spaghetti bolognese KD style, 148–50
  Spaghetti with herbs and olives, 177–8
  Spaghetti with lentil sauce, 196–7
Spanish-style omelette, 118–9
Spices, 21, 175
Spicy potatoes in tomato sauce, 186–8
Spicy quick roast chicken salad with salsa
    dressing, 79–80
Spicy vegetable peanut satay, 192–4
Spinach
  Buttered purée of spinach with nutmeg,
    206, 225
  Layered spinach and carrots, 224–5
  Stir fried spinach and bean sprouts, 232–3
Spring medley of stuffed vegetables, 144–6
Starch thickeners, 25, 30, 46
Starch-rich foods, 21, 253
Stewed apricot smoothie with whole
    blueberries, 39–40
Stewed fruit compote, 35
Stir fried spinach and bean sprouts, 232–3
Stir fry with any vegetables Thai-style,
    230–32
Stir fry of a variety of Mix With Any
    vegetables, 228–30
Stir frying, 227–33
Stocks, 46–7, 48
  Basic vegetable stock, 48–9
  Chicken stock, 50–51
  fish, 47
  protein, 47
  Quick vegetable stock, 49
  vegetable, 46–7
Strawberries
  Banana and strawberry smoothie, 39
  Summer berries and yogurt with
    blackcurrant coulis, 36
Stuffed leek rarebit, 123–4
Stuffed pork fillets, 155–7
Stuffing: Herb stuffing, 206
Sub acid fruits, 21
Suet, 21
Sugar, 21, 30, 32, 174, 252, 253, 254
Sultanas, 21
Summer berries and yogurt with
    blackcurrant coulis, 36
Summer tomato salsa, 281–2
Summer vegetable cous cous, 179–81
Swedes, 211
  Purée of swede, 222
Sweet pepper coulis, 276–7

Sweet potatoes, 185
Tabbouleh, 95–6
Tacos, 190
Tartare sauce, 279
Tartlets
  Mushroom tartlets, 128–30
  Treacle tartlets, 264–5
Tatin-style tart of peppers and onions with
    sour cream and chives, 130–32
Tea, 23, 24
Temperature
  food and, 27–8
  oven, 288
10% Rule, KD, 24–5
Textures, food and, 27
Thick vegetable soup, 57–8
Tiramisu KD, 262–4
Tomatoes, 119
  Bacon, onion and tomato quiche, 125–6
  Basic tomato sauce, 271–2
  Liver in tomato sauce, 169–70
  Pasta salad with sun dried tomato
    dressing, 93–4
  Rich tomato sauce, 272–3
  Scrambled eggs with mushrooms,
    tomatoes and bacon, 41–2
  Summer tomato salsa, 281–2
  Tomato and ginger sauce, 110–11
  Tomato and onion side salad, 246
Toxicity, 18, 22
Treacle tartlets, 264–5
Tuna
  Griddle fried tuna, 161–2
  Niçoise-style tuna salad, 85–6
Turkey
  Turkey, bacon and walnut salad, 80–81
  Turkey satay, 167–9
Turnips, 140, 143–4, 211
Twice-cooked duck salad, 75–7
Twigg, Stephen M.: The Kensington Diet,
    18, 24, 31

Vanilla essence, 21
Vegans, 175
Vegetable juices, 21, 24, 208
Vegetable oils, 21
Vegetable stock cubes/extracts, 47
Vegetable stocks, 46–7
Vegetables, 21, 24, 25, 26
  Autumn medley of stuffed vegetables,
    140–44
  Buttered purée of spinach with nutmeg,
    206, 225

carbohydrates, 21, 174
Casserole of beans and vegetables with
    filled dumplings, 203–6
Chinese salmon and vegetables soup,
    67–8
grated mix, 219–21
Green salsa, 280
Green side salad, 247
Herby green side salad, 247–8
julienne mix, 219
mashed and puréed mix, 221–4
Medley of seasonal steamed vegetables,
    226–7
'Mix with Any' foods, 21, 208
Mix With Any vegetable casserole, 241–3
Mixed root penne-style 'pasta' with herbs,
    215–6
Mixed vegetable curry, 248–50
Oriental-style shredded vegetable crudités,
    110–12
Oven cooked ratatouille, 238–9
'pasta', 209–17
Polenta stacked with ratatouille
    vegetables, 190–92
Potatoes and root vegetables boulangère
    style, 188–90
Pressed terrine of vegetables, 236–8
Quick braised red cabbage, 155, 237
Quick sauté ratatouille, 239–41
and rice, 181
Roasted Mediterranean vegetables, 233–4
Roasted winter vegetables, 235–6
Root soup, 58–9
Rösti and seasonal vegetables, 136–8
in salads, 72
Shredded vegetable crudités with classic
    sauces, 108–10
Side salad of grated Mix With Any
    vegetables, 220–21
Spicy vegetable peanut satay, 192–4
Spring medley of stuffed vegetables,
    144–6
steaming mix, 226–7
Stir fry with any vegetables Thai-style,
    230–32
Stir fry with a variety of Mix With Any
    vegetables, 228–30
stir frying, 227–33

stuffed, 138–46
and sugar, 253
Summer vegetable cous cous, 179–81
Thick vegetable soup, 57–8
vegetable preparation and cooking KD
    style, 209–10
vegetable 'rice', 217–19
Vegetable rice curry, 183–4
Warm vegetable salads, 102–4
and weight control, 25
and wheat, 176
see also individual vegetables
Vegetarians, 26, 175
Vinaigrettes, 102
    Basic vinaigrette, 73–4
    Variations, 103
    Fennel vinaigrette, 277–8
    Herb and onion vinaigrette, 109
    Warm herb vinaigrette, 277
Vinegar, 21
Violence, in children, 22

Walking, 25
Walnuts
    Goat's cheeses and crudités with walnuts,
        269
    Turkey, bacon and walnut salad, 80–81
    Warm walnut and anchovy dip, 107–8
Warm herb vinaigrette, 277
Warm salad of mixed mushrooms, 104–5
Warm vegetable salads, 102–4
Warm walnut and anchovy dip, 107–8
Watercress soup, 51–2
Weight control, 24–5
Wheat, 21, 23, 26, 33, 46, 127, 176
    Wheat bread crostini, 134
    Wheat croutons, 68–9
Wheat flour, 30
Whole foods, 19
Wine, 24, 253–4

Yeast extracts, 23
Yogurt, 21, 32, 46, 147
    Summer berries and yogurt with
        blackcurrant coulis, 36
    Yogurt with chopped nuts, 267
    Yogurt and mint sauce, 108